A Spiral Workbook
for
Discrete Mathematics

Harris Kwong

Dept. of Math. Sci.
SUNY Fredonia

Open SUNY Textbooks

2015

©2015 Harris Kwong

ISBN: 978-1-942341-16-1 (e-book)

978-1-942341-18-5 (print)

This publication was made possible by a SUNY Innovative Instruction Technology Grant (IITG). IITG is a competitive grants program open to SUNY faculty and support staff across all disciplines. IITG encourages development of innovations that meet the Power of SUNY's transformative vision.

Published by Open SUNY Textbooks
Milne Library
State University of New York at Geneseo
Geneseo, NY 14454

About the Book

A Spiral Workbook for Discrete Mathematics covers the standard topics in a sophomore-level course in discrete mathematics: logic, sets, proof techniques, basic number theory, functions, relations, and elementary combinatorics, with an emphasis on motivation. The text explains and clarifies the unwritten conventions in mathematics, and guides the students through a detailed discussion on how a proof is revised from its draft to a final polished form. Hands-on exercises help students understand a concept soon after learning it. The text adopts a spiral approach: many topics are revisited multiple times, sometimes from a different perspective or at a higher level of complexity, in order to slowly develop the student's problem-solving and writing skills.

About the Author

Harris Kwong is a mathematics professor at SUNY Fredonia. He was born and raised in Hong Kong. After finishing high school there, he came to the United States to further his education. He received his B.S. and M.S. degrees from the University of Michigan, and Ph.D. from the University of Pennsylvania. His research focuses on combinatorics, number theory, and graph theory. His work appears in many international mathematics journals. Besides research articles, he also contributes frequently to the problems and solutions sections of *Mathematics Monthly*, *Mathematics Magazine*, *College Journal of Mathematics*, and *Fibonacci Quarterly*. He gives thanks and praises to God for his success.

About Open SUNY Textbooks

Open SUNY Textbooks is an open access textbook publishing initiative established by State University of New York libraries and supported by SUNY Innovative Instruction Technology Grants. This initiative publishes high-quality, cost-effective course resources by engaging faculty as authors and peer-reviewers, and libraries as publishing service and infrastructure. The pilot launched in 2012, providing an editorial framework and service to authors, students and faculty, and establishing a community of practice among libraries. Participating libraries in the 2012-2013 pilot include SUNY Geneseo, College at Brockport, College of Environmental Science and Forestry, SUNY Fredonia, Upstate Medical University, and University at Buffalo, with support from other SUNY libraries and SUNY Press. To date, the project has published 10 open textbooks. More information can be found at http://textbooks.opensuny.org.

Preface

There are many discrete mathematics textbooks available, so why did I decide to invest my time and energy to work on something that perhaps only I myself would appreciate?

Mathematical writings are full of jargon and conventions that, without proper guidance, are difficult for beginners to follow. In the past, students were expected to pick them up along the way on their own. Those who failed to do so would be left behind. Looking back, I consider myself lucky. It was by God's grace that I survived all those years. Now, when I teach a mathematical concept, I discuss its motivation, explain why it is important, and provide a lot of examples. I dissect the proofs thoroughly to make sure everyone understands them. In brief, I want to show my students how to analyze mathematical problems.

Most textbooks typically hide all these details. They only show you the final polished products. By training, mathematicians love short and elegant proofs. This is reflected in their own writing. Yes, the results are beautiful, but it is a mystery how mathematicians come up with such ideas. I want a textbook that discusses mathematical concepts in greater detail. I want to teach my students how to read and write mathematical arguments. Since I could not find a textbook that suited my needs, I started writing lecture notes to supplement the main text. Marginal notes, hands-on exercises, summaries, and section exercises were subsequently added at different stages. The lecture notes have evolved into a full-length text.

Discrete mathematics is a rich subject, full of many interesting topics. Often, it is taught to both mathematics and computer science majors. Due to the limit in space, this text addresses mainly the needs of the mathematics majors. Consequently, we will concentrate on logic and proof techniques, and apply them to sets, basic number theory, and functions. In the last two chapters, we discuss relations and combinatorics, as many students will find them useful in other courses.

Since the intended audience of the text is mathematics majors, I use a number of examples from calculus. By design, I hope this can help the students review what they have learned, and see that discrete mathematics forms the foundation of many mathematical arguments.

Discrete mathematics is often a required course in computer science. I find it hard and unjust to serve two different groups of students in the same textbook. Although this text could be used in a typical first semester discrete mathematics class for the computer science majors, they need to consult another text for the second semester course. Here are two that serve this purpose well:

- Alan Doerr and Kenneth Levasseur, *Applied Discrete Structures*.
- Miguel A. Lerma, *Notes on Discrete Mathematics*.

Both are available on-line.

Why do I call this a workbook? There are many hands-on exercises designed to help students understand a new concept before they move on to the next. I believe the title *Workbook* reflects the nature of the book, because I expect the students to work on the hands-on exercises. But why spiral? Because the pedagogy is inspired by the spiral method. The idea is to revisit some themes and results several times throughout the course and each time further deepen your understanding. You will find some problems pop up more than once, and are solved in a different way each time. In other instances, a concept you learned earlier will be viewed from a new perspective, thus adding a new dimension to it.

I am indebted to the anonymous reviewers, whose numerous valuable comments helped to shape the workbook in its current form. I would also like to express my great appreciation to Scott Richmond of Reed Library at the State University of New York at Fredonia, who provided many helpful suggestions and editorial assistance.

The reason I developed this workbook is to help students learn discrete mathematics. If this workbook proves to be a failure, I am the one to blame. If you find this workbook serves its intended purposes, I give all the glory to God, in whom I believe and trust.

Harris Kwong
April 21, 2015

Contents

Chapter 1

An Introduction

1.1 An Overview

What is discrete mathematics? Roughly speaking, it is the study of discrete objects. Here, discrete means "containing distinct or unconnected elements." Examples include:

- Determining whether a mathematical argument is logically correct.
- Studying the relationship between finite sets.
- Counting the number of ways to arrange objects in a certain pattern.
- Analyzing processes that involve a finite number of steps.

Here are a few reasons why we study discrete mathematics:

- To develop our ability to understand and create mathematical arguments.
- To provide the mathematical foundation for advanced mathematics and computer science courses.

In this text, we will cover these five topics:

1. *Logic and Proof Techniques*. Logic allows us to determine if a certain argument is valid. We will also learn several basic proof techniques.

2. *Sets*. We study the fundamental properties of sets, and we will use the proof techniques we learned to prove important results in set theory.

3. *Basic Number Theory*. Number theory is one of the oldest branches of mathematics; it studies properties of integers. Again, we will use the proof techniques we learned to prove some basic facts in number theory.

4. *Relations and Functions*. Relations and functions describe the relationship between the elements from two sets. They play a key role in mathematics.

5. *Combinatorics*. Combinatorics studies the arrangement of objects. For instance, one may ask, in how many ways can we form a five-letter word. It is used in many disciplines beyond mathematics.

All of these topics are crucial in the development of your mathematical maturity. The importance of some of these concepts may not be apparent at the beginning. As time goes on, you will slowly understand why we cover such topics. In fact, you may not fully appreciate the subjects until you start taking advanced courses in mathematics.

This is a very challenging course partly because of its intensity. We have to cover many topics that appear totally unrelated at first. This is also the first time many students have to study mathematics in depth. You will be asked to write up your mathematical argument clearly, precisely, and rigorously, which is a new experience for most of you.

Learning how to think mathematically is far more important than knowing how to do all the computations. Consequently, the principal objective of this course is to help you develop the analytic skills you need to learn mathematics. To achieve this goal, we will show you the motivation behind the ideas, explain the results, and dissect why some solution methods work while others do not.

1.2   Suggestions to Students

All mathematics courses are difficult. It takes hard work and patience to learn mathematics. Rote memorization does *not* work. Here are some suggestions that you may find helpful:

1. Do *not* skip classes.

2. Read the text, including the examples, *before* the lecture; review what you have learned after each lecture.

3. Do the exercises.

    (a) First, study the examples in the book.
    (b) Make an effort to understand how and why a solution works, and remember how certain types of problems should be solved.
    (c) When you do a problem, ask yourself if you have seen something similar before; if you have, follow the steps in its solution.
    (d) After solving a problem, look for alternate solutions, analyze and compare their differences.

4. Get help from the instructor, your friends, and whatever facility your college provides.

5. Develop good study habits.

    (a) Keep working every day: study the book, your own lecture notes, and, most important of all, do the exercises at the end of each section.
    (b) Form a study group of two to three students, and meet on a regular basis to study together.
    (c) Check the solutions for any nonsense or discrepancies.
    (d) Learn how to solve the problems systematically.

6. Perseverance. Do not give up easily.

7. Be willing to help your classmates. Trying to explain something to others is the best way to learn anything new.

Attitude is the real difference between success and failure. Nothing comes easy. To succeed, you have to work hard. But you also need to learn how to learn mathematics the right way.

- Do not rely on memorizing formulas or procedures by rote. Instead, try to understand the concepts and ideas behind them. It is important to learn when and how to use them.

- Of course, it does not mean that you need not memorize anything at all. On the contrary, many basic results and definitions need to be memorized. You may find it helpful to use a highlighter to mark the definitions and keywords that you have trouble recalling, and I urge you to review them frequently.

- Do not compartmentalize the material; all sections are connected in one way or another. Consequently, as you move along from chapter to chapter and from section to section, try to observe the connections between the concepts you have learned. Without saying, it is understood that you need to remember what you had learned earlier.

- Write down all intermediate and partial results *clearly*. For instance, if the value of x is 7, do not just jot down the number 7; instead, write $x = 7$. Otherwise, you may forget what 7 is after just a few minutes. In brief, present your results in such a way that they can be read and understood by *everyone* in the class.

- While we are on the subject, let us comment briefly how to write up a solution. *Take your homework assignments seriously.* Keep in mind: to study for a test, you may want to review your homework, so you need to be able to read your own work. Write everything clearly and neatly. The process of writing out everything correctly helps you think about what you write. Very often, incoherent and incomprehensible writing is an indication of lack of understanding of the subject matter.

- When doing your homework assignments, start with a draft, then look over it carefully, check the spelling and grammar, and revise the solution. Make sure you write in complete sentences and use correct notations. If necessary, you may have to polish it further. Before turning in the final version, be sure to check again for any mistakes that you may have overlooked.

How should a student use this workbook?

1. Read the workbook *before* class, and study the workbook *again* after each class.
2. Read and study the examples in the workbook.
3. Do the hands-on exercises.
4. Do the section exercises.

1.3 How to Read and Write Mathematics

Reading mathematics is difficult for beginners. It takes patience and practice to learn how to read mathematics. You may need to read a sentence or a paragraph several times before you understand it completely. There are writing styles and notational conventions that you acquire only by reading and paying attention to how mathematics is written. As we proceed with the course, we will discuss the details. As a starter, let us offer several suggestions.

- Make sure you know the definition of mathematical terms, the meaning and proper usage of mathematical symbols and notations. Although this may sound obvious, many beginners have difficulty understanding a mathematical argument because they fail to recall the exact meaning of certain mathematical concepts.

- Often, the reason behind a claim lies in the sentence before it. Sometimes it could be found in the preceding paragraph, and it is not unusual that you may need to check several sentences or paragraphs before it. You need to take an active role in reading mathematics, and you need to remember what you have read.

- Mathematicians prefer short and elegant proofs. To do this, they suppress the details of what they consider as "obvious" reasons. But what is obvious to one reader may not be that obvious to another. At any rate, for practical reasons, it is impossible to include every minute step in a mathematical argument. Consequently, keep your pencil and paper next to you, and be ready to check the calculation and fill in the missing details.

- It may help to try out some examples just to see how an argument works.

- After you finish reading a proof, go over it one more time, and try to summarize its key steps (in other words, try to draw an outline of the proof) in your own words.

Writing mathematics is even harder! It takes much longer to learn how to write mathematics. Of course, the most important thing about a mathematical argument is its correctness. When we say "good" mathematical writing, we are talking about precision, clarity, and sound logic.

- Be precise! For example, do not just say "it" when it is unclear which quantity you are referring to. This is particularly true in a lengthy argument. In this regard, it helps to identify and hence distinguish different quantities by their names such as x, y, z, etc.

- Use mathematical terms correctly! A common mistake is confusing an expression with an equation. An equation has an equal sign, as in

$$x + y = 5,$$

but an expression does not, as in

$$x + y.$$

- Likewise, the following is an inequality:

$$x + y \geq 5.$$

Do not call it an equation!

- Do not abuse the word "solve." For instance, many students would say "solve $5^2 + 7^3$." A more appropriate saying should be "compute the value of $5^2 + 7^3$," or simply "evaluate $5^2 + 7^3$."

In the beginning, it helps to follow what others do. This again means you need to read a lot of mathematical writing, and pick up styles that you are comfortable with. We often follow some conventions (unwritten rules, if you prefer) that everyone follows.

Example 1.3.1   Consider this argument for showing that $(x - y)(x + y) = x^2 - y^2$:

> We want to show that
> $$(x - y)(x + y) = x^2 - y^2.$$
> After expanding the product on the left-hand side, we find
> $$= x^2 + xy - yx - y^2 = x^2 - y^2,$$
> which is what we want to prove.

The logic and mathematics in the argument are correct, but not the notation. In formal writing, each equation should be a stand-alone equation. The last equation is incomplete, because it does not have anything on the left-hand side of the equal sign. Here is a proper way to write the argument:

> We want to show that
> $$(x - y)(x + y) = x^2 - y^2.$$
> After expanding the product on the left-hand side, we find
> $$(x - y)(x + y) = x^2 + xy - yx - y^2 = x^2 - y^2,$$
> which is what we want to prove.

The fix is simple: just repeat the left-hand side.   ▲

Example 1.3.2   Short and simple mathematical expressions or equations such as $a^2 + b^2 = c^2$ can be written within a paragraph. Longer ones and expressions or equations that are important should be displayed separately, and centered, on their own lines, as in

$$x^3 - y^3 = (x - y)(x^2 + xy + y^2).$$

If we intend to refer to the equation later, assign a number to it, and enclose the number within parentheses:

$$x^2 - y^2 = (x - y)(x + y). \tag{1.1}$$

Now, for example, we can say, because of (1.1), we find

$$135 = 144 - 9 = 12^2 - 3^2 = (12 - 3)(12 + 3) = 9 \cdot 15.$$

For a longer equation such as

$$(x + y)^2 = (x + y)(x + y) = x^2 + xy + xy + y^2 = x^2 + 2xy + y^2,$$

it may look better and easier to follow if we break it up into several lines, and line them up along the equal signs:

$$\begin{aligned}
(x + y)^2 &= (x + y)(x + y) \\
&= x^2 + xy + xy + y^2 \\
&= x^2 + 2xy + y^2.
\end{aligned}$$

Although we display the equation in three lines, they together form *one* equation. The equal signs at the beginning of the second and third lines indicate that they are the continuation of the previous line. Since this is actually one long equation, we only need to say $(x + y)^2$ once, namely, at the beginning.

When part of the right-hand side extends beyond the margin, you may want to balance the look of the entire equation by repositioning the left-hand side:

$$\begin{aligned}
(x^2 + 2xy + y^2)&(x^2 + 2xy + y^2) \\
&= x^4 + 2x^3y + x^2y^2 + 2x^3y + 4x^2y^2 + 2xy^3 + x^2y^2 + 2xy^3 + y^4 \\
&= x^4 + 4x^3y + 6x^2y^2 + 4xy^3 + y^4.
\end{aligned}$$

In the multi-line display format, always write the equal signs at the *beginning* of the lines. Do not forget to align the equal signs.

When part of the right-hand side is too long to display as a single piece, we may split it into multiple pieces:

$$\begin{aligned}
(x + y)^5 &= (x + y)^2(x + y)^3 \\
&= (x^2 + 2xy + y^2)(x^3 + 3x^2y + 3xy^2 + y^3) \\
&= x^5 + 3x^4y + 3x^3y^2 + x^2y^3 + 2x^4y + 6x^3y^2 + 6x^2y^3 + 2xy^4 \\
&\quad + x^3y^2 + 3x^2y^3 + 3xy^4 + y^5 \\
&= x^5 + 5x^4y + 10x^3y^2 + 10x^2y^3 + 5xy^4 + y^5.
\end{aligned}$$

It is a common practice to use indentation to indicate the continuation of part of a line into the next.   ▲

There will be more discussion as we continue. Let us not forget: the best way to learn is to watch and observe how others do it. Reading is a must! Reading and analyzing technical papers will surely improve your mathematical knowledge as well as your writing.

1.4   Proving Identities

There are many methods that one can use to prove an identity. The simplest is to use algebraic manipulation, as we have demonstrated in the previous examples. In an algebraic proof, there are three acceptable approaches:

- *From left to right*: expand or simplify the left-hand side until you obtain the right-hand side.

- *From right to left*: expand or simplify the right-hand side until you obtain the left-hand side.

- *Meet in the middle*: expand or simplify the left-hand side and the right-hand side *separately* until you obtain the same result from both sides.

Example 1.4.1   To prove that

$$x^3 - y^3 = (x - y)(x^2 + xy + y^2),$$

we start from the right-hand side, because it is more complicated than the left-hand side. The proof proceeds as follows:

$$
\begin{aligned}
(x - y)(x^2 + xy + y^2) &= x^3 - x^2 y + x^2 y - xy^2 + xy^2 - y^3 \\
&= x^3 - y^3.
\end{aligned}
$$

Remember: start from one side and work on it until you obtain the other side.   ▲

Example 1.4.2   The following "proof" of

$$x^4 + x^2 y^2 + y^4 = (x^2 + xy + y^2)(x^2 - xy + y^2)$$

is *incorrect*:

*A **wrong** proof.*

$$
\begin{aligned}
x^4 + x^2 y^2 + y^4 &= (x^2 + xy + y^2)(x^2 - xy + y^2) \\
&= x^4 - x^3 y + x^2 y^2 + x^3 y - x^2 y^2 + xy^3 + x^2 y^2 - xy^3 + y^4 \\
&= x^4 + x^2 y^2 + y^4.
\end{aligned}
$$

Here is the reason. When we place

$$x^4 + x^2 y^2 + y^4 = (x^2 + xy + y^2)(x^2 - xy + y^2)$$

at the start of the proof, by convention, we are proclaiming that $x^4 + x^2 y^2 + y^4$ is indeed equal to $(x^2 + xy + y^2)(x^2 - xy + y^2)$. However, this is what we are asked to prove. Before we have actually proved that it is true, we do not know *yet*, whether they are equal. Therefore, it is wrong to start the proof with it.   ▲

Example 1.4.3   For the same reason, the following "proof" of the identity

$$x^3 - y^3 = (x - y)(x^2 + xy + y^2)$$

is *unacceptable*:

*Another **wrong** proof.*

$$
\begin{aligned}
x^3 - y^3 &= (x - y)(x^2 + xy + y^2) \\
x^3 - y^3 &= x^3 - x^2 y + x^2 y - xy^2 + xy^2 - y^3 \\
x^3 - y^3 &= x^3 - y^3
\end{aligned}
$$

By putting $x^3 - y^3$ on the left-hand side of every line, this becomes (by convention) a collection of three equations. In a nutshell, the argument starts with an equation and we simplify until we obtain something we know is true. If this format is valid, we can "prove" that $21 = 6$, as follows:

$$
\begin{array}{rcl}
21 & = & 6 \\
6 & = & 21 \\
27 & = & 27
\end{array}
$$

By writing $21 = 6$ at the beginning of the proof, what we really say is "*Assume* $21 = 6$ is true." But this is what we *intend* to prove. Thus, in effect, we are putting the cart in front of the horse, which is logically incorrect. There is another explanation why this proof is incorrect. We shall discuss it in Section 2.3. ▲

In brief: we *cannot* start with the given identity and simplify both sides until we obtain an equality (or an equation of the form $0 = 0$).

Example 1.4.4 Show that $\frac{1}{6} k(k+1)(2k+1) + (k+1)^2 = \frac{1}{6}(k+1)(k+2)(2k+3)$.

Solution 1: We can use the "meet in the middle" approach. Recall that we cannot simplify both sides *simultaneously*. Instead, we should expand the two sides *separately*, and then compare the results. We also suggest adding more writing (in words) to help with the explanation.

> After expansion, the left-hand side becomes
>
> $$
> \begin{aligned}
> \tfrac{1}{6} k(k+1)(2k+1) + (k+1)^2 & = \tfrac{1}{6}(2k^3 + 3k^2 + k) + (k^2 + 2k + 1) \\
> & = \tfrac{1}{3} k^3 + \tfrac{3}{2} k^2 + \tfrac{13}{6} k + 1.
> \end{aligned}
> $$
>
> The right-hand side expands into
>
> $$
> \begin{aligned}
> \tfrac{1}{6}(k+1)(k+2)(2k+3) & = \tfrac{1}{6}(2k^3 + 9k^2 + 13k + 6) \\
> & = \tfrac{1}{3} k^3 + \tfrac{3}{2} k^2 + \tfrac{13}{6} k + 1.
> \end{aligned}
> $$
>
> Since both sides yield the same result, they must be equal.

Although the proof is correct, it requires two sets of computation. It is much easier to use either the left-to-right or the right-to-left approach.

Solution 2: A better alternative is to start from the left-hand side and simplify it until we obtain the right-hand side. Our secret weapon is factorization:

> $$
> \begin{aligned}
> \tfrac{1}{6} k(k+1)(2k+1) + (k+1)^2 & = \tfrac{1}{6}(k+1)[k(2k+1) + 6(k+1)] \\
> & = \tfrac{1}{6}(k+1)(2k^2 + 7k + 6) \\
> & = \tfrac{1}{6}(k+1)(k+2)(2k+3).
> \end{aligned}
> $$

This approach is usually better and safer, because no messy computation is involved. ▲

Hands-On Exercise 1.4.1 Show that

$$
\frac{k(k+1)(k+2)}{3} + (k+1)(k+2) = \frac{(k+1)(k+2)(k+3)}{3}.
$$

Be sure to use one of the three methods we discussed above.

$\triangle$

Summary and Review

- There are only three ways to prove an identity: left to right, right to left, or meet in the middle.
- *Never* prove an identity by simplifying both sides simultaneously.

Exercises 1.4

1. Let x and y be any real numbers. Prove that

$$(x+y)^3 = x^3 + 3x^2y + 3xy^2 + y^3.$$

2. Let x and y be any real numbers. Prove that

$$(a-b)^4 = a^4 - 4a^4b + 6a^2b^2 - 4ab^3 + b^4.$$

3. Prove that, for any distinct real numbers x and y,

$$\frac{x^3 - y^3}{x - y} = x^2 + xy + y^2.$$

4. Prove that, for any integer k,

$$\frac{k(k+1)(k+2)(k+3)}{4} + (k+1)(k+2)(k+3) = \frac{(k+1)(k+2)(k+3)(k+4)}{4}.$$

5. Prove that, for any integer k,

$$\frac{k^2(k+1)^2}{4} + (k+1)^3 = \frac{(k+1)^2(k+2)^2}{4}.$$

Chapter 2

Logic

2.1 Propositions

The rules of logic allow us to distinguish between valid and invalid arguments. Besides mathematics, logic has numerous applications in computer science, including the design of computer circuits and the construction of computer programs. To analyze whether a certain argument is valid, we first extract its syntax.

Example 2.1.1   These two arguments:

- If $x + 1 = 5$, then $x = 4$. Therefore, if $x \neq 4$, then $x + 1 \neq 5$.

- If I watch Monday night football, then I will miss the following Tuesday 8 A.M. class. Therefore, if I do not miss my Tuesday 8 A.M. class, then I did not watch football the previous Monday night.

use the same format:

> If p then q. Therefore, if q is false then p is false.

If we can establish the validity of this type of argument, then we have proved *at once* that both arguments are legitimate. In fact, we have also proved that any argument using the same format is also credible.   ▲

Hands-On Exercise 2.1.1   Can you give another argument that uses the same format in the last example?

△

In mathematics, we are interested in statements that can be proved or disproved. We define a ***proposition*** (sometimes called a ***statement***, or an ***assertion***) to be a sentence that is either true or false, but not both.

Example 2.1.2   The following sentences:

- Barack Obama is the president of the United States.

- $2 + 3 = 6$.

are propositions, because each of them is either true or false (but not both).   ▲

Example 2.1.3   These two sentences:

- Ouch!

- What time is it?

are not propositions because they do not proclaim anything; they are exclamation and question, respectively.   ▲

Example 2.1.4   Explain why the following sentences are *not* propositions:

(a) $x + 1 = 2$.

(b) $x - y = y - x$.

(c) $A^2 = 0$ implies $A = 0$.

Solution: (a) This equation is not a statement because we cannot tell whether it is true or false unless we know the value of x. It is true when $x = 1$; it is false for other x-values. Since the sentence is sometimes true and sometimes false, it cannot be a statement.

(b) For the same reason, since $x - y = y - x$ is sometimes true and sometimes false, it cannot be a statement.

(c) This looks like a statement because it appears to be true all the time. Yet, this is *not* a statement, because we never say what A represents. The claim is true if A is a real number, but it is not always true if A is a matrix[1]. Thus, it is not a proposition.   ▲

Hands-On Exercise 2.1.2   Explain why these sentences are not propositions:

(a) He is the quarterback of our football team.

(b) $x + y = 17$.

(c) $AB = BA$.

△

Example 2.1.5   Although the sentence "$x + 1 = 2$" is not a statement, we can change it into a statement by adding some condition on x. For instance, the following is a true statement:

$$\text{For some real number } x, \text{ we have } x + 1 = 2.$$

and the statement

$$\text{For all real numbers } x, \text{ we have } x + 1 = 2.$$

is false. The parts of these two statements that say "for some real number x" and "for all real numbers x" are called quantifiers. We shall study them in Section 2.6.   ▲

---

[1]Some students may not be familiar with matrices. A matrix is rectangular array of numbers. Matrices are important tools in mathematics. The product of two matrices of appropriate sizes is defined in a rather unusual way. It is the peculiar way that two matrices are multiplied that makes matrices so useful in mathematics. The square of a matrix is of course the product of the matrix with itself. It is well-defined only when the matrix is a square matrix. As it turns out, the order of multiplication of two matrices is important. In other words, given any two matrices A and B, it is not always true that $AB = BA$.

Example 2.1.6 Saying that

"A statement is not a proposition if we *cannot* decide whether it is true or false."

is different from saying that

"A statement is not a proposition if we do not know
how to verify whether it is true or false."

The more important issue is whether the truth value of the statement can be determined in theory. Consider the sentence

Every even integer greater than 2 can be written as the sum of two primes.

Nobody has ever proved or disproved this claim, so we do not know whether it is true or false, even though computational data suggest it is true. Nevertheless, it *is* a proposition because it is either true or false but not both. It is impossible for this sentence to be true sometimes, and false at other times. With the advancement of mathematics, someone may be able to either prove or disprove it in the future. The example above is the famous *Goldbach Conjecture*, which dates back to 1742. ▲

We usually use the lowercase letters p, q and r to represent propositions. This can be compared to using variables x, y and z to denote real numbers. Since the truth values of p, q, and r vary, they are called *propositional variables*. A proposition has only two possible values: it is either true or false. We often abbreviate these values as T and F, respectively.

Given a proposition p, we form another proposition by changing its truth value. The result is called the *negation* of p, and is denoted $\neg p$ or $\sim p$, both of which are pronounced as "not p." The similarity between the notations $\neg p$ and $-x$ is obvious.

We can also write the negation of p as $\bar{p}$, which is pronounced as "p bar." The truth value of $\bar{p}$ is opposite of that of p. Hence, if p is true, then $\bar{p}$ would be false; and if p is false, then $\bar{p}$ would be true. We summarize these results in a *truth table*:

p	$\bar{p}$
T	F
F	T

Example 2.1.7 Find the negation of the following statements:

(a) George W. Bush is the president of the United States.
(b) It is not true that New York is the largest state in the United States.
(c) x is a real number such that $x = 4$.
(d) x is a real number such that $x < 4$.

If necessary, you may rephrase the negated statements, and change a mathematical notation to a more appropriate one.

Solution: (a) George W. Bush is not the president of the United States.

(b) It is true that New York is the largest state in the United States.

(c) The phrase "x is a real number" describes what kinds of numbers we are considering. The main part of the proposition is the proclamation that $x = 4$. Hence, we only need to negate "$x = 4$". The answer is:

x is a real number such that $x \neq 4$.

(d) x is a real number such that $x \geq 4$. ▲

Hands-On Exercise 2.1.3 Negate the following statements:

(a) x is an integer greater than 7.

(b) We can factor 144 into a product of prime numbers.

(c) The number 64 is a perfect square.

$\triangle$

Since we will be studying numbers throughout this course, it is convenient to introduce some notations to facilitate our discussion. Let

$$\begin{aligned}
\mathbb{N} &= \text{the set of natural numbers (positive integers)}, \\
\mathbb{Z} &= \text{the set of integers}, \\
\mathbb{R} &= \text{the set of real numbers, and} \\
\mathbb{Q} &= \text{the set of rational numbers}.
\end{aligned}$$

Recall that a rational number is a number that can be expressed as a ratio of two integers. Hence, a rational number can be written as $\frac{m}{n}$ for some integers m and n, where $n \neq 0$. If you use a word processor, and cannot find, for example, the symbol $\mathbb{N}$, you may use bold face **N** as a replacement.

We usually use uppercase letters such as A, B, C, S and T to represent sets, and denote their elements by the corresponding lowercase letters a, b, c, s, and t, respectively. To indicate that b is an element of the set B, we adopt the notation

$$b \in B \qquad [\text{pronounced as "b belongs to B"}].$$

Occasionally, we also use the notation

$$B \ni b \qquad [\text{pronounced as "B contains b"}].$$

Consequently, saying $x \in \mathbb{R}$ is another way of saying x is a real number.

Denote the set of positive real numbers, the set of negative real numbers, and the set of nonzero real numbers, by inserting the appropriate sign in the superscript:

$$\begin{aligned}
\mathbb{R}^+ &= \text{the set of all positive real numbers}, \\
\mathbb{R}^- &= \text{the set of all negative real numbers}, \\
\mathbb{R}^* &= \text{the set of all nonzero real numbers}.
\end{aligned}$$

The same convention applies to $\mathbb{Z}$ and $\mathbb{Q}$. Notice that $\mathbb{Z}^+$ is same as $\mathbb{N}$.

The meaning of kS.

In addition, if S is a set of numbers, and k is a number, we sometimes use the notation kS to indicate the set of numbers obtained by multiplying k to every number in S.

Example 2.1.8   The notation $2\mathbb{Z}$ denotes the set of all even integers. Take note that an even integer can be positive, negative, or even zero.   ▲

Summary and Review

- A proposition (statement or assertion) is a sentence which is either always true or always false.
- The negation of the statement p is denoted $\neg p$, $\sim p$, or $\overline{p}$.
- We can describe the effect of a logical operation by displaying a truth table which covers all possibilities (in terms of truth values) involved in the operation.

- The notations $\mathbb{R}$, $\mathbb{Q}$, $\mathbb{Z}$, and $\mathbb{N}$ represent the set of real numbers, rational numbers, integers, and natural numbers (positive integers), respectively.
- If S denotes a set of numbers, S^+ means the set of positive numbers in S, S^- means the set of negative numbers in S, and S^* means the set of nonzero numbers in S.
- If S denotes a set of numbers, and k is a real number, then kS means the set of numbers obtained by multiplying k to every number in S.

Exercises 2.1

1. Indicate which of the following are propositions (assume that x and y are real numbers).

    (a) The integer 36 is even.
    (b) Is the integer $3^{15} - 8$ even?
    (c) The product of 3 and 4 is 11.
    (d) The sum of x and y is 12.
    (e) If $x > 2$, then $x^2 \geq 3$.
    (f) $5^2 - 5 + 3$.

2. Which of the following are propositions (assume that x is a real number)?

    (a) $2\pi + 5\pi = 7\pi$.
    (b) The product of x^2 and x^3 is x^6.
    (c) It is not possible for $3^{15} - 7$ to be both even and odd.
    (d) If the integer x is odd, is x^2 odd?
    (e) The integer $2^{524287} - 1$ is prime.
    (f) $1.7 + .2 = 4.0$.

3. Determine the truth values of these statements:

    (a) The product of x^2 and x^3 is x^6 for any real number x.
    (b) $x^2 > 0$ for any real number x.
    (c) The number $3^{15} - 8$ is even.
    (d) The sum of two odd integers is even.

4. Determine the truth values of these statements:

    (a) $\pi \in \mathbb{Z}$.
    (b) $1^3 + 2^3 + 3^3 = 3^2 \cdot 4^2/4$.
    (c) u is a vowel.
    (d) This statement is both true and false.

5. Negate the statements in Problem 4.

6. Determine the truth values of these statements:

    (a) $\sqrt{2} \in \mathbb{Z}$ \qquad (b) $-1 \notin \mathbb{Z}^+$ \qquad (c) $0 \in \mathbb{N}$
    (d) $\pi \in \mathbb{R}$ \qquad (e) $\frac{4}{2} \in \mathbb{Q}$ \qquad (f) $1.5 \in \mathbb{Q}$

7. Determine whether these statements are true or false:

    (a) $0 \in \mathbb{Q}$ \qquad (b) $0 \in \mathbb{Z}$ \qquad (c) $-4 \in \mathbb{Z}$
    (d) $-4 \in \mathbb{N}$ \qquad (e) $2 \in 3\mathbb{Z}$ \qquad (f) $-18 \in 3\mathbb{Z}$

8. Negate the following statements about the real number x:

    (a) $x > 0$ \qquad (b) $x \leq -5$ \qquad (c) $7 \leq x$

9. Explain why $7\mathbb{Q} = \mathbb{Q}$. Is it still true that $0\mathbb{Q} = \mathbb{Q}$?

10. Find the number(s) k such that $k\mathbb{Z} = \mathbb{Z}$.

2.2   Conjunctions and Disjunctions

Given two real numbers x and y, we can form a new number by means of addition, subtraction, multiplication, or division, denoted $x + y$, $x - y$, $x \cdot y$, and x/y, respectively. The symbols $+$, $-$, $\cdot$, and $/$ are **binary operators** because they all work on two **operands**. In fact, the negative sign in $-x$ can be regarded as a **unary operator** that changes the sign of x.

In a similar manner, from one or more logical statements, we can form a **compound statement** by joining them with **logical operators**, which are also called **logical connectives** because they are used to connect logical statements. Obviously, negation is a unary operation.

Since a compound statement is itself a statement, it is either true or false. Therefore, we define a logical operation by describing the truth value of the resulting compound statement. The first two binary operations we shall study are conjunction and disjunction. They perform the "and" and "or" operations, respectively.

name	meaning	notation	truth value
conjunction	p and q	$p \wedge q$	true if both p and q are true, false otherwise
disjunction	p or q	$p \vee q$	false if both p and q are false, true otherwise

Their truth values are summarized in the following truth table:

p	q	$p \wedge q$	$p \vee q$
T	T	T	T
T	F	F	T
F	T	F	T
F	F	F	F

Example 2.2.1   Do not use mathematical notations as abbreviation in writing. For example, do *not* write "$x \wedge y$ are real numbers" if you want to say "x and y are real numbers."

In fact, the phrase "$x \wedge y$ are real numbers" is syntactically incorrect. Since $\wedge$ is a binary *logical* operator, it is used to connect two logical statements. Here, the "x" before $\wedge$ is not a logical statement. Therefore we cannot write "$x \wedge y$ are real numbers."

Incidentally, the statement "x and y are real numbers" is actually a conjunction. It means "x is a real number and y is a real number," or symbolically,

$$(x \in \mathbb{R}) \wedge (y \in \mathbb{R}).$$

It is wrong to write "$x \wedge y \in \mathbb{R}$." Can you explain why?   ▲

Hands-On Exercise 2.2.1   Write "x and y are rational" as a conjunction, first in words, then in mathematical symbols.

△

Example 2.2.2   The statement "New York is the largest state in the United States and New York City is the state capital of New York" is clearly a conjunction. A conjunction of two statements is true only when both statements are true. Since New York is not the largest state in the United States, the conjunction is false.

In general, in a conjunction of two statements, if the first statement is false, no further consideration of the second statement is necessary since we know the conjunction must be false. In computer science, this is referred to as the **short circuit evaluation**.   ▲

Example 2.2.3   The statement "$\sqrt{30}$ is greater than 6 or $\sqrt{30}$ is less than 5" can be expressed symbolically as

$$\left(\sqrt{30} > 6\right) \vee \left(\sqrt{30} < 5\right).$$

Both statements "$\sqrt{30} > 6$" and "$\sqrt{30} < 5$" are false. Hence, their disjunction is also false.   ▲

Example 2.2.4   Determine the truth values of the following statements:

(a) $\left(\sqrt{30} > 5\right) \wedge \left(\sqrt{30} > 7\right)$

(b) Either $\left(\sqrt{30} < 5\right)$ or $\left(\sqrt{30} > 7\right)$

Solution: (a) Since $\sqrt{30} > 5$ is true, but $\sqrt{30} > 7$ is false, their conjunction is false.

(b) Since $\sqrt{30} < 5$ is false, and $\sqrt{30} > 7$ is also false, their disjunction is false.   ▲

Hands-On Exercise 2.2.2   Determine the truth values of the following statements:

(a) $\left(\sqrt{30} < 5\right)$ and $\left(\sqrt{30} > 7\right)$.

(b) $\left(\sqrt{30} > 5\right) \vee \left(\sqrt{30} < 7\right)$.

Be sure to show your reasons.   △

Example 2.2.5   What does "$0 \leq x \leq 1$" really mean, logically?

Solution: It means the conjunction "$(0 \leq x) \wedge (x \leq 1)$." Hence, given a real number x, to test whether $0 \leq x \leq 1$, we have to check whether $0 \leq x$ *and* $x \leq 1$.   ▲

"$0 \leq x \leq 1$" means "$0 \leq x$ and $x \leq 1$."

Hands-On Exercise 2.2.3   Write $5 < x < 8$ as a conjunction.

△

Hands-On Exercise 2.2.4   Many students assume that they can negate "$0 \leq x \leq 1$" by reversing the signs. However, neither "$0 \geq x \geq 1$" nor "$0 > x > 1$" is the correct negation. For example, what does "$0 \geq x \geq 1$" really mean? Actually, the statement "$0 \geq x \geq 1$" is syntactically correct, and it is always false. Can you explain why?

The negation of "$0 \leq x \leq 1$" is **not** *"$0 \geq x \geq 1$."*

△

In the everyday usage of most languages, when we say "p or q," we normally mean **exclusive or**, which means either p or q is true, but not both. An example is "I either pass or fail this course," which really means

Either I pass this course or I fail this course.

Sometimes, as illustrated in the statement

Either you pass this course, or I pass this course.

the connective "or" can be interpreted as an **inclusive or**. The actual meaning of "or" in human languages depends on the context. In mathematics, however, "or" *always* means inclusive or.

Summary and Review

- The conjunction "p and q" is denoted "$p \wedge q$". It is true only when both p and q are true.
- The disjunction "p or q" is denoted "$p \vee q$". It is false only when both p and q are false.
- The inequality "$a < x < b$" is actually a conjunction, it means "$(a < x) \wedge (x < b)$".
- Likewise, the phrase "x and y are rational" is also a conjunction, it means "x is rational and y is rational." Symbolically, we can write "$x \in \mathbb{Q} \wedge y \in \mathbb{Q}$."

Exercises 2.2

1. Let p, q, and r represent the following statements:

   p: Sam had pizza last night.
   q: Chris finished her homework.
   r: Pat watched the news this morning.

   Give a formula (using appropriate symbols) for each of these statements:

   (a) Sam had pizza last night and Chris finished her homework.
   (b) Chris did not finish her homework and Pat watched the news this morning.
   (c) Sam did not have pizza last night or Chris did not finish her homework.
   (d) Either Chris finished her homework or Pat watched the news this morning, but not both.

2. Define the propositional variables p, q, and r as in Problem 1. Express, in words, the statements represented by the following formulas:

   (a) $p \vee q$
   (b) $q \wedge r$
   (c) $(p \wedge q) \vee r$
   (d) $\overline{p} \vee r$

3. Consider the following statements:

   p: Niagara Falls is in New York.
   q: New York City is the state capital of New York.
   r: New York City will have more than 40 inches of snow in 2525.

   The statement p is true, but the statement q is false. Represent each of the following statements by a formula. What are their truth values if r is true? What if r is false?

   (a) Niagara Falls is in New York and New York City is the state capital of New York.
   (b) Niagara Falls is in New York or New York City is the state capital of New York.
   (c) Either Niagara Falls is in New York and New York City is the state capital of New York, or New York City will have more than 40 inches of snow in 2525.
   (d) New York City is not the state capital of New York and New York City will have more than 40 inches of snow in 2525.

4. Determine the truth values of these statements:

   (a) $(0 \in \mathbb{Q}) \wedge (-4 \in \mathbb{Z})$ (b) $(-4 \in \mathbb{N}) \vee (3 \in 2\mathbb{Z})$

5. Determine the truth values of these statements:

   (a) $(-3 > -2) \wedge (\sqrt{3} > 2)$ (b) $(4^2 - 5^2 \leq 0) \vee (\sqrt{3^2 + 4^2} = 3 + 4)$

6. Construct the truth tables for the following formulas:

   (a) $p \wedge \overline{q}$ (b) $\overline{p} \vee q$ (c) $\overline{p \wedge q}$

7. Rewrite the following expressions as conjunction:

    (a) $4 \leq x \leq 7$ (b) $4 < x \leq 7$ (c) $4 \leq x < 7$

8. In words, the inequality $0 < x < 1$ means "x is between 0 and 1." Its negation means x is outside this range. Hence, the negation is "$x \leq 0$ or $x \geq 1$." Find the negation of the following inequalities:

    (a) $0 \leq x \leq 4$ (b) $-2 < x \leq 5$ (c) $1.76 \leq x < \sqrt{5}$

9. In volleyball it is important to know which team is serving, because a team scores a point only if that team is serving and wins a volley. If the serving team loses the volley, then the other team gets to serve. Thus, to keep score in a volleyball game between teams A and B, it may be useful to define propositional variables p and q, where p is true if team A is serving (hence false if team B is serving); and q is true if team A wins the current volley (hence false if team B wins it).

    (a) Give a formula that is true if team A scores a point and is false otherwise.
    (b) Give a formula that is true if team B scores a point and is false otherwise.
    (c) Give a formula that is true if the serving team loses the current volley and is false otherwise.
    (d) Give a formula whose truth value determines whether the serving team will serve again.

10. The exclusive or operation, denoted $p \veebar q$, means "p or q, but not both."

    (a) Express $p \veebar q$ as a logic statement.
    (b) Construct the truth table for $p \veebar q$.

2.3   Implications

Most theorems in mathematics appear in the form of compound statements called conditional and biconditional statements. We shall study biconditional statement in the next section. Conditional statements are also called implications.

Definition. An *implication* is the compound statement of the form "if p, then q." It is denoted $p \Rightarrow q$, which is read as "p implies q." It is false only when p is true and q is false, and is true in all other situations.

p	q	$p \Rightarrow q$
T	T	T
T	F	F
F	T	T
F	F	T

The statement p in an implication $p \Rightarrow q$ is called its **hypothesis**, **premise**, or **antecedent**, and q the **conclusion** or **consequence**. $\diamond$

Implications come in many disguised forms. There are several alternatives for saying $p \Rightarrow q$. The most common ones are

- p implies q,
- p only if q,
- q if p,
- q, provided that p.

All of them mean $p \Rightarrow q$.

Implications play a key role in logical argument. If an implication is known to be true, then whenever the hypothesis is met, the consequence must be true as well. This is why an implication is also called a ***conditional statement***.

Example 2.3.1   The quadratic formula asserts that

$$b^2 - 4ac > 0 \quad \Rightarrow \quad ax^2 + bx + c = 0 \text{ has two distinct real solutions.}$$

Consequently, the equation $x^2 - 3x + 1 = 0$ has two distinct real solutions because its coefficients satisfy the inequality $b^2 - 4ac > 0$.   ▲

Hands-On Exercise 2.3.1   More generally,

- If $b^2 - 4ac > 0$, then the equation $ax^2 + bx + c = 0$ has two distinct real solutions. In fact, $ax^2 + bx + c = a(x - r_1)(x - r_2)$, where $r_1 \neq r_2$ are the two distinct roots.

- If $b^2 - 4ac = 0$, then the equation $ax^2 + bx + c = 0$ has only one real solution r. In such an event, $ax^2 + bx + c = a(x - r)^2$. Consequently, we call r a repeated root.

- If $b^2 - 4ac = 0$, then the equation $ax^2 + bx + c = 0$ has no real solution.

Use these results to determine how many solutions these equations have:

(a) $4x^2 + 12x + 9 = 0$

(b) $2x^2 - 3x - 4 = 0$

(c) $x^2 + x = -1$

△

Example 2.3.2   We have remarked earlier that many theorems in mathematics are in the form of implications. Here is an example:

$$\text{If } |r| < 1, \text{ then } 1 + r + r^2 + r^3 + \cdots = \tfrac{1}{1-r}.$$

It means, symbolically, $|r| < 1 \Rightarrow 1 + r + r^2 + r^3 + \cdots = \tfrac{1}{1-r}$.   ▲

Hands-On Exercise 2.3.2   Express the following statement in symbol:

$$\text{If } x > y > 0, \text{ then } x^2 > y^2.$$

△

Example 2.3.3   If a father promises his kids, "If tomorrow is sunny, we will go to the beach," the kids will take it as a true statement. Consequently, if they wake up the next morning and find it sunny outside, they expect they will go to the beach. The father breaks his promise (hence making the implication false) only when it is sunny but he does not take his kids to the beach.

   If it is cloudy outside the next morning, they do not know whether they will go to the beach, because no conclusion can be drawn from the implication (their father's promise) if the weather is bad. Nonetheless, they may still go to the beach, even if it rains! Since their father does not contradict his promise, the implication is still true.   ▲

Many students are bothered by the validity of an implication even when the hypothesis is false. It may help if we understand how we use an implication. Assume we want to show that a certain statement q is true.

(i) First, we find a result of the form $p \Rightarrow q$. If we cannot find one, we have to prove that $p \Rightarrow q$ is true.

(ii) Next, show that the hypothesis p is fulfilled.

(iii) These two steps together allow us to draw the conclusion that q must be true.

Consequently, if p is false, we are not expected to use the implication $p \Rightarrow q$ at all. Since we are not are going to use it, we can define its truth value to anything we like. Nonetheless, we have to maintain consistency with other logical connectives. We will give a justification of our choice at the end of the next section.

Example 2.3.4   To show that "if $x = 2$, then $x^2 = 4$" is true, we need not worry about those x-values that are not equal to 2, because the implication is immediately true if $x \neq 2$. It suffices to assume that $x = 2$, and try to prove that we *will* get $x^2 = 4$. Since we do have $x^2 = 4$ when $x = 2$, the validity of the implication is established.

In contrast, to determine whether the implication "if $x^2 = 4$, then $x = 2$" is true, we assume $x^2 = 4$, and try to determine whether x *must* be 2. Since $x = -2$ makes $x^2 = 4$ true but $x = 2$ false, the implication is false.

In general, to disprove an implication, it suffices to find a counterexample that makes the hypothesis true and the conclusion false.   ▲

We can use a counterexample to disprove a claim.

Hands-On Exercise 2.3.3   Determine whether these two statements are true or false:

(a) If $(x - 2)(x - 3) = 0$, then $x = 2$.

(b) If $x = 2$, then $(x - 2)(x - 3) = 0$.

Explain.

△

Example 2.3.5   Although we said examples can be used to disprove a claim, examples alone can *never* be used as proofs. If you are asked to show that

Examples cannot be used as proofs.

$$\text{if } x > 2, \text{ then } x^2 > 4,$$

you cannot prove it by *checking* just a few values of x, because you may find a counterexample after trying a few more calculations. Therefore, examples are only for illustrative purposes, they are *not* acceptable as proofs.   ▲

Example 2.3.6   The statement

"If a triangle PQR is isosceles, then two of its angles have equal measure."

takes the form of an implication $p \Rightarrow q$, where

p :   The triangle PQR is isosceles
q :   Two of the angles of the triangle PQR have equal measure

In this example, we have to rephrase the statements p and q, because each of them should be a stand-alone statement. If we leave q as "two of its angles have equal measure," it is not clear what "its" is referring to. In addition, it is a good habit to spell out the details. It helps us focus our attention on what we are investigating.   ▲

Example 2.3.7   The statement

"A square must also be a parallelogram."

can be expressed as an implication: "if the quadrilateral $PQRS$ is a square, then the quadrilateral $PQRS$ is a parallelogram."

Likewise, the statement

"All isosceles triangles have two equal angles."

can be rephrased as "if the triangle PQR is isosceles, then the triangle PQR has two equal angles." Since we have expressed the statement in the form of an implication, we no longer need to include the word "all." ▲

Hands-On Exercise 2.3.4   Rewrite each of these logical statements:

(a) Any square is also a parallelogram.

(b) A prime number is an integer.

(c) All polynomials are differentiable.

as an implication $p \Rightarrow q$. Specify what p and q are. △

Example 2.3.8   What does "p unless q" translate into, logically speaking? We know that p is true, provided that q does not happen. It means, in symbol, $\overline{q} \Rightarrow p$. Therefore,

The quadrilateral $PQRS$ is not a square
unless the quadrilateral $PQRS$ is a parallelogram

is the same as saying

If a quadrilateral $PQRS$ is not a parallelogram,
then the quadrilateral $PQRS$ is not a square.

Equivalently, "p unless q" means $\overline{p} \Rightarrow q$, because q is a necessary condition that prevents p from happening. ▲

Given an implication $p \Rightarrow q$, we define three related implications:

- Its **converse** is defined as $q \Rightarrow p$.
- Its **inverse** is defined as $\overline{p} \Rightarrow \overline{q}$.
- Its **contrapositive** is defined as $\overline{q} \Rightarrow \overline{p}$.

Among them, the contrapositive $\overline{q} \Rightarrow \overline{p}$ is the most important one. We shall study it again in the next section.

Example 2.3.9   The converse, inverse, and contrapositive of "$x > 2 \Rightarrow x^2 > 4$" are listed below.

$$\begin{array}{lll} \text{converse:} & x^2 > 4 & \Rightarrow & x > 2, \\ \text{inverse:} & x \le 2 & \Rightarrow & x^2 \le 4, \\ \text{contrapositive:} & x^2 \le 4 & \Rightarrow & x \le 2. \end{array}$$

We can change the notation when we negate a statement. If it is appropriate, we may even rephrase a sentence to make the negation more readable. ▲

Hands-On Exercise 2.3.5   List the converse, inverse, and contrapositive of the statement "if p is prime, then $\sqrt{p}$ is irrational."

$\triangle$

The inverse of an implication is seldom used in mathematics, so we will only study the truth values of the converse and contrapositive.

p	q	$p \Rightarrow q$	$q \Rightarrow p$	$\overline{q}$	$\overline{p}$	$\overline{q} \Rightarrow \overline{p}$
T	T	T	T	F	F	T
T	F	F	T	T	F	F
F	T	T	F	F	T	T
F	F	T	T	T	T	T

An implication and its contrapositive always have the same truth value, but this is not true for the converse. What this means is, even though we know $p \Rightarrow q$ is true, there is no guarantee that $q \Rightarrow p$ is also true. This is an important observation, especially when we have a theorem stated in the form of an implication. So let us say it again:

> The converse of a theorem in the form of an implication may not be true.

Accordingly, if you only know that $p \Rightarrow q$ is true, do not assume that its converse $q \Rightarrow p$ is also true. Likewise, if you are asked to prove that $p \Rightarrow q$ is true, do not attempt to prove $q \Rightarrow p$, because these two implications are not the same.

Example 2.3.10   We know that $p \Rightarrow q$ does not necessarily mean we also have $q \Rightarrow p$. This important observation explains the invalidity of the "proof" of $21 = 6$ in Example 1.4.3.

$$
\begin{aligned}
21 &= 6 \\
6 &= 21 \\
27 &= 27
\end{aligned}
$$

The argument we use here consists of three equations, but they are not individual unrelated equations. They are connected by implication.

$$
\begin{aligned}
& 21 = 6 \\
\Rightarrow \quad & 6 = 21 \\
\Rightarrow \quad & 27 = 27
\end{aligned}
$$

Since implications are not reversible, even though we do have $27 = 27$, we cannot use this fact to prove that $21 = 6$. After all, an implication is true if its hypothesis is false. Therefore, having a true implication does not mean that its hypothesis must be true. In this example, the logic is sound, but it does not prove that $21 = 6$. ▲

There are two other ways to describe an implication $p \Rightarrow q$ in words. They are completely different from the ones we have seen thus far. They focus on whether we can tell one of the two components p and q is true or false if we know the truth value of the other.

- p is a **sufficient condition** for q
- q is a **necessary condition** for p.

They are difficult to remember, and can be easily confused. You may want to visualize it pictorially:

$$\boxed{\text{sufficient condition} \Rightarrow \text{necessary condition.}}$$

The idea is, assuming that $p \Rightarrow q$ is true, then

- For q to be true, it is enough to know or show that p is true. Hence, knowing p is true alone is sufficient for us to draw the conclusion the q must also be true.

- For p to be true, it is necessary to have q be true as well. Thus, knowing q is true does not necessarily mean that p must be true.

Example 2.3.11   Consider the implication

$$x = 1 \Rightarrow x^2 = 1.$$

If $x = 1$, we must have $x^2 = 1$. So, knowing $x = 1$ is enough for us to conclude that $x^2 = 1$. We say that $x = 1$ is a sufficient condition for $x^2 = 1$.

If $x = 1$, it is necessarily true that $x^2 = 1$, because, for example, it is impossible to have $x^2 = 2$. Nonetheless, knowing $x^2 = 1$ alone is not enough for us to decide whether $x = 1$, because x can be -1. Therefore, $x^2 = 1$ is *not* a sufficient condition for $x = 1$. Instead, $x^2 = 1$ is only a necessary condition for $x = 1$.   ▲

Hands-On Exercise 2.3.6   Write these statements:

(a) For $x^2 > 1$, it is sufficient that $x > 1$.

(b) For $x^2 > 1$, it is necessary that $x > 1$.

in the form of $p \Rightarrow q$. Be sure to specify what p and q are.

$\triangle$

Summary and Review

- An implication $p \Rightarrow q$ is false only when p is true and q is false.
- This is how we typically use an implication. Assume we want to show that q is true. We have to find or prove a theorem that says $p \Rightarrow q$. Next, we need to show that hypothesis p is met, hence it follows that q must be true.
- An implication can be described in several other ways. Can you name a few of them?
- Converse, inverse, and contrapositive are obtained from an implication by switching the hypothesis and the consequence, sometimes together with negation.
- In an implication $p \Rightarrow q$, the component p is called the sufficient condition, and the component q is called the necessary condition.

Exercises 2.3

1. Let p, q, and r represent the following statements:

> p: Sam had pizza last night.
> q: Chris finished her homework.
> r: Pat watched the news this morning.

Give a formula (using appropriate symbols) for each of these statements:

(a) If Sam had pizza last night then Chris finished her homework.
(b) Pat watched the news this morning only if Sam had pizza last night.
(c) Chris finished her homework if Sam did not have pizza last night.
(d) It is not the case that if Sam had pizza last night, then Pat watched the news this morning.
(e) Sam did not have pizza last night and Chris finished her homework implies that Pat watched the news this morning.

2. Define the propositional variables as in Problem 1. Express in words the statements represented by the following formulas.

(a) $q \Rightarrow r$
(b) $p \Rightarrow (q \wedge r)$
(c) $\bar{p} \Rightarrow (q \vee r)$
(d) $r \Rightarrow (p \vee q)$

3. Consider the following statements:

> p: Niagara Falls is in New York.
> q: New York City is the state capital of New York.
> r: New York City will have more than 40 inches of snow in 2525.

The statement p is true, and the statement q is false. Represent each of the following statements by a formula. What is their truth value if r is true? What if r is false?

(a) If Niagara Falls is in New York, then New York City is the state capital of New York.
(b) Niagara Falls is in New York only if New York City will have more than 40 inches of snow in 2525.
(c) Niagara Falls is in New York or New York City is the state capital of New York implies that New York City will have more than 40 inches of snow in 2525.
(d) For New York City to be the state capital of New York, it is necessary that New York City will have more than 40 inches of snow in 2525.
(e) For Niagara Falls to be in New York, it is sufficient that New York City will have more than 40 inches of snow in 2525.

4. Express each of the following compound statements symbolically:

(a) If the triangle ABC is equilateral, then it is isosceles.
(b) If $\sqrt{47089}$ is greater than 200 and $\sqrt{47089}$ is an integer, then $\sqrt{47089}$ is prime. *Recall that $\mathbb{Z}$ means the set of all integers.*
(c) If $\sqrt{47089}$ is greater than 200, then, if $\sqrt{47089}$ is prime, it is greater than 210.
(d) The line L_1 is perpendicular to the line L_2 and the line L_2 is parallel to the line L_3 implies that L_1 is perpendicular to L_3.
(e) If $x^3 - 3x^2 + x - 3 = 0$, then either x is positive or x is negative or $x = 0$.

5. Express each of the following compound statements in symbols.

(a) $x^3 - 3x^2 + x - 3 = 0$ only if $x = 3$.
(b) A necessary condition for $x^3 - 3x^2 + x - 3 = 0$ is $x = 3$.

(c) A sufficient condition for $x^3 - 3x^2 + x - 3 = 0$ is $x = 3$.

(d) If e^π is a real number, then e^π is either rational or irrational.

(e) All NFL players are huge.

6. Find the converse, inverse, and contrapositive of the following implication:

If the quadrilateral $ABCD$ is a rectangle, then $ABCD$ is a parallelogram.

7. Construct the truth tables for the following expressions:

(a) $(p \wedge q) \vee r$ (b) $(p \vee q) \Rightarrow (p \wedge r)$

Hint: To help you get started, fill in the blanks.

(a)

p	q	r	$p \wedge q$	$(p \wedge q) \vee r$
T	T	T		
T	T	F		
T	F	T		
T	F	F		
F	T	T		
F	T	F		
F	F	T		
F	F	F		

(b)

p	q	r	$p \vee q$	$p \wedge r$	$(p \vee q) \Rightarrow (p \wedge r)$
T	T	T			
T	T	F			
T	F	T			
T	F	F			
F	T	T			
F	T	F			
F	F	T			
F	F	F			

8. Construct the truth tables for the following expressions:

(a) $(p \Rightarrow q) \vee (\bar{p} \Rightarrow q)$ (b) $(p \Rightarrow q) \wedge (\bar{p} \Rightarrow q)$

9. Determine (you may use a truth table) the truth value of p if

(a) $(p \wedge q) \Rightarrow (q \vee r)$ is false   (b) $(q \wedge r) \Rightarrow (p \wedge q)$ is false

10. Assume $p \Rightarrow q$ is true.

(a) If p is true, must q be true? Explain.

(b) If p is false, must q be true? Explain.

(c) If q is true, must p be false? Explain.

(d) If q if false, must p be false? Explain.

2.4   Biconditional Statements

The *biconditional statement* "p if and only if q," denoted $p \Leftrightarrow q$, is true when both p and q carry the same truth value, and is false otherwise. It is sometimes abbreviated as "p iff q." Its truth table is depicted below.

p	q	$p \Leftrightarrow q$
T	T	T
T	F	F
F	T	F
F	F	T

Example 2.4.1   The following biconditional statements

- $2x - 5 = 0 \Leftrightarrow x = 5/2$,
- $x > y \Leftrightarrow x - y > 0$,

are true, because, in both examples, the two statements joined by $\Leftrightarrow$ are true or false simultaneously.   ▲

A biconditional statement can also be defined as the compound statement

$$(p \Rightarrow q) \wedge (q \Rightarrow p).$$

This explains why we call it a biconditional statement. A biconditional statement is often used
to define a new concept.

Example 2.4.2 A number is even if and only if it is a multiple of 2. Mathematically, this
means

$$n \text{ is even} \Leftrightarrow n = 2q \text{ for some integer } q.$$

It follows that for any integer m,

$$mn = m \cdot 2q = 2(mq).$$

Since mq is an integer (because it is a product of two integers), by definition, mn is even. This
shows that the product of any integer with an even integer is always even.   ▲

Hands-On Exercise 2.4.1 Complete the following statement:

$$n \text{ is odd} \Leftrightarrow \qquad\qquad .$$

Use this to prove that if n is odd, then n^2 is also odd.

                                                                                              △

Example 2.4.3 The operation "exclusive or" can be defined as

$$p \veebar q \Leftrightarrow (p \vee q) \wedge \overline{(p \wedge q)}.$$

See Problem 10 in Exercises 2.2.   ▲

When we have a complex statement involving more than one logical operation, care must be
taken to determine which operation should be carried out first. The **precedence** or **priority** is
listed below.

Connectives	Priority
$\neg$	Highest
$\wedge$	
$\vee$	$\vdots$
$\Rightarrow$	
$\Leftrightarrow$	Lowest

This is the order in which the operations should be carried out if the logical expression is read
from left to right. To override the precedence, use parentheses.

Example 2.4.4 The precedence of logical operations can be compared to those of arithmetic
operations.

Operations	Priority
– (Negative)	Highest
Exponentiation	⋮
Multiplication/Division	⋮
Addition/Subtraction	Lowest

For example, $yz^{-3} \neq (yz)^{-3}$. To evaluate yz^{-3}, we have to perform exponentiation first. Hence, $yz^{-3} = y \cdot z^{-3} = \frac{y}{z^3}$.

Another example: the notation x^{2^3} means x raised to the power of 2^3, hence $x^{2^3} = x^8$; it should *not* be interpreted as $(x^2)^3$, because $(x^2)^3 = x^6$.   ▲

Example 2.4.5   It is not true that $p \Leftrightarrow q$ can be written as "$p \Rightarrow q \wedge q \Rightarrow p$," because it would mean, technically,

$$p \Rightarrow (q \wedge q) \Rightarrow p.$$

The correct notation is $(p \Rightarrow q) \wedge (q \Rightarrow p)$.   ▲

Hands-On Exercise 2.4.2   Insert parentheses in the following formula

$$p \Rightarrow q \wedge r$$

to identify the proper procedure for evaluating its truth value. Construct its truth table.

△

Hands-On Exercise 2.4.3   Insert parentheses in the following formula

$$p \wedge q \Leftrightarrow \overline{p} \vee \overline{q}.$$

to identify the proper procedure for evaluating its truth value. Construct its truth table.

△

We close this section with a justification of our choice in the truth value of $p \Rightarrow q$ when p is false. The truth value of $p \Rightarrow q$ is obvious when p is true.

p	q	$p \Rightarrow q$
T	T	T
T	F	F
F	T	?
F	F	?

We want to decide what are the best choices for the two missing values so that they are consistent with the other logical connectives. Observe that if $p \Rightarrow q$ is true, and q is false, then p must be false as well, because if p were true, with q being false, then the implication $p \Rightarrow q$ would have been false. For instance, if we promise

"If tomorrow is sunny, we will go to the beach"

but we do not go to the beach tomorrow, then we know tomorrow must not be sunny. This means the two statements $p \Rightarrow q$ and $\bar{q} \Rightarrow \bar{p}$ should share the same truth value.

When both p and q are false, then both $\bar{p}$ and $\bar{q}$ are true. Hence $\bar{q} \Rightarrow \bar{p}$ should be true, consequently so is $p \Rightarrow q$. Thus far, we have the following partially completed truth table:

p	q	$p \Rightarrow q$
T	T	T
T	F	F
F	T	?
F	F	T

If the last missing entry is F, the resulting truth table would be identical to that of $p \Leftrightarrow q$. To distinguish $p \Leftrightarrow q$ from $p \Rightarrow q$, we have to define $p \Rightarrow q$ to be true in this case.

Summary and Review

- A biconditional statement $p \Leftrightarrow q$ is the combination of the two implications $p \Rightarrow q$ and $q \Rightarrow p$.
- The biconditional statement $p \Leftrightarrow q$ is true when both p and q have the same truth value, and is false otherwise.
- A biconditional statement is often used in defining a notation or a mathematical concept.

Exercises 2.4

1. Let p, q, and r represent the following statements:

   p: Sam had pizza last night.
   q: Chris finished her homework.
   r: Pat watched the news this morning.

   Give a formula (using appropriate symbols) for each of these statements.

   (a) Sam had pizza last night if and only if Chris finished her homework.
   (b) Pat watched the news this morning iff Sam did not have pizza last night.
   (c) Pat watched the news this morning if and only if Chris finished her homework and Sam did not have pizza last night.
   (d) In order for Pat to watch the news this morning, it is necessary and sufficient that Sam had pizza last night and Chris finished her homework.

2. Define the propositional variables as in Problem 1. Express in words the statements represented by the following formulas:

   (a) $q \Leftrightarrow r$ (b) $p \Leftrightarrow (q \wedge r)$
   (c) $\bar{p} \Leftrightarrow (q \vee r)$ (d) $r \Leftrightarrow (p \vee q)$

3. Consider the following statements:

   p: Niagara Falls is in New York.
   q: New York City is the state capital of New York.
   r: New York City will have more than 40 inches of snow in 2525.

   The statement p is true, and the statement q is false. Represent each of the following statements by a formula. What is their truth value if r is true? What if r is false?

(a) Niagara Falls is in New York if and only if New York City is the state capital of New York.

(b) Niagara Falls is in New York iff New York City will have more than 40 inches of snow in 2525.

(c) Niagara Falls is in New York or New York City is the state capital of New York if and only if New York City will have more than 40 inches of snow in 2525.

4. Express each of the following compound statements symbolically:

   (a) The product $xy = 0$ if and only if either $x = 0$ or $y = 0$.
   (b) The integer $n = 4$ if and only if $7n - 5 = 23$.
   (c) A necessary condition for $x = 2$ is $x^4 - x^2 - 12 = 0$.
   (d) A sufficient condition for $x = 2$ is $x^4 - x^2 - 12 = 0$.
   (e) For $x^4 - x^2 - 12 = 0$, it is both sufficient and necessary to have $x = 2$.
   (f) The sum of squares $x^2 + y^2 > 1$ iff both x and y are greater than 1.

5. Determine the truth values of the following statements (assuming that x and y are real numbers):

   (a) The product $xy = 0$ if and only if either $x = 0$ or $y = 0$.
   (b) The sum of squares $x^2 + y^2 > 1$ iff both x and y are greater than 1.
   (c) $x^2 - 4x + 3 \quad 0 \Leftrightarrow x - 3$.
   (d) $x^2 > y^2 \Leftrightarrow x > y$.

6. Determine the truth values of the following statements (assuming that x and y are real numbers):

   (a) u is a vowel if and only if b is a consonant.
   (b) $x^2 + y^2 = 0$ if and only if $x = 0$ and $y = 0$.
   (c) $x^2 - 4x + 4 = 0$ if and only if $x = 2$.
   (d) $xy \neq 0$ if and only if x and y are both positive.

7. We have seen that a number n is even if and only if $n = 2q$ for some integer q. Accordingly, what can you say about an odd number?

8. We also say that an integer n is even if it is divisible by 2, hence it can be written as $n = 2q$ for some integer q, where q represents the quotient when n is divided by 2. Thus, n is even if it is a multiple of 2. What if the integer n is a multiple of 3? What form must it take? What if n is not a multiple of 3?

2.5   Logical Equivalences

A **tautology** is a proposition that is always true, regardless of the truth values of the propositional variables it contains. A proposition that is always false is called a **contradiction**. A proposition that is neither a tautology nor a contradiction is called a **contingency**.

Example 2.5.1   From the following truth table

p	$\overline{p}$	$p \vee \overline{p}$	$p \wedge \overline{p}$
T	F	T	F
F	T	T	F

we gather that $p \vee \overline{p}$ is a tautology, and $p \wedge \overline{p}$ is a contradiction.

In words, $p \vee \overline{p}$ says that either the statement p is true, or the statement $\overline{p}$ is true (that is, p is false). This claim is always true.

The compound statement $p \wedge \overline{p}$ claims that p is true, and at the same time, $\overline{p}$ is also true (which means p is false). This is clearly impossible. Hence, $p \wedge \overline{p}$ must be false.   ▲

Example 2.5.2   Show that $(p \Rightarrow q) \Leftrightarrow (\bar{q} \Rightarrow \bar{p})$ is a tautology.

Solution: We can use a truth table to verify the claim.

p	q	$p \Rightarrow q$	$\bar{q}$	$\bar{p}$	$\bar{q} \Rightarrow \bar{p}$	$(p \Rightarrow q) \Leftrightarrow (\bar{q} \Rightarrow \bar{p})$
T	T	T	T	F	F	T
F	T	T	F	T	T	T
F	F	T	T	T	T	T

Note how we work on each component of the compound statement separately before putting them together to obtain the final answer.   ▲

Example 2.5.3   Show that the argument

"If p and q, then r. Therefore, if not r, then not p or not q."

is valid. In other words, show that the logic used in the argument is correct.

Solution: Symbolically, the argument says

$$[(p \wedge q) \Rightarrow r] \Rightarrow [\bar{r} \Rightarrow (\bar{p} \vee \bar{q})]. \tag{2.1}$$

We want to show that it is a tautology. It is easy to verify with a truth table. We can also argue that this compound statement is always true by showing that it can never be false.

Suppose, on the contrary, that (2.1) is false for some choices of p, q, and r. Then

$$(p \wedge q) \Rightarrow r \quad \text{must be true,} \qquad \text{and} \qquad \bar{r} \Rightarrow (\bar{p} \vee \bar{q}) \quad \text{must be false.}$$

For the second implication to be false, we need

$$\bar{r} \quad \text{to be true,} \qquad \text{and} \qquad \bar{p} \vee \bar{q} \quad \text{to be false.}$$

They in turn imply that r is false, and both $\bar{p}$ and $\bar{q}$ are false; hence both p and q are true. This would make $(p \wedge q) \Rightarrow r$ false, contradicting the assumption that it is true. Thus, (2.1) cannot be false, it must be a tautology.   ▲

Hands-On Exercise 2.5.1   Use a truth table to show that

$$[(p \wedge q) \Rightarrow r] \Rightarrow [\bar{r} \Rightarrow (\bar{p} \vee \bar{q})]$$

is a tautology.

Solution: We need eight combinations of truth values in p, q, and r. We list the truth values according to the following convention. In the first column for the truth values of p, fill the upper half with T and the lower half with F. In the next column for the truth values of q, repeat the same pattern, separately, with the upper half and the lower half. So we split the upper half of the second column into two halves, fill the top half with T and the lower half with F. Likewise, split the lower half of the second column into two halves, fill the top half with T and the lower half with F. Repeat the same pattern with the third column for the truth values of r, and so on if we have more propositional variables.

Complete the following table:

p	q	r	$p \wedge q$	$(p \wedge q) \Rightarrow r$	$\bar{r}$	$\bar{p}$	$\bar{q}$	$\bar{p} \vee \bar{q}$	$\bar{r} \Rightarrow (\bar{p} \vee \bar{q})$	$[(p \wedge q) \Rightarrow r] \Rightarrow [\bar{r} \Rightarrow (\bar{p} \vee \bar{q})]$
T	T	T								
T	T	F								
T	F	T								
T	F	F								
F	T	T								
F	T	F								
F	F	T								
F	F	F								

Question: If there are four propositional variables in a proposition, how many rows are there in the truth table?   △

Definition.   Two logical formulas p and q are said to be ***logically equivalent***, denoted

$$p \equiv q,$$

if $p \Leftrightarrow q$ is a tautology.   ◇

Do not write $p = q$;
instead, write $p \equiv q$.

We are *not* saying that p is equal to q. Since p and q represent two different statements, they cannot be the same. What we are saying is, they always produce the same truth value, regardless of the truth values of the underlying propositional variables. That is why we write $p \equiv q$ instead of $p = q$.

Example 2.5.4   We have learned that

$$p \Leftrightarrow q \equiv (p \Rightarrow q) \wedge (q \Rightarrow p),$$

which is the reason why we call $p \Leftrightarrow q$ a biconditional statement.   ▲

Example 2.5.5   Use truth tables to verify the following equivalent statements.

(a) $p \Rightarrow q \equiv \overline{p} \vee q$.
(b) $p \wedge (q \vee r) \equiv (p \wedge q) \vee (p \wedge r)$.

Solution: The truth tables for (a) and (b) are depicted below.

p	q	$p \Rightarrow q$	$\overline{p}$	$\overline{p} \vee q$
T	T	T	F	T
T	F	F	F	F
F	T	T	T	T
F	F	T	T	T

p	q	r	$q \vee r$	$p \wedge (q \vee r)$	$p \wedge q$	$q \wedge r$	$(p \wedge q) \vee (p \wedge r)$
T	T	T	T	T	T	T	T
T	T	F	T	T	T	F	T
T	F	T	T	T	F	T	T
T	F	F	F	F	F	F	F
F	T	T	T	F	F	F	F
F	T	F	T	F	F	F	F
F	F	T	T	F	F	F	F
F	F	F	T	F	F	F	F

Example (a) is an important result. It says that $p \Rightarrow q$ is true when one of these two things happen: (i) when p is false, (ii) otherwise (when p is true) q must be true.   ▲

Hands-On Exercise 2.5.2   Use truth tables to establish these logical equivalences.

(a) $p \Rightarrow q \equiv \overline{q} \Rightarrow \overline{p}$
(b) $p \vee p \equiv p$
(c) $p \wedge q \equiv \overline{\overline{p} \vee \overline{q}}$
(d) $p \Leftrightarrow q \equiv (p \Rightarrow q) \wedge (q \Rightarrow p)$

Solution: We have set up the table for (a), and leave the rest to you.

p	q	$p \Rightarrow q$	$\overline{q}$	$\overline{p}$	$\overline{q} \Rightarrow \overline{p}$
T	T				
T	F				
F	T				
F	F				

$\triangle$

Hands-On Exercise 2.5.3   The logical connective exclusive or, denoted $p \veebar q$, means either p or q but not both. Consequently,

$$p \veebar q \equiv (p \vee q) \wedge \overline{(p \wedge q)} \equiv (p \wedge \overline{q}) \vee (\overline{p} \wedge q).$$

Construct a truth table to verify this claim.

$\triangle$

Properties of Logical Equivalence. Denote by T and F a tautology and a contradiction, respectively. We have the following properties for any propositional variables p, q, and r.

1. **Commutative properties**: $p \vee q \equiv q \vee p,$
    $p \wedge q \equiv q \wedge p.$

2. **Associative properties**: $(p \vee q) \vee r \equiv p \vee (q \vee r),$
    $(p \wedge q) \wedge r \equiv p \wedge (q \wedge r).$

3. **Distributive laws**: $p \vee (q \wedge r) \equiv (p \vee q) \wedge (p \vee r),$
    $p \wedge (q \vee r) \equiv (p \wedge q) \vee (p \wedge r).$

4. **Idempotent laws**: $p \vee p \equiv p,$
    $p \wedge p \equiv p.$

5. **De Morgan's laws**: $\overline{p \vee q} \equiv \overline{p} \wedge \overline{q},$
    $\overline{p \wedge q} \equiv \overline{p} \vee \overline{q}.$

6. **Laws of the excluded middle**, or **inverse laws**: $p \vee \overline{p} \equiv T,$
    $p \wedge \overline{p} \equiv F.$

7. **Identity laws**: $p \vee F \equiv p,$
    $p \wedge T \equiv p.$

8. **Domination laws**: $p \vee T \equiv T,$
    $p \wedge F \equiv F.$

Two VERY important logical equivalences. Memorize them!

9. Equivalence of an implication and its contrapositive: $p \Rightarrow q \equiv \overline{q} \Rightarrow \overline{p}$.

10. Writing an implication as a disjunction: $p \Rightarrow q \equiv \overline{p} \vee q$.

Be sure you memorize the last two equivalences, because we will use them frequently in the rest of the course.

Remark.   These properties are not easy to recall. Instead of focusing on the symbolic formulas, try to understand their meanings. Let us explain them in words, and compare them to similar operations on the real numbers,

1. ***Commutative properties***: In short, they say that "the order of operation does not matter." It does not matter which of the two logical statements comes first, the result from conjunction and disjunction always produces the same truth value. Compare this to addition of real numbers: $x + y = y + x$. Subtraction is not commutative, because it is not always true that $x - y = y - x$. This explains why we have to make sure that an operation is commutative.

2. ***Associative properties***: Roughly speaking, these properties also say that "the order of operation does not matter." However, there is a key difference between them and the commutative properties.

   - Commutative properties apply to operations on *two* logical statements, but associative properties involves *three* logical statements. Since $\wedge$ and $\vee$ are *binary* operations, we can only work on a pair of statements at a time. Given the three statements p, q, and r, appearing in that order, which pair of statements should we operate on first? The answer is: it does not matter. It is the order of *grouping* (hence the term associative) that does not matter in associative properties.

   - The important consequence of the associative property is: since it does not matter on which pair of statements we should carry out the operation first, we can eliminate the parentheses and write, for example,

     $$p \vee q \vee r$$

     without worrying about any confusion.

   - Not all operations are associative. Subtraction is not associative. Given three numbers 5, 7, and 4, in that order, how should we carry out two subtractions? Which interpretation should we use:

     $$(5 - 7) - 4, \qquad \text{or} \qquad 5 - (7 - 4)?$$

     Since they lead to different results, we have to be careful where to place the parentheses.

3. ***Distributive laws***: When we mix two *different* operations on three logical statements, one of them has to work on a pair of statements first, forming an "inner" operation. This is followed by the "outer" operation to complete the compound statement. Distributive laws say that we can distribute the "outer" operation over the inner one.

4. ***Idempotent laws***: When an operation is applied to a pair of identical logical statements, the result is the same logical statement. Compare this to the equation $x^2 = x$, where x is a real number. It is true only when $x = 0$ or $x = 1$. But the logical equivalences $p \vee p \equiv p$ and $p \wedge p \equiv p$ are true for all p.

5. ***De Morgan's laws***: When we negate a disjunction (respectively, a conjunction), we have to negate the two logical statements, and change the operation from disjunction to conjunction (respectively, from conjunction to a disjunction).

6. **Laws of the excluded middle**, or **inverse laws**: Any statement is either true or false, hence $p \vee \overline{p}$ is always true. Likewise, a statement cannot be both true and false at the same time, hence $p \wedge \overline{p}$ is always false.

7. **Identity laws**: Compare them to the equation $x \cdot 1 = x$: the value of x is unchanged after multiplying by 1. We call the number 1 the multiplicative identity. For logical operations, the identity for disjunction is F, and the identity for conjunction is T.

8. **Domination laws**: Compare them to the equation $x \cdot 0 = 0$ for real numbers: the result is always 0, regardless of the value x. The "zero" for disjunction is T, and the "zero" for conjunction is F.   ◇

Example 2.5.6   What is the negation of $2 \leq x \leq 3$? Give a logical explanation as well as a graphical explanation.

Solution: The inequality $2 \leq x \leq 3$ means

$$(2 \leq x) \wedge (x \leq 3).$$

Its negation, according to De Morgan's laws, is

$$(2 > x) \vee (x > 3).$$

The inequality $2 \leq x \leq 3$ yields a closed interval. Its negation yields two open intervals. Their graphical representations on the real number line are depicted below.

$$(2 \leq x) \wedge (x \leq 3) \qquad\qquad\qquad (2 > x) \vee (x > 3)$$

Take note of the two endpoints 2 and 3. They change from inclusion to exclusion when we take negation.   ▲

Hands-On Exercise 2.5.4   Since $0 \leq x \leq 1$ means "$0 \leq x$ and $x \leq 1$," its negation should be "$0 > x$ or $x > 1$," which is often written as "$x < 0$ or $x > 1$." Explain why it is inappropriate, and indeed incorrect, to write "$0 > x > 1$."   *See Example 2.2.5.*

                                                                                   △

Example 2.5.7   Expand $(p \wedge q) \vee (r \wedge s)$.

Solution: Compare this problem to the expansion of $(x + y)(u + v)$. We use the distributive law twice to obtain

$$\begin{aligned}
(x + y)(u + v) &= x(u + v) + y(u + v) \\
&= xu + xv + yu + yv.
\end{aligned}$$

Let us follow the same procedure to expand $(p \wedge q) \vee (r \wedge s)$. We need to apply the distributive law twice. The first time, regard $(r \wedge s)$ as a single statement, and distribute it over $p \wedge q$. In the second round, distribute p and q, separately, over $r \wedge s$. The complete solution is shown below.

$$\begin{aligned}
(p \wedge q) \vee (r \wedge s) &\equiv [p \vee (r \wedge s)] \wedge [q \vee (r \wedge s)] \\
&\equiv (p \vee r) \wedge (p \vee s) \wedge (q \vee r) \wedge (q \vee s).
\end{aligned}$$

We can also proceed as follows:

$$(p \wedge q) \vee (r \wedge s) \quad \equiv \quad [(p \wedge q) \vee r] \wedge [(p \wedge q) \vee s]$$
$$\equiv \quad (p \vee r) \wedge (q \vee r) \wedge (p \vee s) \wedge (q \vee s).$$

The two results are identical because $\wedge$ is commutative.   ▲

Hands-On Exercise 2.5.5   Expand $(p \vee q) \wedge (r \vee s)$.

△

Example 2.5.8   We have used a truth table to verify that

$$[(p \wedge q) \Rightarrow r] \Rightarrow [\overline{r} \Rightarrow (\overline{p} \vee \overline{q})]$$

is a tautology. We can use the properties of logical equivalence to show that this compound statement is logically equivalent to T. This kind of proof is usually more difficult to follow, so it is a good idea to supply the explanation in each step. Here is a complete proof:

$$[(p \wedge q) \Rightarrow r] \Rightarrow [\overline{r} \Rightarrow (\overline{p} \vee \overline{q})] \quad \equiv \quad \overline{(p \wedge q) \Rightarrow r} \vee [\overline{r} \Rightarrow (\overline{p} \vee \overline{q})] \quad \text{(implication as disjunction)}$$
$$\equiv \quad \overline{(p \wedge q) \Rightarrow r} \vee [\overline{\overline{p} \vee \overline{q}} \Rightarrow r] \quad \text{(implication as disjunction)}$$
$$\equiv \quad \overline{(p \wedge q) \Rightarrow r} \vee [(p \wedge q) \Rightarrow r] \quad \text{(De Morgan's law)}$$
$$\equiv \quad T \qquad\qquad\qquad\qquad\qquad\qquad \text{(inverse law)}$$

This is precisely what we called the left-to-right method for proving an identity (in this case, a logical equivalence).   ▲

Example 2.5.9   Write $\overline{p \Rightarrow q}$ as a conjunction.

Wrong ways to negate an implication.

Solution: It is important to remember that

$$\overline{p \Rightarrow q} \not\equiv q \Rightarrow p,$$

and

$$\overline{p \Rightarrow q} \not\equiv \overline{p} \Rightarrow \overline{q}$$

either. Instead, since $p \Rightarrow q \equiv \overline{p} \vee q$, it follows from De Morgan's law that

$$\overline{p \Rightarrow q} \equiv \overline{\overline{p} \vee q} \equiv p \wedge \overline{q}.$$

How to negate an implication?

Alternatively, we can argue as follows. Interpret $\overline{p \Rightarrow q}$ as saying $p \Rightarrow q$ is false. This requires p to be true and q to be false, which translates into $p \wedge \overline{q}$. Thus, $\overline{p \Rightarrow q} \equiv p \wedge \overline{q}$.   ▲

Summary and Review

- Two logical statements are logically equivalent if they always produce the same truth value.
- Consequently, $p \equiv q$ is same as saying $p \Leftrightarrow q$ is a tautology.
- Beside distributive and De Morgan's laws, remember these two equivalences as well; they are very helpful when dealing with implications.

$$p \Rightarrow q \equiv \overline{q} \Rightarrow \overline{p} \qquad \text{and} \qquad p \Rightarrow q \equiv \overline{p} \vee q.$$

Exercises 2.5

1. Use a truth table to verify the De Morgan's law $\overline{p \vee q} \equiv \overline{p} \wedge \overline{q}$.

2. Use truth tables to verify the two associative properties.

3. Construct a truth table for each formula below. Which ones are tautologies?

    (a) $(\overline{p} \vee q) \Rightarrow p$
    (b) $(p \Rightarrow q) \vee (p \Rightarrow \overline{q})$
    (c) $(p \Rightarrow q) \Rightarrow r$

4. Use truth tables to verify these logical equivalences.

    (a) $(p \wedge q) \Leftrightarrow p \equiv p \Rightarrow q$
    (b) $(p \wedge q) \Rightarrow r \equiv p \Rightarrow (\overline{q} \vee r)$
    (c) $(p \Rightarrow \overline{q}) \wedge (p \Rightarrow \overline{r}) \equiv p \wedge \overline{(q \vee r)}$

5. Use only the properties of logical equivalences to verify (b) and (c) in Problem 4.

6. Determine whether formulas u and v are logically equivalent (you may use truth tables or properties of logical equivalences).

    (a) $u : (p \Rightarrow q) \wedge (p \Rightarrow \overline{q})$ $\quad\quad$ $v : \overline{p}$
    (b) $u : p \Rightarrow q$ $\quad\quad$ $v : q \Rightarrow p$
    (c) $u : p \Leftrightarrow q$ $\quad\quad$ $v : q \Leftrightarrow p$
    (d) $u : (p \Rightarrow q) \Rightarrow r$ $\quad\quad$ $v : p \Rightarrow (q \Rightarrow r)$

7. Find the converse, inverse, and contrapositive of these implications.

    (a) If triangle ABC is isosceles and contains an angle of 45 degrees, then ABC is a right triangle.
    (b) If quadrilateral $ABCD$ is a square, then it is both a rectangle and a rhombus.
    (c) If quadrilateral $ABCD$ has two sides of equal length, then it is either a rectangle or a rhombus.

8. Negate the following implications:

    (a) $x^2 > 0 \Rightarrow x > 0$.
    (b) If $PQRS$ is a square, then $PQRS$ is a parallelogram.
    (c) If $n > 1$ is prime, then $n + 1$ is composite.
    (d) If x and y are integers such that $xy \geq 1$, then either $x \geq 1$ or $y \geq 1$.

9. Determine whether the following formulas are true or false:

    (a) $\overline{p \Leftrightarrow q} \equiv \overline{p} \Leftrightarrow \overline{q}$
    (b) $(p \Rightarrow q) \vee (p \Rightarrow \overline{q}) \equiv \overline{p}$
    (c) $p \Rightarrow q \equiv q \Rightarrow p$

10. Determine whether the following formulas are true or false:

    (a) $(p \Rightarrow q) \Rightarrow r \equiv p \Rightarrow (q \Rightarrow r)$
    (b) $p \Rightarrow (q \vee r) \equiv (p \Rightarrow q) \vee (p \Rightarrow r)$
    (c) $p \Rightarrow (q \wedge r) \equiv (p \Rightarrow q) \wedge (p \Rightarrow r)$

11. Which of the following statements are equivalent to the statement "if $x^2 > 0$, then $x > 0$"?

    (a) If $x > 0$, then $x^2 > 0$.
    (b) If $x \leq 0$, then $x^2 \leq 0$.
    (c) If $x^2 \leq 0$, then $x \leq 0$.
    (d) If $x^2 \not> 0$, then $x \not> 0$.

12. Determine whether the following formulas are tautologies, contradictions, or neither:

   (a) $(p \Rightarrow q) \wedge \overline{p}$
   (b) $(p \Rightarrow \overline{q}) \wedge (p \wedge q)$
   (c) $(p \Rightarrow \overline{q}) \wedge q$

13. Simplify the following formulas:

   (a) $p \wedge (p \wedge q)$ (b) $\overline{\overline{p} \vee q}$ (c) $\overline{p \Rightarrow \overline{q}}$

14. Simplify the following formulas:

   (a) $(p \Rightarrow \overline{q}) \wedge (\overline{q} \Rightarrow p)$ (b) $\overline{p \wedge \overline{q}}$ (c) $p \wedge (\overline{p} \vee q)$

2.6   Logical Quantifiers

The expression

$$x > 5$$

is neither true nor false. In fact, we cannot even determine its truth value unless we know the value of x. This is an example of a **propositional function**, because it behaves like a function of x, it becomes a proposition when a specific value is assigned to x. Propositional functions are also called **predicates**.

Example 2.6.1   Denote the propositional function "$x > 5$" by $p(x)$. We often write

$$p(x): \quad x > 5.$$

It is not a proposition because its truth value is undecidable, but $p(6)$, $p(3)$ and $p(-1)$ are propositions.   ▲

Example 2.6.2   Define

$$q(x,y): \quad x + y = 1.$$

Which of the following are propositions; which are not?

   (a) $q(x, y)$
   (b) $q(x, 3)$
   (c) $q(1, 1)$
   (d) $q(5, -4)$

For those that are, determine their truth values.

Solution: Both (a) and (b) are not propositions, because they contain at least one variable. Both (c) and (d) are propositions; $q(1, 1)$ is false, and $q(5, -4)$ is true.   ▲

Hands-On Exercise 2.6.1   Determine the truth values of these statements, where $q(x, y)$ is defined in Example 2.6.2.

   (a) $q(5, -7)$

   (b) $q(-6, 7)$

   (c) $q(x + 1, -x)$

△

Although a propositional function is not a proposition, we can form a proposition by means of **quantification**. The idea is to specify whether the propositional function is true for all or for some values that the underlying variables can take on.

Definition. The **universal quantification** of $p(x)$ is the proposition in any of the following forms:

- $p(x)$ is true for all values of x.
- For all x, $p(x)$.
- For each x, $p(x)$.
- For every x, $p(x)$.
- Given any x, $p(x)$.

All of them are symbolically denoted by

$$\forall x \, p(x),$$

which is pronounced as

"for all x, $p(x)$".

The symbol $\forall$ is called the **universal quantifier**, and can be extended to several variables. $\Diamond$

Write $\forall$, not A.

Example 2.6.3 The statement

"For any real number x, we always have $x^2 \geq 0$"

is true. Symbolically, we can write

$$\forall x \in \mathbb{R} \, (x^2 \geq 0), \qquad \text{or} \qquad \forall x \, (x \in \mathbb{R} \Rightarrow x^2 \geq 0).$$

The second form is a bit wordy, but could be useful in some situations. ▲

Example 2.6.4 The statement

$$\forall x \in \mathbb{R} \, (x > 5)$$

is false because x is not always greater than 5. To disprove a claim, it suffices to provide only one counterexample. We can use $x = 4$ as a counterexample.

However, examples cannot be used to prove a universally quantified statement. Consider the statement

$$\forall x \in \mathbb{R} \, (x^2 \geq 0).$$

By direct calculations, one may demonstrate that $x^2 \geq 0$ is true for many x-values. But it does not *prove* that it is true for *every* x, because there may be a counterexample that we have not found yet. We have to use mathematical and logical argument to prove a statement of the form "$\forall x \, p(x)$." ▲

Counterexamples can be used to disprove a claim.

Examples alone do not prove a statement of the form "$\forall x \, p(x)$".

Example 2.6.5 The statement

"Every Discrete Mathematics student has taken Calculus I and Calculus II"

is clearly a universally quantified proposition. To express it in a logical formula, we can use an implication:

$$\forall x \, (x \text{ is a Discrete Mathematics student} \Rightarrow x \text{ has taken Calculus I and Calculus II})$$

An alternative is to say

$$\forall x \in S \, (x \text{ has taken Calculus I and Calculus II})$$

where S represents the set of all Discrete Mathematics students. Although the second form looks simpler, we must define what S stands for. ▲

See Example 2.6.3.

Definition.   The *existential quantification* of $p(x)$ takes one of these forms:

- There exists an x such that $p(x)$.
- For some x, $p(x)$.
- There is some x such that $p(x)$.

Write ∃, not E.

We write, in symbol,

$$\exists x \, p(x),$$

which is pronounced as

"There exists x such that $p(x)$."

The symbol $\exists$ is called the *existential quantifier*. It can be extended to several variables. ◇

One example suffices to prove a statement of the form "$\exists x \, p(x)$."

Example 2.6.6   To prove that a statement of the form "$\exists x \, p(x)$" is true, it suffices to find an example of x such that $p(x)$ is true. Using this guideline, can you determine whether these two propositions

(a) $\exists x \in \mathbb{R} \, (x > 5)$

(b) $\exists x \in \mathbb{R} \, (\sqrt{x} = 0)$

are true?

Solution: (a) True. For example: $x = 6$.

(b) True. For example: $x = 0$.   ▲

Example 2.6.7   The proposition

"There exists a prime number x such that $x + 2$ is also prime"

is true. We call such a pair of primes *twin primes*.   ▲

Hands-On Exercise 2.6.2   Name a few more examples of twin primes.

                                                                                                          △

Example 2.6.8   The proposition

"There exists a real number x such that $x > 5$"

can be expressed, symbolically, as

$$\exists x \in \mathbb{R} \, (x > 5), \qquad \text{or} \qquad \exists x \, (x \in \mathbb{R} \wedge x > 5).$$

Notice that in an existential quantification, we use $\wedge$ instead of $\Rightarrow$ to specify that x is a real number.   ▲

Hands-On Exercise 2.6.3   Determine the truth value of each of the following propositions:

(a) For any prime number x, the number $x + 1$ is composite.

(b) For any prime number $x > 2$, the number $x + 1$ is composite.

(c) There exists an integer k such that $2k + 1$ is even.

(d) For all integers k, the integer $2k$ is even.

(e) For any real number x, if x^2 is an integer, then x is also an integer.

$\triangle$

Hands-On Exercise 2.6.4   The proposition

"The square of any real number is positive"

is a universal quantification

"For any real number x, $x^2 > 0$."

Is it true or false?

$\triangle$

Example 2.6.9   When multiple quantifiers are present, the order in which they appear is important. Determine whether these two statements are true or false.

(a) $\forall x \in \mathbb{Z}\, \exists y \in \mathbb{R}^* \,(xy < 1)$

(b) $\exists y \in \mathbb{R}^* \,\forall x \in \mathbb{Z}\, (xy < 1)$

Here, $\mathbb{R}^*$ denotes the set of all nonzero real numbers.

Solution: (a) To prove that the statement is true, we need to show that no matter what integer x we start with, we can always find a nonzero real number y such that $xy < 1$. For $x \leq 0$, we can pick $y = 1$, which makes $xy = x \leq 0 < 1$. For $x > 0$, let $y = \frac{1}{x+1}$, then $xy = \frac{x}{x+1} < 1$. This concludes the proof that the first statement is true.

(b) Let $y = 1$. Can we find an integer x such that $xy \not< 1$? Definitely! For example, we can set $x = 2$. This counterexample shows that the second statement is false. ▲

Hands-On Exercise 2.6.5   True or false: $\exists y \in \mathbb{R}\,\forall x \in \mathbb{Z}\,(xy < 1)$?

$\triangle$

Example 2.6.10   Many theorems in mathematics can be expressed as quantified statements. Consider

"If x is rational and y is irrational, then $x + y$ is irrational."

This is same as saying

"Whenever x is rational and y is irrational, then $x + y$ is irrational."

The keyword "whenever" suggests that we should use a universal quantifier.

$$\forall x, y \, (x \text{ is rational} \land y \text{ is irrational} \Rightarrow x + y \text{ is irrational}).$$

It can also be written as

$$\forall x \in \mathbb{Q} \, \forall y \notin \mathbb{Q} \, (x + y \text{ is irrational}).$$

Although this form looks complicated and seems difficult to understand (primarily because it is quite symbolic, hence appears to be abstract and incomprehensible to many students), it provides an easy form for negation. See the discussion below.

The fact that an implication can be expressed as a universally quantified statement sounds familiar. See Example 2.3.7.   ▲

We shall learn several basic proof techniques in Chapter 3. Some of them require negating a logical statement. Since many mathematical results are stated as quantified statements, it is necessary for us to learn how to negate a quantification. The rule is rather simple. Interchange $\forall$ and $\exists$, and negate the statement that is being quantified. In other words,

$$\overline{\forall x \, p(x)} \equiv \exists x \, \overline{p(x)}, \qquad \text{and} \qquad \overline{\exists x \, p(x)} \equiv \forall x \, \overline{p(x)}.$$

If we have $\forall x \in \mathbb{Z}$, we only change it to $\exists x \in \mathbb{Z}$ when we take negation. It should *not* be negated as $\exists x \notin \mathbb{Z}$. The reason is: we are only negating the quantification, not the membership of x. In symbols, we write

$$\overline{\forall x \in \mathbb{Z} \, p(x)} \equiv \exists x \in \mathbb{Z} \, \overline{p(x)}.$$

The negation of "$\exists x \in \mathbb{Z} \, p(x)$" is obtained in a similar manner.

Example 2.6.11   We find

$$\overline{\forall x \in \mathbb{Z} \, \exists y \in \mathbb{R}^* \, (xy < 1)} \equiv \exists x \in \mathbb{Z} \, \forall y \in \mathbb{R}^* \, (xy \geq 1),$$

and

$$\overline{\exists y \in \mathbb{R}^* \, \forall x \in \mathbb{Z} \, (xy < 1)} \equiv \forall y \in \mathbb{R}^* \, \exists x \in \mathbb{Z} \, (xy \geq 1).$$

Remember that we do not change the membership of x and y.   ▲

Recall how to negate an implication.

Hands-On Exercise 2.6.6   Negate the propositions in Hands-On Exercise 2.6.3.

△

Example 2.6.12   The statement

"All real numbers x satisfy $x^2 \geq 0$"

can be written as, symbolically, $\forall x \in \mathbb{R} \, (x^2 \geq 0)$. Its negation is $\exists x \in \mathbb{R} \, (x^2 < 0)$. In words, it says "There exists a real number x that satisfies $x^2 < 0$."   ▲

Hands-On Exercise 2.6.7   Negate the statement

"Every Discrete Mathematics student has taken Calculus I and Calculus II."

△

Summary and Review

- There are two ways to quantify a propositional function: universal quantification and existential quantification.
- They are written in the form of "$\forall x\, p(x)$" and "$\exists x\, p(x)$" respectively.
- To negate a quantified statement, change $\forall$ to $\exists$, and $\exists$ to $\forall$, and then negate the statement.

Exercises 2.6

1. Consider these propositional functions:

$$
\begin{array}{ll}
p(n): & n \text{ is prime} \\
q(n): & n \text{ is even} \\
r(n): & n > 2
\end{array}
$$

   Express these formulas in words:

   (a) $\exists n \in \mathbb{Z}\,(p(n) \wedge q(n))$
   (b) $\forall n \in \mathbb{Z}\,[r(n) \Rightarrow p(n) \vee q(n)]$
   (c) $\exists n \in \mathbb{Z}\,[p(n) \wedge (q(n) \vee r(n)]$
   (d) $\forall n \in \mathbb{Z}\,[(p(n) \wedge r(n)) \Rightarrow \overline{q(n)}]$

2. Give a formula for each of the following statements:

   (a) For every even integer n there exists an integer k such that $n = 2k$.
   (b) There exists a right triangle T that is an isosceles triangle.
   (c) Given any quadrilateral Q, if Q is a parallelogram and Q has two adjacent sides that are perpendicular, then Q is a rectangle.

   Recall that the set of all even integers can be written as $2\mathbb{Z}$.

3. Determine whether these statements are true or false:

   (a) There exists an even prime integer.
   (b) There exist integers s and t such that $1 < s < t < 187$ and $st = 187$.
   (c) There is an integer m such that both $m/2$ is an integer and, for every integer k, $m/(2k)$ is not an integer.
   (d) Given any real numbers x and y, $x^2 - 2xy + y^2 > 0$.
   (e) For every integer n, there exists an integer m such that $m > n^2$.

4. Determine whether these statements are true or false:

   (a) There is a rational number x such that $x^2 \leq 0$.
   (b) There exists a number x such that for every real number y, $xy = 0$.
   (c) For all $x \in \mathbb{Z}$, either x is even, or x is odd.
   (d) There exists a unique number x such that $x^2 = 1$.

5. Find the negation (in simplest form) of each formula.

   (a) $\forall x < 0\, \forall y, z \in \mathbb{R}\,(y < z \Rightarrow xy > xz)$
   (b) $\forall x \in \mathbb{Z}\,[p(x) \vee q(x)]$
   (c) $\forall x, y \in \mathbb{R}\,[p(x, y) \Rightarrow q(x, y)]$

6. Negate the following statements:

   (a) For all real numbers x, there exists an integer y such that $p(x, y)$ implies $q(x, y)$.
   (b) There exists a rational number x such that for all integers y, either $p(x, y)$ or $r(x, y)$ is true.
   (c) For all integers x, there exists an integer y such that if $p(x, y)$ is true, then there exists an integer z so that $q(x, y, z)$ is true.

7. For each statement, (i) represent it as a formula, (ii) find the negation (in simplest form) of this formula, and (iii) express the negation in words.

   (a) For all real numbers x and y, $x + y = y + x$.
   (b) For every positive real number x there exists a real number y such that $y^2 = x$.
   (c) There exists a real number y such that, for every integer x, $2x^2 + 1 > x^2 y$.

8. For each statement, (i) represent it as a formula, (ii) find the negation (in simplest form) of this formula, and (iii) express the negation in words.

   (a) There exist rational numbers x_1 and x_2 such that $x_1 < x_2$ and $x_1^3 - x_1 > x_2^3 - x_2$.
   (b) For all real numbers x and y there exists an integer z such that $2z = x + y$.
   (c) For all real numbers x_1 and x_2, if $x_1^3 + x_1 - 2 = x_2^3 + x_2 - 2$, then $x_1 = x_2$.

9. The easiest way to negate the proposition

   "A square must be a parallelogram"

   is to say

   "It is not true that a square must be a parallelogram."

   Yet, it is not the same as saying

   "A square must not be a parallelogram."

   Can you explain why? What are other ways to express its negation in words?

10. Negate these statements:

   (a) All squared numbers are positive.
   (b) All basketball players are over 6 feet tall.
   (c) No quarterback is under 6 feet tall.

Chapter 3

Proof Techniques

3.1 An Introduction to Proof Techniques

A proof is a logical argument that verifies the validity of a statement. A good proof must be correct, but it also needs to be clear enough for others to understand. In the following sections, we want to show you how to write mathematical arguments. It takes practice to learn how to write mathematical proofs; you have to keep trying! We would like to start with some suggestions.

1. **Write at the level of your peers**. A common question asked by many students is: how much detail should I include in a proof? One simple guideline is to write at the level that your peers can understand. Although you can skip the detailed computation, be sure to include the major steps in an argument.

2. **Use symbols and notations appropriately**. Do not use mathematical symbols as abbreviations. For example, do not write "x is a number > 4." Use "x is a number greater than 4" instead. Do not use symbols excessively either. It is often clearer if we express our idea in words. Finally, do not start a sentence with a symbol, as in "Suppose $xy > 0$. x and y have the same signs." It would look better if we combine the two sentences, and write "Suppose $xy > 0$, then x and y have the same signs."

3. **Display long and important equations separately**. Make the key mathematical results stand out by displaying them separately on their own. Be sure to center these expressions. Number them if you need to refer to them later. See Examples 1.3.1 and 1.3.2.

4. **Write in complete sentences, with proper usage of grammar and punctuation**. A proof is, after all, a piece of writing. It should conform to the usual writing rules. Use complete sentences, and do not forget to check the grammar and punctuation.

5. **Start with a draft**. Prepare a draft. When you feel it is correct, start revising it: check the accuracy, remove redundancy, and simplify the sentence structure. Organize the argument into short paragraphs to enhance the readability of a proof. Go over the proof and refine it further.

Some proofs only require direct computation.

Example 3.1.1 Let a and b be two rational numbers such that $a < b$. Show that the weighted average $\frac{1}{3}a + \frac{2}{3}b$ is a rational number between a and b.

Solution: Since a and b are rational numbers, we can write $a = \frac{m}{n}$ and $b = \frac{p}{q}$ for some integers m, n, p, and q, where $n, q \neq 0$. Then

$$\frac{1}{3}a + \frac{2}{3}b = \frac{1}{3} \cdot \frac{m}{n} + \frac{2}{3} \cdot \frac{p}{q} = \frac{mq + 2np}{3nq}$$

is clearly a rational number because $mq + 2np$ and $3np$ are integers, and $3nq \neq 0$. Since $a < b$, we know $b - a > 0$. It follows that

$$\left(\frac{1}{3} a + \frac{2}{3} b \right) - a = \frac{2}{3} (b - a) > 0,$$

which means $\frac{1}{3} a + \frac{2}{3} b > a$. In a similar fashion, we also find $\frac{1}{3} a + \frac{2}{3} b < b$. Thus, $\frac{1}{3} a + \frac{2}{3} b$ is a rational number between a and b.   ▲

Hands-On Exercise 3.1.1   Show that $\frac{1}{3} a + \frac{2}{3} b$ is closer to b than to a.

Hint: Compute the distance between a and $\frac{1}{3} a + \frac{2}{3} b$, and compare it to the distance between $\frac{1}{3} a + \frac{2}{3} b$ and b.

△

Sometimes, we can use a ***constructive proof*** when a proposition claims that certain values or quantities exist.

Example 3.1.2   Prove that every positive integer can be written in the form of $2^e t$ for some nonnegative integer e and some odd integer t.

Remark.   The problem statement only says "every positive integer." It often helps if we assign a name to the integer; it will make it easier to go through the discussion. Consequently, we customarily start a proof with the phrase "Let n be ... "   ◇

Solution: Let n be a positive integer. Keep dividing n by 2 until an odd number t remains. Let e be the number of times we factor out a copy of 2. It is clear that e is nonnegative, and we have found $n = 2^e t$.   ▲

Hands-On Exercise 3.1.2   Express 6, 40, 32, and 15 in the form stated in Example 3.1.2.

△

Example 3.1.3   Given any positive integer n, show that there exist n consecutive composite positive integers.

Solution: For each positive integer n, we claim that the n integers

$$(n+1)! + 2, \quad (n+1)! + 3, \quad \ldots \quad (n+1)! + n, \quad (n+1)! + (n+1)$$

are composite. Here is the reason. For each i, where $2 \leq i \leq n+1$, the integer

$$
\begin{aligned}
(n+1)! + i &= 1 \cdot 2 \cdot 3 \cdots (i-1)i(i+1) \cdots (n+1) + i \\
&= i\left[1 \cdot 2 \cdot 3 \cdots (i-1)(i+1) \cdots (n+1) + 1 \right]
\end{aligned}
$$

is divisible by i and greater than i, and hence is composite.   ▲

Hands-On Exercise 3.1.3 Construct five consecutive positive integers that are composite. Verify their compositeness by means of factorization.

$\triangle$

Example 3.1.4 Let m and n be positive integers. Show that, if mn is even, then an $m \times n$ chessboard can be fully covered by non-overlapping dominoes.

Remark. This time, the names m and n have already been assigned to the two positive integers. Thus, we can refer to them in the proof without an introduction.

Solution: Since mn is even, one of the two integers m and n must be even. Without loss of generality (since the other case is similar), we may assume m, the number of rows, is even. Then $m = 2t$ for some integer t. Each column can be filled with $m/2 = t$ non-overlapping dominoes placed vertically. As a result, the entire chessboard can be covered with nt non-overlapping vertical dominoes. ▲

Hands-On Exercise 3.1.4 Show that, between any two rational numbers a and b, where $a < b$, there exists another rational number.

Hint: Try the midpoint of the interval $[a, b]$.

$\triangle$

Hands-On Exercise 3.1.5 Show that, between any two rational numbers a and b, where $a < b$, there exists another rational number closer to b than to a.

Hint: Use a weighted average of a and b.

$\triangle$

Sometimes a non-constructive proof can be used to show the existence of a certain quantity that satisfies some conditions. We have learned two such existence theorems from calculus.

Theorem 3.1.1 (Mean Value Theorem) *Let f be a differentiable function defined over a closed interval $[a, b]$. Then there exists a number c strictly inside the open interval (a, b) such that $f'(c) = \frac{f(b)-f(a)}{b-a}$.*

Theorem 3.1.2 (Intermediate Value Theorem) *Let f be a function that is continuous over a closed interval $[a, b]$. Then f assumes all values between $f(a)$ and $f(b)$. In other words, for any value t between $f(a)$ and $f(b)$, there exists a number c inside $[a, b]$ such that $f(c) = t$.*

Both results only guarantee the existence of a number c with some specific property; they do not tell us how to find this number c. Nevertheless, the Mean-Value Theorem plays a very important role in analysis; many of its applications are beyond the scope of this course. We could, however, demonstrate an application of the Intermediate Value Theorem.

Corollary 3.1.3 *Let f be a continuous function defined over a closed interval $[a, b]$. If $f(a)$ and $f(b)$ have opposite signs, then the equation $f(x) = 0$ has a solution between a and b.*

Proof: According to the Intermediate Value Theorem, $f(x)$ can take on any value between $f(a)$ and $f(b)$. Since they have opposite signs, 0 is a number between them. Hence, $f(c) = 0$ for some number c between a and b.   ∎

Example 3.1.5   The function $f(x) = 5x^3 - 2x - 1$ is a polynomial function, which is known to be continuous over the real numbers. Since $f(0) = -1$ and $f(1) = 2$, Corollary 3.1.3 implies that there exists a number between 0 and 1 such that $5x^3 - 2x - 1 = 0$.   ▲

Hands-On Exercise 3.1.6   Show that the equation $1 + x \cos x = 0$ has at least one real solution between 0 and $\frac{\pi}{2}$.

Hint: No function is mentioned here, so you need to define a function, say $g(x)$. Next, you need to make sure that $g(x)$ is continuous. What else do you need to do before you can apply Corollary 3.1.3?

△

Summary and Review

- Sometimes we can prove a statement by showing how the result can be obtained through a construction, and we can describe the construction in an algorithm.
- Sometimes all we need to do is apply an existence theorem to verify the existence of a certain quantity.

Exercises 3.1

1. Show that a chessboard with 7 rows and 12 columns can be covered by non-overlapping dominoes.

2. Show that there is a rational number between 1 and 5 whose distance from 5 is seven times as long as its distance from 1.

3. Show that the equation $x^3 - 12x + 2 = 0$ has at least three real solutions.

4. Show that if the equation $(x^2 + 4)(x - 2)(3x + 5) = 0$ has a real solution, the solution must be either $x = 2$ or $x = -\frac{5}{3}$.

5. Show that given any rational number x, there exists an integer y such that $x^2 y$ is an integer.

   Hint: Since x is rational, we can write $x = \frac{m}{n}$ for some integers m and n, where $n \neq 0$. All you need to do is to describe y in terms of m and n.

6. Show that given any rational number x, and any positive integer k, there exists an integer y such that $x^k y$ is an integer.

7. Show that there exists an integer n such that n, $n + 2$ and $n + 4$ are all primes.

8. Find a counterexample to the following claim: For any positive integer n, if n is prime, then $n^2 + 4$ is also prime.

3.2   Direct Proofs

To show that a statement q is true, follow these steps:

1. Either find a result that states $p \Rightarrow q$, or prove that $p \Rightarrow q$ is true.
2. Show or verify that p is true.
3. Conclude that q must be true.

The logic is valid because if $p \Rightarrow q$ is true and p is true, then q must be true. Symbolically, we are saying that the logical formula

$$[(p \Rightarrow q) \wedge p] \Rightarrow q$$

is a tautology (we can easily verify this with a truth table). Symbolically, we present the argument as

$$p \Rightarrow q$$
$$\underline{\hspace{1cm} p \hspace{1cm}}$$
$$\therefore \quad q$$

Such an argument is called **modus ponens** or the **law of detachment**.

Example 3.2.1   The argument

$$b^2 > 4ac \Rightarrow ax^2 + bx + c = 0 \text{ has two real solutions.}$$
$$\underline{x^2 - 5x + 6 \text{ satisfies } b^2 > 4ac. \hspace{2cm}}$$
$$\therefore \quad x^2 - 5x + 6 = 0 \text{ has two real solutions.}$$

is an example of modus ponens.   ▲

It is clear that implications play an important role in mathematical proofs. If we have a sequence of implications, we could join them "head to tail" to form another implication:

$$p \Rightarrow q$$
$$\underline{q \Rightarrow r}$$
$$\therefore \quad p \Rightarrow r$$

This is called the **law of syllogism**.

Example 3.2.2   The argument

German shepherds are dogs.
Dogs are mammals.
$$\underline{\text{Mammals are vertebrates.} \hspace{2cm}}$$
$$\therefore \quad \text{German shepherds are vertebrates.}$$

is valid because of the law of syllogism.   ▲

The big question is, how can we prove an implication? The most basic approach is the **direct proof**:

1. Assume p is true.   *Proving $p \Rightarrow q$ via*
2. Deduce from p that q is true.   *a direct proof.*

The important thing to remember is: use the information derived from p to show that q is true. This is how a typical direct proof may look:

> *Proof:*   Assume p is true. Then ...
>
> Because of p, we find ...
>
>   ... Therefore q is true.   ∎

Example 3.2.3   Prove that if an $m \times n$ chessboard can be fully covered by non-overlapping dominoes, then mn must be even.

Solution: Assume the chessboard can be covered by non-overlapping dominoes, and let t be the number of dominoes that cover the chessboard. Then the chessboard must contain $2t$ squares. Hence $mn = 2t$, which means mn must be an even number.   ▲

Before we continue with more examples, we would like to introduce the formal definition of even and odd integers.

Definition.   An integer is ***even*** if it can be written as $2q$ for some integer q, and ***odd*** if it can be written as $2q + 1$ for some integer q.   ◇

We do not have to use q to denote the integer that, when multiplied by 2, produces an even integer. Any letter will work, provided that we mention it is an integer. For example, if n is an even integer, then we can write $n = 2t$ for some integer t. The notion of even integers can be further generalized.

Definition.   Let m be a nonzero integer. An integer is said to be a ***multiple*** of m if it can be written as mq for some integer q.   ◇

We are now ready to study more examples.

Example 3.2.4   Show that the square of an odd integer is odd.

Solution: Let n be an odd integer. Then $n = 2t + 1$ for some integer t, and

$$n^2 = (2t + 1)^2 = 4t^2 + 4t + 1 = 2(2t^2 + 2t) + 1,$$

where $2t^2 + 2t$ is an integer. Hence, n^2 is odd.   ▲

Hands-On Exercise 3.2.1   Let n be an integer. Show that if n is odd, then n^3 is odd.

△

Example 3.2.5   Show that the product of two odd integers is odd.

Describe your goal.   *Solution:*   Let x and y be two odd integers. We want to prove that xy is odd. Then $x = 2s + 1$ and $y = 2t + 1$ for some integers s and t, and

$$xy = (2s + 1)(2t + 1) = 4st + 2s + 2t + 1 = 2(2st + s + t) + 1,$$

where $2st + s + t$ is an integer. Therefore, xy is odd.   ▲

In this proof, we need to use two different quantities s and t to describe x and y because they need not be the same. If we write $x = 2s + 1$ and $y = 2s + 1$, we are in effect saying that $x = y$. We have to stress that s and t are integers, because just saying $x = 2s + 1$ and $y = 2t + 1$ does not guarantee x and y are odd. For instance, the even number 4 can be written as $2 \cdot \frac{3}{2} + 1$, *Pay attention to* which is of the form $2s + 1$. It is obvious that 4 is not odd. Even though we can write a number *the details!* in the form $2s + 1$, it does not necessarily mean the number must be odd, *unless* we know with certainty that s is an integer. This example illustrates the importance of paying attention to the details in our writing.

Example 3.2.6   Show that if $x^3 - 7x^2 + x - 7 = 0$, then $x = 7$.

Solution: Assume $x^3 - 7x^2 + x - 7 = 0$. Since

$$x^3 - 7x^2 + x - 7 = x^2(x - 7) + (x - 7) = (x^2 + 1)(x - 7),$$

if it is equal to zero, we need either $x^2 + 1 = 0$, or $x - 7 = 0$. Since $x^2 + 1$ can never be zero, we must have $x - 7 = 0$; thus $x = 7$.   ▲

Hands-On Exercise 3.2.2   Show that if $x^3 + 6x^2 + 12x + 8 = 0$, then $x = -2$.

△

The last example demonstrates a technique called ***proof by cases***. There are two possibilities, namely, either (i) $x^2 + 1 = 0$, or (ii) $x - 7 = 0$. The final conclusion is drawn after we study these two cases separately.

Example 3.2.7   Show that if an integer n is not divisible by 3, then $n^2 - 1$ must be a multiple of 3.

Remark.   The letter n has been used to identify the integer of interest to us, and it appears in the hypothesis of the implication that we want to prove. Nonetheless, many authors would start their proofs with the familiar phrase "Let n be ... ."   ◇

Solution: Let n be an integer that is not divisible by 3. When it is divided by 3, the remainder is 1 or 2. Hence, $n = 3q + 1$ or $n = 3q + 2$ for some integer q.

- Case 1: If $n = 3q + 1$ for some integer q, then

$$n^2 - 1 = 9q^2 + 6q = 3(3q^2 + 2q),$$

  where $3q^2 + 2q$ is an integer.

- Case 2: If $n = 3q + 2$ for some integer q, then

$$n^2 - 1 = 9q^2 + 12q + 3 = 3(3q^2 + 4q + 1),$$

  where $3q^2 + 4q + 1$ is an integer.

In both cases, we have shown that $n^2 - 1$ is a multiple 3.   ▲

Hands-On Exercise 3.2.3   Show that $n^3 + n$ is even for all $n \in \mathbb{N}$.

△

Hands-On Exercise 3.2.4   Show that $n(n + 1)(2n + 1)$ is divisible by 6 for all $n \in \mathbb{N}$.

Hint: One of the two integers n and $n + 1$ must be even, so we already know that the product $n(n + 1)(2n + 1)$ is a multiple of 2. Hence, it remains to show that it is also a multiple of 3. Consider three cases: $n = 3q$, $n = 3q + 1$, or $n = 3q + 2$, where q is an integer.

$\triangle$

We close our discussion with two common fallacies (logical errors). The first one is the *fallacy of the inverse* or the *denial of the antecedent*:

$$p \Rightarrow q$$
$$\frac{\overline{p}}{\therefore \ \overline{q}}$$

This in effect proves the inverse $\overline{p} \Rightarrow \overline{q}$, which we know is *not* logically equivalent to the original implication. Hence, this is an incorrect method for proving an implication.

Example 3.2.8   Is the following argument

     Dictionaries are valuable.
     <u>This book is not a dictionary.</u>
   $\therefore$ This book is not valuable.

valid? Why?   ▲

Another common mistake is known as the *fallacy of the converse* or the *affirmation of the consequence*:

$$p \Rightarrow q$$
$$\frac{q}{\therefore \ p}$$

This only proves the converse $q \Rightarrow p$. Since the converse is *not* logically equivalent to the original implication, this is an incorrect way to prove an implication.

Example 3.2.9   Is this argument

     No medicine tastes good.
     <u>This drink tastes bad.</u>
   $\therefore$ This must be medicine.

a valid argument? Why?   ▲

Summary and Review

- To prove an implication $p \Rightarrow q$, start by assuming that p is true. Use the information from this assumption, together with any other known results, to show that q must also be true.
- If necessary, you may break p into several cases $p_1, p_2, \ldots$, and prove each implication $p_i \Rightarrow q$ (separately, one at a time) as indicated above.
- Be sure to write the mathematical expressions clearly. Use different variables if the quantities involved may not be the same.

- To get started, write down the given information, the assumption, and what you want to prove.
- In the next step, use the definition if necessary, and rewrite the information in mathematical notations. The point is, try to obtain some mathematical equations or logical statements that we can manipulate.

Exercises 3.2

1. Prove or disprove: $2^n + 1$ is prime for all nonnegative integer n.

2. Show that for any integer $n \geq 5$, the integers n, $n+2$ and $n+4$ cannot be all primes.

   Hint: If n is a multiple of 3, then n itself is composite, and the proof will be complete. So we may assume n is not divisible by 3. Then what would n look like, and, what can you say about $n+2$ and $n+4$?

3. Let n be an integer.

   (a) Show that if n is odd, then n^2 is also odd.
   (b) Show that if n is odd, then n^4 is also odd.
   (c) A *corollary* is a result that can be derived easily from another result. Derive (b) as a corollary of (a).
   (d) Show that if m and n are odd, then so is mn.
   (e) Show that if m is even, and n is odd, then mn is even.

4. Prove that, for any odd integer n, the number $2n^2 + 5n + 4$ must be odd.

5. Let n be an integer.

   (a) Prove that if n is a multiple of 3, then n^2 is also a multiple of 3.
   (b) Prove that if n is a multiple of 7, then n^3 is also a multiple of 7.

6. Prove that if n is not a multiple of 3, then n^2 is also not a multiple of 3.

   Hint: If n is not a multiple of 3, then $n = 3q + 1$ or $n = 3q + 2$ for *some* integer q.

7. Use the facts that

   (i) $\sqrt{2}$ is irrational, and
   (ii) if x is irrational, then $\sqrt{x}$ is also irrational,

   to prove that $\sqrt[8]{2}$ is irrational.

8. Recall that we can use a counterexample to disprove an implication. Show that the following claims are false:

   (a) If x and y are integers such that $x^2 > y^2$, then $x > y$.
   (b) If n is a positive integer, then $n^2 + n + 41$ is prime.

9. Explain why the following arguments are invalid:

   (a) Let n be an integer. If n^2 is odd, then n is odd. Therefore, n must be odd.
   (b) Let n be an integer. If n is even, then n^2 is also even. As an integer, n^2 could be odd. Hence, n cannot be even. Therefore, n must be odd.

10. Analyze the following reasoning:

    (a) Let S be a set of real numbers. If x is in S, then x^2 is in S. But x is not in S, hence x^2 is not in S.
    (b) Let S be a set of real numbers. If x is in S, then x^2 is in S. Therefore, if x^2 is in S, then x is in S.

3.3   Indirect Proofs

Instead of proving $p \Rightarrow q$ directly, it is sometimes easier to prove it indirectly. There are two kinds of **indirect proofs**: the proof by contrapositive, and the proof by contradiction.

The **proof by contrapositive** is based on the fact that an implication is equivalent to its contrapositive. Therefore, instead of proving $p \Rightarrow q$, we may prove its contrapositive $\overline{q} \Rightarrow \overline{p}$. Since it is an implication, we could use a direct proof:

Proof by contrapositive.

1. Assume $\overline{q}$ is true (hence, assume q is false).
2. Show that $\overline{p}$ is true (that is, show that p is false).

The proof may proceed as follow:

> *Proof:* We want to prove the contrapositive of the stated result. Assume q is false, ...
>
> $\vdots$
>
> ...   Therefore p is false.   ∎

Example 3.3.1   Let n be an integer. Show that if n^2 is even, then n is also even.

Remember to describe your goal.

Solution: Proof by contrapositive: We want to prove that if n is odd, then n^2 is odd. If n is odd, then $n = 2t + 1$ for some integer t. Hence,

$$n^2 = 4t^2 + 4t + 1 = 2(2t^2 + 2t) + 1$$

is odd. This completes the proof.   ▲

Example 3.3.2   Show that if n is a positive integer such that the sum of its positive divisors is $n + 1$, then n is prime.

Solution: We shall prove the contrapositive of the given statement. We want to prove that if n is composite, then the sum of its positive divisors is not $n + 1$. Let n be a composite number. Then its divisors include 1, n, and at least one other positive divisor x different from 1 and n. So the sum of its positive divisors is at least $1 + n + x$. Since x is positive, we gather that

$$1 + n + x > 1 + n.$$

We deduce that the sum of the divisors cannot be $n + 1$. Therefore, if the sum of the divisors of n is precisely $n + 1$, then n must be prime.   ▲

Example 3.3.3   Let x be a real number. Prove that if $x^3 - 7x^2 + x - 7 = 0$, then $x = 7$.

Solution: Assume $x \neq 7$, then

$$x^3 - 7x^2 + x - 7 = x^2(x - 7) + (x - 7) = (x^2 + 1)(x - 7) \neq 0.$$

Thus, if $x^3 - 7x^2 + x - 7 = 0$, then $x = 7$.   ▲

Hands-On Exercise 3.3.1   Let x be a real number. Prove that if $(2x^2 + 3)(x + 5)(x - 7) = 0$, then either $x = -5$, or $x = 7$.

△

Hands-On Exercise 3.3.2 Let x and y be two real numbers. Prove that if $x \neq 0$ and $y \neq 0$, then $xy \neq 0$.

$\triangle$

Another indirect proof is the **proof by contradiction**. To prove that $p \Rightarrow q$, we proceed as follows:

Proof by contradiction.

1. Suppose $p \Rightarrow q$ is false; that is, assume that p is true and q is false.
2. Argue until we obtain a contradiction, which could be any result that we know is false.

How does this prove that $p \Rightarrow q$? Assuming that the logic used in every step in the argument is correct, yet we still end up with a contradiction, then the only possible flaw must come from the supposition that $p \Rightarrow q$ is false. Consequently, $p \Rightarrow q$ must be true.

This is what a typical proof by contradiction may look like:

> *Proof:* Suppose $p \Rightarrow q$ is false. Then p is true and q is false. Then
> ...
>
> ⋮
>
> ..., which is a contradiction. Therefore, $p \Rightarrow q$ must be true. ■

There is a more general form for proving a statement r, which needs not be an implication. To prove the proposition r by contradiction, we follow these steps:

Another form of proof by contradiction.

1. Suppose r is false.
2. Argue until we obtain a contradiction.

> *Proof:* Suppose r is false. Then ...
>
> ⋮
>
> ..., which is a contradiction. Therefore, r must be true. ■

Example 3.3.4 Show that if $x^3 - 7x^2 + x - 7 = 0$, then $x = 7$.

Solution: Assume $x^3 - 7x^2 + x - 7 = 0$, we want to show that $x = 7$. Suppose $x \neq 7$, then $x - 7 \neq 0$, and

$$0 = x^3 - 7x^2 + x - 7 = x^2(x - 7) + (x - 7) = (x^2 + 1)(x - 7)$$

would have implied that $x^2 + 1 = 0$, which is impossible. Therefore, we must have $x = 7$. ▲

Example 3.3.5 Show that if P is a point not on a line L, then there exists exactly one perpendicular line from P onto L.

Solution: Suppose we can find more than one perpendicular line from P onto L. Pick any two of them, and denote their intersections with L as Q and R. Then we have a triangle PQR, where the angles PQR and PRQ are both $90°$. This implies that the sum of the interior angles of the triangle PQR exceeds $180°$, which is impossible. Hence, there is only one perpendicular line from P onto L.   ▲

Example 3.3.6   Show that if $x^2 < 5$, then $|x| < \sqrt{5}$.

Solution: Assume $x^2 < 5$, we want to show that $|x| < \sqrt{5}$. Suppose, on the contrary, we have $|x| \geq \sqrt{5}$. Then either $x \geq \sqrt{5}$, or $x \leq -\sqrt{5}$. If $x \geq \sqrt{5}$, then $x^2 \geq 5$. If $x \leq -\sqrt{5}$, we again have $x^2 \geq 5$. In either case, we have a contradiction. Hence $|x| < \sqrt{5}$.   ▲

Hands-On Exercise 3.3.3   Prove that if $x^2 \geq 49$, then $|x| \geq 7$.

△

Example 3.3.7   Prove that the logical formula

$$[(p \Rightarrow q) \wedge p] \Rightarrow q$$

is a tautology.

Solution: Suppose $[(p \Rightarrow q) \wedge p] \Rightarrow q$ is false for some statements p and q. Then we find

- $(p \Rightarrow q) \wedge p$ is true, and
- q is false.

For the conjunction $(p \Rightarrow q) \wedge p$ to be true, we need

- $p \Rightarrow q$ to be true, and
- p to be true.

Having p true and q false would make $p \Rightarrow q$ false. This directly contradicts what we have found. Therefore, the logical formula $[(p \Rightarrow q) \wedge p] \Rightarrow q$ is always true, hence it is a tautology.   ▲

Example 3.3.8   Prove, by contradiction, that if x is rational and y is irrational, then $x + y$ is irrational.

Solution: Let x be a rational number and y an irrational number. We want to show that $x + y$ is irrational. Suppose, on the contrary, that $x + y$ is rational. Then

$$x + y = \frac{m}{n}$$

for some integers m and n, where $n \neq 0$. Since x is rational, we also have

$$x = \frac{p}{q}$$

for some integers p and q, where $q \neq 0$. It follows that

$$\frac{m}{n} = x + y = \frac{p}{q} + y.$$

Hence,

$$y = \frac{m}{n} - \frac{p}{q} = \frac{mq - np}{nq},$$

where $mq - np$ and nq are both integers, with $nq \neq 0$. This makes y rational, which contradicts the assumption that y is irrational. Thus, $x + y$ cannot be rational, it must be irrational. ▲

Hands-On Exercise 3.3.4 Prove that

$$\sqrt{x + y} \neq \sqrt{x} + \sqrt{y}$$

for any positive real numbers x and y.

Hint. The words "for any" suggest this is a universal quantification. Be sure you negate the problem statement properly.

△

Example 3.3.9 Prove that $\sqrt{2}$ is irrational.

Solution: Suppose, on the contrary, $\sqrt{2}$ is rational. Then we can write

$$\sqrt{2} = \frac{m}{n}$$

for some positive integers m and n such that m and n do not share any common divisor except 1 (hence $\frac{m}{n}$ is in its simplest term). Squaring both sides and cross-multiplying yields

$$2n^2 = m^2.$$

Thus, 2 divides m^2. Consequently, 2 must also divide m. Then we can write $m = 2s$ for some integer s. The equation above becomes

$$2n^2 = m^2 = (2s)^2 = 4s^2.$$

Hence,

$$n^2 = 2s^2,$$

which implies that 2 divides n^2; thus, 2 also divides n. We have proved that both m and n are divisible by 2. This contradicts the assumption that m and n do not share any common divisor. Therefore, $\sqrt{2}$ must be irrational. ▲

Hands-On Exercise 3.3.5 Prove that $\sqrt{3}$ is irrational.

△

Very often, a proof by contradiction can be rephrased into a proof by contrapositive or even a direct proof, both of which are easier to follow. If this is the case, rewrite the proof.

Example 3.3.10   Show that $x^2 + 4x + 6 = 0$ has no real solution. In symbols, show that $\nexists x \in \mathbb{R}\, (x^2 + 4x + 6 = 0)$.

Solution: Consider the following proof by contradiction:

> Suppose there exists a real number x such that $x^2 + 4x + 6 = 0$. Using calculus, it can be shown that the function $f(x) = x^2 + 4x + 6$ has an absolute minimum at $x = -2$. Thus, $f(x) \geq f(-2) = 2$ for any x. This contradicts the assumption that there exists an x such that $x^2 + 4x + 6 = 0$. Thus, $x^2 + 4x + 6 = 0$ has no real solution.

A close inspection reveals that we do not really need a proof by contradiction. The crux of the proof is the fact that $x^2 + 4x + 6 \geq 2$ for all x. This already shows that $x^2 + 4x + 6$ could never be zero. It is easier to use a direct proof, as follows.

> Using calculus, we find that the function $f(x) = x^2 + 4x + 6$ has an absolute minimum at $x = -2$. Therefore, for any x, we always have $f(x) \geq f(-2) = 2$. Hence, there does not exist any x such that $x^2 + 4x + 6 = 0$.

Do you agree that the second proof (the direct proof) is more elegant?   ▲

Recall that a biconditional statement $p \Leftrightarrow q$ consists of two implications $p \Rightarrow q$ and $q \Rightarrow p$. Hence, to prove $p \Leftrightarrow q$, we need to establish these two "directions" separately.

Example 3.3.11   Let n be an integer. Prove that n^2 is even if and only if n is even.

Solution: ($\Rightarrow$)   We first prove that if n^2 is even, then n must be even. We shall prove its contrapositive: if n is odd, then n^2 is odd. If n is odd, then we can write $n = 2t + 1$ for some integer t. Then

$$n^2 = (2t + 1) = 4t^2 + 4t + 1 = 2(2t^2 + 2t) + 1,$$

where $2t^2 + 2t$ is an integer. Thus, n^2 is odd.

($\Leftarrow$)   Next, we prove that if n is even, then n^2 is even. If n is even, we can write $n = 2t$ for some integer t. Then

$$n^2 = (2t)^2 = 4t^2 = 2 \cdot 2t^2,$$

where $2t^2$ is an integer. Hence, n^2 is even, which completes the proof.   ▲

Hands-On Exercise 3.3.6   Let n be an integer. Prove that n is odd if and only if n^2 is odd.

△

Summary and Review

- We can use indirect proofs to prove an implication.
- There are two kinds of indirect proofs: proof by contrapositive and proof by contradiction.
- In a proof by contrapositive, we actually use a direct proof to prove the contrapositive of the original implication.
- In a proof by contradiction, we start with the supposition that the implication is false, and use this assumption to derive a contradiction. This would prove that the implication must be true.
- A proof by contradiction can also be used to prove a statement that is not of the form of an implication. We start with the supposition that the statement is false, and use this assumption to derive a contradiction. This would prove that the statement must be true.
- Sometimes a proof by contradiction can be rewritten as a proof by contrapositive or even a direct proof. If this is true, rewrite the proof.

Exercises 3.3

1. Let n be an integer. Prove that if n^2 is even, then n must be even. Use

   (a) A proof by contrapositive.

   (b) A proof by contradiction.

   Remark: The two proofs are very similar, but the wording is slightly different, so be sure you present your proofs clearly.

2. Let n be an integer. Show that if n^2 is a multiple of 3, then n must also be a multiple of 3. Use

   (a) A proof by contrapositive.

   (b) A proof by contradiction.

3. Let n be an integer. Prove that if n is even, then $n^2 = 4s$ for some integer s.

4. Let m and n be integers. Show that $mn = 1$ implies that $m = 1$ or $m = -1$.

5. Let x be a real number. Prove by contrapositive: if x is irrational, then $\sqrt{x}$ is irrational. Apply this result to show that $\sqrt[4]{2}$ is irrational, using the assumption that $\sqrt{2}$ is irrational.

6. Let x and y be real numbers such that $x \neq 0$. Prove that if x is rational, and y is irrational, then xy is irrational.

7. Prove that $\sqrt{5}$ is irrational.

8. Prove that $\sqrt[3]{2}$ is irrational.

9. Let a and b be real numbers. Show that if $a \neq b$, then $a^2 + b^2 \neq 2ab$.

10. Use contradiction to prove that, for all integers $k \geq 1$,

$$2\sqrt{k+1} + \frac{1}{\sqrt{k+1}} \geq 2\sqrt{k+2}.$$

11. Let m and n be integers. Show that mn is even if and only if m is even or n is even.

12. Let x and y be real numbers. Show that $x^2 + y^2 = 0$ if and only if $x = 0$ and $y = 0$.

13. Prove that, if x is a real number such that $0 < x < 1$, then $x(1 - x) \leq \frac{1}{4}$.

14. Let m and n be positive integers such that 3 divides mn. Show that 3 divides m, or 3 divides n.

15. Prove that the logical formula

$$(p \Rightarrow q) \vee (p \Rightarrow \overline{q})$$

is a tautology.

16. Prove that the logical formula

$$[(p \Rightarrow q) \wedge (p \Rightarrow \overline{q})] \Rightarrow \overline{p}$$

is a tautology.

3.4   Mathematical Induction: An Introduction

Mathematical induction can be used to prove that an identity is valid for all integers $n \geq 1$. Here is a typical example of such an identity:

$$1 + 2 + 3 + \cdots + n = \frac{n(n+1)}{2}.$$

More generally, we can use mathematical induction to prove that a propositional function $P(n)$ is true for all integers $n \geq 1$.

Mathematical Induction.   To show that a propositional function $P(n)$ is true for all integers $n \geq 1$, follow these steps:

1. **Basis Step**: Verify that $P(1)$ is true.
2. **Inductive Step**: Show that if $P(k)$ is true for some integer $k \geq 1$, then $P(k+1)$ is also true.

The basis step is also called the **anchor step** or the **initial step**. This proof technique is valid because of the next theorem.

Theorem 3.4.1 (Principle of Mathematical Induction) *If $S \subseteq \mathbb{N}$ such that*

(i) $1 \in S$, and
(ii) $k \in S \Rightarrow k + 1 \in S$,

then $S = \mathbb{N}$.

Remark.   Here is a sketch of the proof. From (i), we know that $1 \in S$. It then follows from (ii) that $2 \in S$. Applying (ii) again, we find that $3 \in S$. Likewise, $4 \in S$, then $5 \in S$, and so on. Since this argument can go on indefinitely, we find that $S = \mathbb{N}$.

There is a subtle problem with this argument. It is unclear why "and so on" will work. After all, what does "and so on" or "continue in this manner" really mean? Can it really continue indefinitely? The trouble is, we do not have a formal definition of the natural numbers. It turns out that we cannot completely prove the principle of mathematical induction with just the usual properties for addition and multiplication. Consequently, we will take the theorem as an axiom without giving any formal proof. $\diamond$

Although we cannot provide a satisfactory proof of the principle of mathematical induction, we can use it to justify the validity of the mathematical induction. Let S be the set of integers n for which a propositional function $P(n)$ is true. The basis step of mathematical induction verifies that $1 \in S$. The inductive step shows that $k \in S$ implies $k + 1 \in S$. Therefore, the principle of mathematical induction proves that $S = \mathbb{N}$. It follows that $P(n)$ is true for all integers $n \geq 1$.

The basis step and the inductive step, together, prove that

$$P(1) \Rightarrow P(2) \Rightarrow P(3) \Rightarrow \cdots.$$

Therefore, $P(n)$ is true for all integers $n \geq 1$. Compare induction to falling dominoes. When the first domino falls, it knocks down the next domino. The second domino in turn knocks down the third domino. Eventually, all the dominoes will be knocked down. But it will not happen unless these conditions are met:

Compare induction to the domino effect.

- The first domino must fall to start the motion. If it does not fall, no chain reaction will occur. This is the basis step.

- The distance between adjacent dominoes must be set up correctly. Otherwise, a certain domino may fall down without knocking over the next. Then the chain reaction will stop, and will never be completed. Maintaining the right inter-domino distance ensures that $P(k) \Rightarrow P(k+1)$ for each integer $k \geq 1$.

To prove the implication

$$P(k) \Rightarrow P(k+1)$$

in the inductive step, we need to carry out two steps: assuming that $P(k)$ is true, then using it to prove $P(k+1)$ is also true. So we can refine an induction proof into a 3-step procedure:

1. Verify that $P(1)$ is true.
2. Assume that $P(k)$ is true for some integer $k \geq 1$.
3. Show that $P(k+1)$ is also true.

The second step, the assumption that $P(k)$ is true, is sometimes referred to as the ***inductive hypothesis*** or ***induction hypothesis***. This is how a mathematical induction proof may look:

Proof: We proceed by induction on n. When $n = 1$, the left-hand side of the identity reduces to ... , and the right-hand side becomes .... Hence, the identity holds when $n = 1$. Assume the identity holds when $n = k$ for some integer $k \geq 1$; that is, assume

$$\cdots \tag{3.1}$$

for some integer $k \geq 1$. We want to show that it also holds when $n = k + 1$; that is, we want to show that

$$\cdots$$

Using the inductive hypothesis (3.1), we find

$$\cdots$$

Therefore, the identity also holds when $n = k + 1$. This completes the induction. ∎

The idea behind mathematical induction is rather simple. However, it must be delivered with precision.

(i) Be sure to say "Assume the identity holds for *some* integer $k \geq 1$." Do not say "Assume it holds for *all* integers $k \geq 1$." If we already know the result holds for all $k \geq 1$, then there is no need to prove anything at all.

(ii) Be sure to specify the requirement $k \geq 1$. This ensures that the chain reaction of the falling dominoes starts with the first one.

(iii) Do not say "let $n = k$" or "let $n = k + 1$." The point is, you are not assigning the value of k and $k + 1$ to n. Rather, you are *assuming* that the statement is true *when n equals k*, and using it to show that the statement also holds *when n equals $k + 1$*.

Example 3.4.1   Use mathematical induction to show that

$$1 + 2 + 3 + \cdots + n = \frac{n(n+1)}{2}$$

for all integers $n \geq 1$.

Discussion.   In the basis step, it would be easier to check the two sides of the equation separately. The inductive step is the key step in any induction proof, and the last part, the part that proves $P(k+1)$ is true, is the most difficult part of the entire proof. In this regard, it is helpful to write out exactly what the inductive hypothesis proclaims, and what we really want to prove. In this problem, the inductive hypothesis claims that

$$1 + 2 + 3 + \cdots + k = \frac{k(k+1)}{2}.$$

We want to prove that $P(k+1)$ is also true. What does $P(k+1)$ really mean? It says

$$1 + 2 + 3 + \cdots + (k+1) = \frac{(k+1)(k+2)}{2}.$$

Compare the left-hand sides of these two equations. The first one is the sum of k quantities, and the second is the sum of $k+1$ quantities, and the extra quantity is the last number $k+1$. The sum of the first k terms is precisely what we have on the left-hand side of the inductive hypothesis. Hence, by writing

$$1 + 2 + 3 + \cdots + (k+1) = 1 + 2 + \cdots + k + (k+1),$$

we can regroup the right-hand side as

$$1 + 2 + 3 + \cdots + (k+1) = [1 + 2 + \cdots + k] + (k+1),$$

so that $1 + 2 + \cdots + k$ can be replaced by $\frac{k(k+1)}{2}$, according to the inductive hypothesis. With additional algebraic manipulation, we try to show that the sum does equal to $\frac{(k+1)(k+2)}{2}$. $\diamond$

Solution: We proceed by induction on n. When $n = 1$, the left-hand side of the identity reduces to 1, and the right-hand side becomes $\frac{1 \cdot 2}{2} = 1$; hence, the identity holds when $n = 1$. Assume it holds when $n = k$ for some integer $k \geq 1$; that is, assume that

$$1 + 2 + 3 + \cdots + k = \frac{k(k+1)}{2}$$

for some integer $k \geq 1$. We want to show that it also holds when $n = k + 1$. In other words, we want to show that

$$1 + 2 + 3 + \cdots + (k+1) = \frac{(k+1)(k+2)}{2}.$$

Using the inductive hypothesis, we find

$$
\begin{aligned}
1 + 2 + 3 + \cdots + (k+1) &= 1 + 2 + 3 + \cdots + k + (k+1) \\
&= \frac{k(k+1)}{2} + (k+1) \\
&= (k+1)\left(\frac{k}{2} + 1\right) \\
&= (k+1) \cdot \frac{k+2}{2}.
\end{aligned}
$$

Therefore, the identity also holds when $n = k + 1$. This completes the induction.   ▲

We can use the **summation notation** (also called the **sigma notation**) to abbreviate a sum. For example, the sum in the last example can be written as

$$\sum_{i=1}^{n} i.$$

The letter i is the **index of summation**. By putting $i = 1$ under $\sum$ and n above, we declare that the sum starts with $i = 1$, and ranges through $i = 2$, $i = 3$, and so on, until $i = n$. The quantity that follows $\sum$ describes the pattern of the terms that we are adding in the summation. Accordingly,

$$\sum_{i=1}^{10} i^2 = 1^2 + 2^2 + 3^2 + \cdots + 10^2.$$

In general, the sum of the first n terms in a sequence $\{a_1, a_2, a_3, \dots\}$ is denoted $\sum_{i=1}^{n} a_i$. Observe that

$$\sum_{i=1}^{k+1} a_i = \left(\sum_{i=1}^{k} a_i \right) + a_{k+1},$$

which provides the link between $P(k + 1)$ and $P(k)$ in an induction proof.

Example 3.4.2   Use mathematical induction to show that, for all integers $n \geq 1$,

$$\sum_{i=1}^{n} i^2 = 1^2 + 2^2 + 3^2 + \cdots + n^2 = \frac{n(n+1)(2n+1)}{6}.$$

Solution: We proceed by induction on n. When $n = 1$, the left-hand side reduces to $1^2 = 1$, and the right-hand side becomes $\frac{1 \cdot 2 \cdot 3}{6} = 1$; hence, the identity holds when $n = 1$. Assume it holds when $n = k$ for some integer $k \geq 1$; that is, assume that

$$\sum_{i=1}^{k} i^2 = \frac{k(k+1)(2k+1)}{6}$$

for some integer $k \geq 1$. We want to show that it still holds when $n = k + 1$. In other words, we want to show that

$$\sum_{i=1}^{k+1} i^2 = \frac{(k+1)(k+2)[2(k+1)+1]}{6} = \frac{(k+1)(k+2)(2k+3)}{6}.$$

From the inductive hypothesis, we find

$$\begin{aligned}
\sum_{i=1}^{k+1} i^2 &= \left(\sum_{i=1}^{k} i^2 \right) + (k+1)^2 \\
&= \frac{k(k+1)(2k+1)}{6} + (k+1)^2 \\
&= \tfrac{1}{6}(k+1)[k(2k+1) + 6(k+1)] \\
&= \tfrac{1}{6}(k+1)(2k^2 + 7k + 6) \\
&= \tfrac{1}{6}(k+1)(k+2)(2k+3).
\end{aligned}$$

Therefore, the identity also holds when $n = k + 1$. This completes the induction.   ▲

Example 3.4.3   Use mathematical induction to show that

$$3 + \sum_{i=1}^{n}(3 + 5i) = \frac{(n+1)(5n+6)}{2}$$

for all integers $n \geq 1$.

Solution: Proceed by induction on n. When $n = 1$, the left-hand side reduces to $3 + (3+5) = 11$, and the right-hand side becomes $\frac{2 \cdot 11}{2} = 11$; hence, the identity holds when $n = 1$. Assume it holds when $n = k$ for some integer $k \geq 1$; that is, assume that

$$3 + \sum_{i=1}^{k}(3 + 5i) = \frac{(k+1)(5k+6)}{2}$$

for some integer $k \geq 1$. We want to show that it still holds when $n = k + 1$. In other words, we want to show that

$$3 + \sum_{i=1}^{k+1}(3 + 5i) = \frac{[(k+1)+1][5(k+1)+6]}{2} = \frac{(k+2)(5k+11)}{2}.$$

From the inductive hypothesis, we find

$$
\begin{aligned}
3 + \sum_{i=1}^{k+1}(3 + 5i) &= \left(3 + \sum_{i=1}^{k}(3 + 5i) \right) + [3 + 5(k+1)] \\
&= \frac{(k+1)(5k+6)}{2} + 5k + 8 \\
&= \tfrac{1}{2}[(k+1)(5k+6) + 2(5k+8)] \\
&= \tfrac{1}{2}(5k^2 + 21k + 22) \\
&= \tfrac{1}{2}(k+2)(5k+11).
\end{aligned}
$$

This completes the induction.   ▲

Hands-On Exercise 3.4.1   It is time for you to write your own induction proof. Prove that

$$1 \cdot 2 + 2 \cdot 3 + 3 \cdot 4 + \cdots + n(n+1) = \frac{n(n+1)(n+2)}{3}$$

for all integers $n \geq 1$.

Remark.   We give you a hand on this one, after which, you will be on your own. We lay out the template, all you need to do is fill in the blanks.   ◊

Solution: Proceed by induction on n. When $n = 1$, the left-hand side reduces to $\ldots$,
and the right-hand side becomes $\ldots$. Hence, $\ldots$. Assume the identity holds when $n = k$ for $\ldots$; that is, assume

for some integer $k \geq 1$. We want to show that it also holds when $n = k + 1$; that is, we want to show that

It follows from the inductive hypothesis that

$$= \qquad\qquad\qquad +$$

$$= \qquad +$$

$$= \qquad .$$

This completes the induction. ▲

Hands-On Exercise 3.4.2   Use induction to prove that, for all positive integers n,

$$1 \cdot 2 \cdot 3 + 2 \cdot 3 \cdot 4 + \cdots + n(n+1)(n+2) = \frac{n(n+1)(n+2)(n+3)}{4}.$$

△

Hands-On Exercise 3.4.3   Use induction to prove that, for all positive integers n,

$$1 + 4 + 4^2 + \cdots + 4^n = \frac{1}{3}\left(4^{n+1} - 1\right).$$

$\triangle$

All three steps in an induction proof must be completed; otherwise, the proof may not be correct.

Example 3.4.4   *Never attempt to prove $P(k) \Rightarrow P(k+1)$ by examples alone.* Consider

$$P(n): \qquad n^2 + n + 11 \text{ is prime.}$$

In the inductive step, we want to prove that

$$P(k) \Rightarrow P(k+1) \qquad \text{for } any \ k \geq 1.$$

The following table verifies that it is true for $1 \leq k \leq 8$:

n	1	2	3	4	5	6	7	8	9
$n^2 + n + 11$	13	17	23	31	41	53	67	83	101

Nonetheless, when $n = 10$, $n^2 + n + 11 = 121$ is composite. So $P(9) \nRightarrow P(10)$. The inductive step breaks down when $k = 9$.   ▲

Example 3.4.5   *The basis step is equally important.* Consider proving

$$P(n): \qquad 3n + 2 = 3q \text{ for some integer } q$$

for all $n \in \mathbb{N}$. Assume $P(k)$ is true for some integer $k \geq 1$; that is, assume $3k + 2 = 3q$ for some integer q. Then

$$3(k+1) + 2 = 3k + 3 + 2 = 3 + 3q = 3(1 + q).$$

Therefore, $3(k+1) + 2$ can be written in the same form. This proves that $P(k+1)$ is also true. Does it follow that $P(n)$ is true for all integers $n \geq 1$? We know that $3n + 2$ cannot be written as a multiple of 3. What is the problem?

Solution: The problem is: we need $P(k)$ to be true for at least one value of k so as to start the sequence of implications

$$P(1) \Rightarrow P(2), \qquad P(2) \Rightarrow P(3), \qquad P(3) \Rightarrow P(4), \qquad \ldots$$

The induction fails because we have not established the basis step. In fact, $P(1)$ is false. Since the first domino does not fall, we cannot even start the chain reaction.   ▲

Remark.   Thus far, we have learned how to use mathematical induction to prove identities. In general, we can use mathematical induction to prove a statement about n. This statement can take the form of an identity, an inequality, or simply a verbal statement about n. We shall learn more about mathematical induction in the next few sections.   ◇

Summary and Review

- Mathematical induction can be used to prove that a statement about n is true for all integers $n \geq 1$.
- We have to complete three steps.
- In the basis step, verify the statement for $n = 1$.
- In the inductive hypothesis, assume that the statement holds when $n = k$ for some integer $k \geq 1$.
- In the inductive step, use the information gathered from the inductive hypothesis to prove that the statement also holds when $n = k + 1$.
- Be sure to complete all three steps.
- Pay attention to the wording. At the beginning, follow the template closely. When you feel comfortable with the whole process, you can start venturing out on your own.

Exercises 3.4

1. Use induction to prove that

$$1^3 + 2^3 + 3^3 + \cdots + n^3 = \frac{n^2(n+1)^2}{4}$$

   for all integers $n \geq 1$.

2. Use induction to prove that the following identity holds for all integers $n \geq 1$:

$$1 + 3 + 5 + \cdots + (2n - 1) = n^2.$$

3. Use induction to show that

$$1 + \frac{1}{3} + \frac{1}{3^2} + \cdots + \frac{1}{3^n} = \frac{3}{2}\left(1 - \frac{1}{3^{n+1}}\right)$$

   for all positive integers n.

4. Use induction to establish the following identity for any integer $n \geq 1$:

$$1 - 3 + 9 - \cdots + (-3)^n = \frac{1 - (-3)^{n+1}}{4}.$$

5. Use induction to show that, for any integer $n \geq 1$:

$$\sum_{i=1}^{n} i \cdot i! = (n + 1)! - 1.$$

6. Use induction to prove the following identity for integers $n \geq 1$:

$$\sum_{i=1}^{n} \frac{1}{(2i - 1)(2i + 1)} = \frac{n}{2n + 1}.$$

7. Evaluate $\sum_{i=1}^{n} \frac{1}{i(i + 1)}$ for a few values of n. What do you think the result should be? Use induction to prove your conjecture.

8. Use induction to prove that

$$\sum_{i=1}^{n} (2i - 1)^3 = n^2(2n^2 - 1)$$

   whenever n is a positive integer.

9. Use induction to show that, for any integer $n \geq 1$:

$$1^2 - 2^2 + 3^2 - \cdots + (-1)^{n-1} n^2 = (-1)^{n-1} \frac{n(n+1)}{2}.$$

10. Use mathematical induction to show that

$$\sum_{i=1}^{n} \frac{i+4}{i(i+1)(i+2)} = \frac{n(3n+7)}{2(n+1)(n+2)}$$

for all integers $n \geq 1$.

3.5   More on Mathematical Induction

Besides identities, we can also use mathematical induction to prove a statement about a positive integer n.

Example 3.5.1   Prove that $n(n+1)(2n+1)$ is a multiple of 6 for all integers $n \geq 1$.

See Hands-On
Exercise 3.2.4.

Remark.   We have already seen how to prove this claim using a proof by cases, which is actually an easier way to prove that $n(n+1)(2n+1)$ is divisible by 6. Nonetheless, we shall demonstrate below how to use induction to prove the claim.   ◇

Discussion.   In the inductive hypothesis, it is clear that we are assuming $k(k+1)(2k+1)$ is a multiple of 6. In the inductive step, we want to prove that

$$(k+1)(k+2)[2(k+1)+1] = (k+1)(k+2)(2k+3)$$

is also a multiple of 6. A multiple of 6 can be written as $6q$ for some integer q. Since we have two multiples of 6, we need to write

$$k(k+1)(2k+1) = 6q$$

and

$$(k+1)(k+2)(2k+3) = 6Q$$

to distinguish them. By using the lowercase and uppercase of the same letter, we indicate that they are different values. Yet, because they come from the same letter, they both share some common attribute, in this case, being the quotients when the respective values are divided by 6.

Now, in the inductive step, we need to make use of the equation $k(k+1)(2k+1) = 6q$ from the inductive hypothesis. This calls for connecting the product $(k+1)(k+2)(2k+3)$ to the expression $k(k+1)(2k+1)$. Since they share the common factor $k+1$, what remains to do is write $(k+2)(2k+3)$ in terms of $k(2k+1)$.

We are asked to prove that $n(n+1)(2n+1)$ is a multiple of 6. This is not an identity. Therefore, do not say "assume/show that the *identity* holds when ... ." Instead, say "assume/show that the *claim* is true when ... ."   ◇

Solution: Proceed by induction on n. When $n = 1$, we have $n(n+1)(2n+1) = 1 \cdot 2 \cdot 3 = 6$, which is clearly a multiple of 6. Hence, the claim is true when $n = 1$. Assume the claim is true when $n = k$ for some integer $k \geq 1$; that is, assume that we can write

$$k(k+1)(2k+1) = 6q$$

for some integer q. We want to show that the claim is still true when $n = k+1$; that is, we want to show that

$$(k+1)(k+2)[2(k+1)+1] = (k+1)(k+2)(2k+3) = 6Q$$

for some integer Q. Using the inductive hypothesis, we find

$$
\begin{aligned}
(k+1)(k+2)(2k+3) &= (k+1)(2k^2+7k+6) \\
&= (k+1)[(2k^2+k)+(6k+6)] \\
&= (k+1)[k(2k+1)+6(k+1)] \\
&= k(k+1)(2k+1)+6(k+1)^2 \\
&= 6q+6(k+1)^2 \\
&= 6\left[q+(k+1)^2\right],
\end{aligned}
$$

where $q+(k+1)^2$ is clearly an integer. This completes the induction.   ▲

Hands-On Exercise 3.5.1   Prove that n^2+3n+2 is even for all integers $n \geq 1$.

$\triangle$

Induction can also be used to prove inequalities, which often require more work to finish.

Example 3.5.2   Prove that

$$
1+\frac{1}{4}+\cdots+\frac{1}{n^2} \leq 2-\frac{1}{n}
$$

for all positive integers n.

Draft.   In the inductive hypothesis, we assume that the inequality holds when $n=k$ for some integer $k \geq 1$. This means we assume

$$
\sum_{i=1}^{k} \frac{1}{i^2} \leq 2-\frac{1}{k}.
$$

In the inductive step, we want to show that it also holds when $n=k+1$. In other words, we want to prove that

$$
\sum_{i=1}^{k+1} \frac{1}{i^2} \leq 2-\frac{1}{k+1}.
$$

In order to use the inductive hypothesis, we have to find a connection between these two inequalities. Obviously, we have

$$
\sum_{i=1}^{k+1} \frac{1}{i^2} = \left(\sum_{i=1}^{k} \frac{1}{i^2}\right) + \frac{1}{(k+1)^2}.
$$

Hence, it follows from the inductive hypothesis that

$$\sum_{i=1}^{k+1} \frac{1}{i^2} = \left(\sum_{i=1}^{k} \frac{1}{i^2} \right) + \frac{1}{(k+1)^2} \leq 2 - \frac{1}{k} + \frac{1}{(k+1)^2}.$$

The proof would be complete if we could show that

$$2 - \frac{1}{k} + \frac{1}{(k+1)^2} \leq 2 - \frac{1}{k+1}.$$

There is no guarantee that this idea will work, but this should be the first thing we try.

After rearrangement, the inequality becomes

$$\frac{1}{k+1} + \frac{1}{(k+1)^2} \leq \frac{1}{k},$$

which is equivalent to $\frac{k+2}{(k+1)^2} \leq \frac{1}{k}$. Cross-multiplication yields

$$k(k+2) \leq (k+1)^2.$$

Since

$$k(k+2) = k^2 + 2k, \qquad \text{and} \qquad (k+1)^2 = k^2 + 2k + 1,$$

it is clear that what we want to prove is indeed true.   ◇

Polish It Up!   Next, we rearrange the argument to make it read more smoothly. Essentially all we need is to run the argument *backward*. To improve the flow of the argument, we can prove a separate result on the side before we return to the main argument.   ◇

Proof 1:   Proceed by induction on n. When $n = 1$, the left-hand side becomes 1, and so does the right-hand side; thus, the inequality holds. Assume it holds when $n = k$ for some integer $k \geq 1$:

$$\sum_{i=1}^{k} \frac{1}{i^2} \leq 2 - \frac{1}{k}.$$

We want to show that it also holds when $n = k + 1$:

$$\sum_{i=1}^{k+1} \frac{1}{i^2} \leq 2 - \frac{1}{k+1}.$$

To finish the proof, we need to derive an inequality. Notice that

$$k(k+2) = k^2 + 2k < k^2 + 2k + 1 = (k+1)^2.$$

Hence, after dividing both sides by $k(k+1)^2$, we obtain

$$\frac{k+2}{(k+1)^2} < \frac{1}{k}.$$

This leads to

$$\frac{1}{k+1} + \frac{1}{(k+1)^2} = \frac{(k+1)+1}{(k+1)^2} = \frac{k+2}{(k+1)^2} < \frac{1}{k},$$

which is equivalent to

$$-\frac{1}{k} + \frac{1}{(k+1)^2} < -\frac{1}{k+1}. \tag{3.2}$$

We now return to our original problem. It follows from the inductive hypothesis and (3.2) that

$$\sum_{i=1}^{k+1} \frac{1}{i^2} = \left(\sum_{i=1}^{k} \frac{1}{i^2} \right) + \frac{1}{(k+1)^2}$$

$$\leq 2 - \frac{1}{k} + \frac{1}{(k+1)^2}$$

$$< 2 - \frac{1}{k+1}.$$

Therefore, the inequality still holds when $n = k + 1$, which completes the induction.   ▲

Remark. The key step in the proof is to establish (3.2), which can be done by means of contradiction.   ◇

Proof 2:   Proceed by induction on n. When $n = 1$, the left-hand side becomes 1, and so does the right-hand side; thus, the inequality holds. Assume it holds when $n = k$ for some integer $k \geq 1$:

$$\sum_{i=1}^{k} \frac{1}{i^2} \leq 2 - \frac{1}{k}.$$

We want to show that it also holds when $n = k + 1$:

$$\sum_{i=1}^{k+1} \frac{1}{i^2} \leq 2 - \frac{1}{k+1}.$$

To finish the proof, we need the following inequality. We claim that

$$-\frac{1}{k} + \frac{1}{(k+1)^2} < -\frac{1}{k+1}. \qquad (3.3)$$

Suppose, on the contrary, that

$$-\frac{1}{k} + \frac{1}{(k+1)^2} \geq -\frac{1}{k+1}.$$

Clear the denominators by multiplying $k(k+1)^2$ to both sides of the inequality. We find

$$-(k+1)^2 + k \geq -k(k+1),$$

or equivalently,

$$-k^2 - k - 1 \geq -k^2 - k,$$

which is the same as saying $-1 \geq 0$. This contradiction proves that (3.3) must be true.

We now return to our original problem. It follows from the inductive hypothesis and (3.3) that

$$\sum_{i=1}^{k+1} \frac{1}{i^2} = \left(\sum_{i=1}^{k} \frac{1}{i^2} \right) + \frac{1}{(k+1)^2}$$

$$\leq 2 - \frac{1}{k} + \frac{1}{(k+1)^2}$$

$$< 2 - \frac{1}{k+1}.$$

Therefore, the inequality still holds when $n = k + 1$, which completes the induction.   ▲

Hands-On Exercise 3.5.2   Show that $n < 2^n$ for all integers $n \geq 1$.

$\triangle$

We do not have to start with $n = 1$ in the basis step. We can start with any integer n_0.

Generalization.   To show that $P(n)$ is true for all integers $n \geq n_0$, follow these steps:

1. Verify that $P(n_0)$ is true.
2. Assume that $P(k)$ is true for some integer $k \geq n_0$.
3. Show that $P(k + 1)$ is also true.

The major difference is in the basis step: we need to verify that $P(n_0)$ is true. In addition, in the inductive hypothesis, we need to stress that $k \geq n_0$.

Example 3.5.3   Use mathematical induction to show that

$$\sum_{i=0}^{n} 4^i = \frac{1}{3}(4^{n+1} - 1)$$

for all integers $n \geq 0$.

Solution: Proceed by induction on n. When $n = 0$, the left-hand side reduces to $\sum_{i=0}^{0} 4^i = 4^0 = 1$, and the right-hand side becomes $\frac{1}{3}(4^1 - 1) = \frac{1}{3} \cdot 3 = 1$. Hence, the formula holds when $n = 0$. Assume it holds when $n = k$ for some integer $k \geq 0$; that is, assume

$$\sum_{i=0}^{k} 4^i = \frac{1}{3}(4^{k+1} - 1).$$

We want to show that it also holds when $n = k + 1$; that is,

$$\sum_{i=0}^{k+1} 4^i = \frac{1}{3}(4^{k+2} - 1).$$

Using the inductive hypothesis, we find

$$
\begin{aligned}
\sum_{i=0}^{k+1} 4^i &= \left(\sum_{i=0}^{k} 4^i \right) + 4^{k+1} \\
&= \tfrac{1}{3} \left(4^{k+1} - 1 \right) + 4^{k+1} \\
&= \tfrac{1}{3} \left(4^{k+1} - 1 + 3 \cdot 4^{k+1} \right) \\
&= \tfrac{1}{3} \left(4 \cdot 4^{k+1} - 1 \right) \\
&= \tfrac{1}{3} \left(4^{k+2} - 1 \right),
\end{aligned}
$$

which is what we want to prove, thereby completing the induction.   ▲

Hands-On Exercise 3.5.3   Prove that, for any integer $n \geq 0$,

$$
1 + \frac{2}{3} + \frac{4}{9} + \cdots + \left(\frac{2}{3} \right)^n = 3 \left[1 - \left(\frac{2}{3} \right)^{n+1} \right].
$$

△

Example 3.5.4   Use mathematical induction to show that

$$
n^n \geq 2^n
$$

for all integers $n \geq 2$.

Solution: Proceed by induction on n. When $n = 2$, the inequality becomes $2^2 \geq 2^2$, which is obviously true. Assume it holds when $n = k$ for some integer $k \geq 2$:

$$
k^k \geq 2^k.
$$

We want to show that it still holds when $n = k + 1$:

$$
(k + 1)^{k+1} \geq 2^{k+1}.
$$

Since $k \geq 2$, it follows from the inductive hypothesis that

$$(k+1)^{k+1} \geq k^{k+1} = k \cdot k^k \geq 2 \cdot 2^k = 2^{k+1}.$$

Therefore, the inequality still holds when $n = k + 1$. This completes the induction.   ▲

Summary and Review

- We can use induction to prove a general statement involving an integer n.
- The statement can be an identity, an inequality, or a claim about the property of an expression involving n.
- An induction proof need not start with $n = 1$.
- If we want to prove that a statement is true for all integers $n \geq n_0$, we have to verify the statement for $n = n_0$ in the basis step.
- In addition, we need to assume that $k \geq n_0$ in the inductive hypothesis.

Exercises 3.5

1. Use induction to prove that $n(n+1)(n+2)$ is a multiple of 3 for all integers $n \geq 1$.

2. Use induction to show that $n^3 + 5n$ is a multiple of 6 for any nonnegative integer n.

3. Use induction to prove that

$$2 + \left(1 + \frac{1}{\sqrt{2}} + \frac{1}{\sqrt{3}} + \cdots + \frac{1}{\sqrt{n}}\right) > 2\sqrt{n+1}$$

   for all integers $n \geq 1$.

4. Use induction to prove that

$$2\left(1 + \frac{1}{8} + \frac{1}{27} + \cdots + \frac{1}{n^3}\right) \leq 3 - \frac{1}{n^2}$$

   for all integers $n \geq 1$.

5. Use induction to prove that

$$a + ar + ar^2 + \cdots + ar^n = \frac{a(r^{n+1} - 1)}{r - 1}$$

   for all nonnegative integers n, where a and r are real numbers with $r \neq 1$.

6. Use induction to prove that, for any integer $n \geq 2$,

$$6\sum_{i=2}^{n} i(i+2) = 2n^3 + 9n^2 + 7n - 18.$$

7. Use induction to prove that, for any integer $n \geq 0$,

$$1 - \frac{2}{5} + \frac{4}{25} + \cdots + \left(-\frac{2}{5}\right)^n = \frac{5}{7}\left[1 - \left(-\frac{2}{5}\right)^{n+1}\right].$$

8. Use induction to show that $n! > 2^n$ for all integers $n \geq 4$.

9. Use induction to prove that $n^2 > 4n + 1$ for all integers $n \geq 5$.

10. Prove that $2n + 1 < 2^n$ for all integers $n \geq 3$.

11. Define

$$S_n = \frac{1}{2!} + \frac{2}{3!} + \frac{3}{4!} + \cdots + \frac{n}{(n+1)!}.$$

   (a) Evaluate S_n for $n = 1, 2, 3, 4, 5$.
   (b) Propose a simple formula for S_n.
   (c) Use induction to prove your conjecture for all integers $n \geq 1$.

12. Define $T_n = \displaystyle\sum_{i=0}^{n} \frac{1}{(2i+1)(2i+3)}.$

   (a) Evaluate T_n for $n = 0, 1, 2, 3, 4$.
   (b) Propose a simple formula for T_n.
   (c) Use induction to prove your conjecture for all integers $n \geq 0$.

3.6 Mathematical Induction: The Strong Form

You may have heard of **Fibonacci numbers**. They occur frequently in mathematics and life sciences. They have even been applied to study the stock market! Fibonacci numbers form a sequence every term of which, except the first two, is the sum of the previous two numbers. Mathematically, if we denote the nth Fibonacci number F_n, then

$$F_n = F_{n-1} + F_{n-2}. \tag{3.4}$$

This is called the **recurrence relation** for F_n.

   Some students have trouble using (3.4): we are *not* adding $n-1$ and $n-2$. The subscripts only indicate the *locations* within the Fibonacci sequence. Hence, F_1 means the first Fibonacci number, F_2 the second Fibonacci number, and so forth. Compare this to dropping ten numbers into ten boxes, and each box is labeled with the numbers 1 through 10. Let us use a_i to denote the value in the ith box. When we say a_7, we do not mean the number 7. Instead, we mean the number stored in Box 7. Expressed in words, the recurrence relation (3.4) tells us that the nth Fibonacci number is the sum of the $(n-1)$th and the $(n-2)$th Fibonacci numbers. This is easy to remember: we add the last two Fibonacci numbers to get the next Fibonacci number.

   The recurrence relation implies that we need to start with two initial values. We often start with $F_0 = 0$ (image F_0 as the zeroth Fibonacci number, the number stored in Box 0) and $F_1 = 1$. We combine the recurrence relation for F_n and its initial values together in one definition:

$$\boxed{F_0 = 0, \quad F_1 = 1, \quad F_n = F_{n-1} + F_{n-2}, \quad \text{for } n \geq 2.}$$

We have to specify that the recurrence relation is valid only when $n \geq 2$, because this is the smallest value of n for which we can use the recurrence relation. What happens if you want to find F_1 using this formula? You will get $F_1 = F_0 + F_{-1}$, but F_{-1} is undefined!

   The sum of the zeroth and the first Fibonacci numbers give us the second Fibonacci number:

$$F_2 = F_1 + F_0 = 1 + 0 = 1.$$

Continuing in this fashion, we find

$$
\begin{array}{rcccl}
F_3 & = & F_2 + F_1 & = & 1 + 1 & = & 2, \\
F_4 & = & F_3 + F_2 & = & 2 + 1 & = & 3, \\
F_5 & = & F_4 + F_3 & = & 3 + 2 & = & 5, \\
F_6 & = & F_5 + F_4 & = & 5 + 3 & = & 8, \\
& \vdots & & \vdots & & \vdots & & \vdots
\end{array}
$$

Following this pattern, what are the values of F_7 and F_8?

Fibonacci numbers enjoy many interesting properties, and there are numerous results concerning Fibonacci numbers. As a starter, consider the property

$$F_n < 2^n, \qquad n \geq 1.$$

How would we prove it by induction?

Since we want to prove that the inequality holds for all $n \geq 1$, we should check the case of $n = 1$ in the basis step. When $n = 1$, we have $F_1 = 1$ which is, of course, less than $2^1 = 2$. In the inductive hypothesis, we assume that the inequality holds when $n = k$ for some integer $k \geq 1$; that is, we assume

$$F_k < 2^k$$

for some integer $k \geq 1$. Next, we want to prove that the inequality still holds when $n = k + 1$. So we need to prove that

$$F_{k+1} < 2^{k+1}.$$

To make use of the inductive hypothesis, we need to apply the recurrence relation of Fibonacci numbers. It tells us that F_{k+1} is the sum of the previous two Fibonacci numbers; that is,

$$F_{k+1} = F_k + F_{k-1}.$$

The only thing we know from the inductive hypothesis is $F_k < 2^k$. So, as it stands, it does not tell us much about F_{k+1}.

A remedy is to assume in the inductive hypothesis that the inequality also holds when $n = k - 1$; that is, we also assume that

$$F_{k-1} < 2^{k-1}.$$

Therefore, unlike all the problems we have seen thus far, the inductive step in this problem relies on the last two n-values instead of just one. In terms of dominoes, imagine they are so heavy that we need the combined weight of two dominoes to knock down the next. Then

$$F_{k+1} = F_k + F_{k-1} < 2^k + 2^{k-1} = 2^{k-1}(2+1) < 2^{k-1} \cdot 2^2 = 2^{k+1},$$

which will complete the induction. This modified induction is known as the strong form of mathematical induction. In contrast, we call the ordinary mathematical induction the **weak form** of induction.

The proof still has a minor glitch! To be able to use the inductive hypothesis in the recurrence relation

$$F_{k+1} = F_k + F_{k-1},$$

both subscripts k and $k - 1$ must be at least 1, because the statement claims that $F_n < 2^n$ for all $n \geq 1$. This means we need $k \geq 2$. Consequently, in the basis step, we have to assume the inequality holds for *at least the first two values of n*.

In terms of the domino effect, the chain reaction of the falling dominoes starts at $k = 2$. We have to make sure that the first two dominoes will fall, so that their combined weight will knock down the third domino. Then the combined weight of the second and the third dominoes will knock over the fourth domino. The chain reaction will carry on indefinitely.

Symbolically, the ordinary mathematical induction relies on the implication $P(k) \Rightarrow P(k+1)$. Sometimes, $P(k)$ alone is not enough to prove $P(k + 1)$. In the case of proving $F_n < 2^n$, we actually use

$$[P(k - 1) \wedge P(k)] \Rightarrow P(k + 1).$$

We need to assume in the inductive hypothesis that the result is true when $n = k - 1$ and $n = k$.

More generally, in the strong form of mathematical induction, we can use as many previous cases as we like to prove $P(k + 1)$.

Strong Form of Mathematical Induction. To show that $P(n)$ is true for all $n \geq n_0$, follow these steps:

1. Verify that $P(n)$ is true for some small values of $n \geq n_0$.
2. Assume that $P(n)$ is true for $n = n_0, n_0 + 1, \ldots, k$ for some integer $k \geq n^*$.
3. Show that $P(k+1)$ is also true.

The idea behind the inductive step is to show that

$$[P(n_0) \wedge P(n_0 + 1) \wedge \cdots \wedge P(k-1) \wedge P(k)] \Rightarrow P(k+1).$$

We could use more than one previous case, say, $n = k$, $k-1$, $k-2$, $\ldots$, to establish the next case $n = k+1$.

We may not need to use all of $P(n_0), P(n_0 + 1), \ldots, P(k-1), P(k)$. In fact, we may only need the last few of them, for example, $P(k-3), P(k-2), P(k-1)$ and $P(k)$. The number of previous cases required to establish $P(k+1)$ tells us how many initial cases we have to verify in the basis step. We do not know how many we need until the inductive step. For this reason, it is wise to start with a draft.

Example 3.6.1   Show that $F_n < 2^n$ for all $n \geq 1$.

Remark.   We have already worked on the draft in the discussion above. We know that we need to verify the first two n-values in the basis step, and to assume that the inequality holds for at least two cases.   ◇

Solution: Proceed by induction on n. When $n = 1$ and $n = 2$, we find

$$F_1 = 1 < 2 = 2^1,$$
$$F_2 = 1 < 4 = 2^2.$$

Therefore, the inequality holds when $n = 1, 2$. Assume it holds for $n = 1, 2, \ldots, k$, where $k \geq 2$. In particular, we have

$$F_k < 2^k, \qquad \text{and} \qquad F_{k-1} < 2^{k-1},$$

where $k \geq 2$. Then

$$F_{k+1} = F_k + F_{k-1} < 2^k + 2^{k-1} = 2^{k-1}(2+1) < 2^{k-1} \cdot 2^2 = 2^{k+1}.$$

Hence, the inequality still holds when $n = k+1$, which completes the induction.   ▲

Recurrence relation can be used to define a sequence. For example, if the sequence $\{a_n\}_{n=1}^{\infty}$ is defined recursively by

$$a_n = 3a_{n-1} - 2 \qquad \text{for } n \geq 2,$$

with $a_1 = 4$, then

$$a_2 = 3a_1 - 2 = 3 \cdot 4 - 2 = 10,$$
$$a_3 = 3a_2 - 2 = 3 \cdot 10 - 2 = 28.$$

Identity involving such sequences can often be proved by means of induction.

Example 3.6.2   The sequence $\{b_n\}_{n=1}^{\infty}$ is defined as

$$b_1 = 5, \quad b_2 = 13, \qquad b_n = 5b_{n-1} - 6b_{n-2} \quad \text{for } n \geq 3.$$

Prove that $b_n = 2^n + 3^n$ for all $n \geq 1$.

Solution: Proceed by induction on n. When $n = 1$, the proposed formula for b_n says $b_1 = 2 + 3 = 5$, which agrees with the initial value $b_1 = 5$. When $n = 2$, the proposed formula claims $b_2 = 4 + 9 = 13$, which again agrees with the definition $b_2 = 13$. Assume the formula is valid for $n = 1, 2, \ldots, k$ for some integer $k \geq 2$. In particular, assume

$$b_k = 2^k + 3^k, \qquad \text{and} \qquad b_{k-1} = 2^{k-1} + 3^{k-1}.$$

We want to show that the formula still works when $n = k + 1$. In other words, we want to show that

$$b_{k+1} = 2^{k+1} + 3^{k+1}.$$

Using the recurrence relation and the inductive hypothesis, we find

$$
\begin{aligned}
b_{k+1} &= 5b_k - 6b_{k-1} \\
&= 5(2^k + 3^k) - 6(2^{k-1} + 3^{k-1}) \\
&= 5 \cdot 2^k + 5 \cdot 3^k - 6 \cdot 2^{k-1} - 6 \cdot 3^{k-1} \\
&= 5 \cdot 2^k + 5 \cdot 3^k - 2 \cdot 3 \cdot 2^{k-1} - 2 \cdot 3 \cdot 3^{k-1} \\
&= 5 \cdot 2^k + 5 \cdot 3^k - 3 \cdot 2^k - 2 \cdot 3^k \\
&= 2 \cdot 2^k + 3 \cdot 3^k \\
&= 2^{k+1} + 3^{k+1}
\end{aligned}
$$

which is what we want to establish. This completes the induction, and hence, the claim that $b_n = 2^n + 3^n$.   ▲

Hands-On Exercise 3.6.1   The sequence $\{c_n\}_{n=1}^\infty$ is defined as

$$c_1 = 7, \quad b_2 = 29, \qquad c_n = 5b_{n-1} - 6b_{n-2} \quad \text{for } n \geq 3.$$

Prove that $c_n = 5 \cdot 3^n - 4 \cdot 2^n$ for all integers $n \geq 1$.

△

Example 3.6.3   Show that all integers $n \geq 24$ can be expressed as $4x + 9y$ for some integers $x, y \geq 0$.

Definition.   The expression $4x + 9y$ is called a ***linear combination*** of 4 and 9, and x and y are called the ***coefficients*** of the linear combination.   ◇

Remark.   We want to prove that any sufficiently large integer n can be written as a linear combination of 4 and 9 with nonnegative coefficients. This problem is called the **postage stamp problem** for the obvious reason: can we use only 4-cent and 9-cent stamps to obtain an n-cent postage for all integers $n \geq 24$? Not too surprisingly, it is also called the **money changing problem** (imagine replacing stamps with coins).   ◇

Remark.   The spirit behind mathematical induction (both weak and strong forms) is making use of what we know about a smaller size problem. In the weak form, we use the result from $n = k$ to establish the result for $n = k + 1$. In the strong form, we use some of the results from $n = k, k - 1, k - 2, \ldots$ to establish the result for $n = k + 1$.   ◇

Discussion.   Let us first look at the inductive step, in which we want to show that we can write $k + 1$ as a linear combination of 4 and 9. The key step of any induction proof is to relate the case of $n = k + 1$ to a problem with a smaller size (hence, with a smaller value in n).

Imagine you want to send a letter that requires a $(k+1)$-cent postage, and you can use only 4-cent and 9-cent stamps. You could first put down a 4-cent stamp. Then you still need to come up with the remaining postage of $(k + 1) - 4 = k - 3$ cents. If you could use 4-cent and 9-cent stamps to make up the remaining $(k - 3)$-cent postage, the problem is solved. Therefore, in the inductive hypothesis, we need to assume that it can be done when $n = k - 3$.

For the whole argument to work, $k - 3$ has to be within the range of the n-values that we consider. So we need $k - 3 \geq 24$; that is, we want $k \geq 27$. Consequently, we have to verify the claim for $n = 24, 25, 26, 27$ in the basis step.   ◇

Solution: Proceed by induction on n. We find

$$
\begin{aligned}
24 &= 4 \cdot 6 + 9 \cdot 0, \\
25 &= 4 \cdot 4 + 9 \cdot 1, \\
26 &= 4 \cdot 2 + 9 \cdot 2, \\
27 &= 4 \cdot 0 + 9 \cdot 3.
\end{aligned}
$$

Hence, the claim is true when $n = 24, 25, 26, 27$. Assume it is true when $n = 24, 25, \ldots, k$ for some integer $k \geq 27$. In particular, since $k - 3 \geq 24$, this assumption assures that

$$
k - 3 = 4x + 9y
$$

for some nonnegative integers x and y. It follows that

$$
\begin{aligned}
k + 1 &= 4 + (k - 3) \\
&= 4 + 4x + 9y \\
&= 4(1 + x) + 9y,
\end{aligned}
$$

where $1 + x$ and y are nonnegative integers. This shows that the claim is still true when $n = k + 1$, thereby completing the induction.   ▲

Hands-On Exercise 3.6.2   Show that all integers $n \geq 2$ can be expressed as $2x + 3y$ for some nonnegative integers x and y.

$\triangle$

Summary and Review

- If, in the inductive step, we need to use more than one previous instance of the statement that we are proving, we may use the strong form of the induction.
- In such an event, we have to modify the inductive hypothesis to include more cases in the assumption.
- We also need to verify more cases in the basis step.
- Finally, we need to rewrite the whole proof to make it coherent.

Exercises 3.6

1. Use mathematical induction to prove the identity

$$F_1^2 + F_2^2 + F_3^2 + \cdots + F_n^2 = F_n F_{n+1}$$

for any integer $n \geq 1$.

2. Use induction to prove the following identity for all integers $n \geq 1$:

$$F_1 + F_3 + F_5 + \cdots + F_{2n-1} = F_{2n}.$$

3. Use induction to prove that

$$\frac{F_1}{F_2 F_3} + \frac{F_2}{F_3 F_4} + \frac{F_3}{F_4 F_5} + \cdots + \frac{F_{n-2}}{F_{n-1} F_n} = 1 - \frac{1}{F_n}$$

for all integers $n \geq 3$.

4. Use induction to prove that any integer $n \geq 8$ can be written as a linear combination of 3 and 5 with nonnegative coefficients.

5. A football team may score a field goal for 3 points or[1] a touchdown (with conversion) for 7 points. Prove that, for any integer $n \geq 12$, it is possible for a football team to score n points with field goals and touchdowns.

6. An island country only issues 1-cent, 5-cent and 9-cent coins. Due to shortage in copper, all 1-cent coins were recalled. Prove that, using just 5-cent and 9-cent coins, one can pay an n-cent purchase for any $n \geq 32$.

---

[1] Although it is possible for a team to score 2 points for a safety or 8 points for a touchdown with a two-point conversion, we would not consider these possibilities in this simplified version of a real football game.

7. The sequence $\{b_n\}_{n=1}^{\infty}$ is defined recursively by

$$b_n = 3b_{n-1} - 2 \qquad \text{for } n \geq 2,$$

with $b_1 = 4$. Use induction to prove that $b_n = 3^n + 1$ for all $n \geq 1$.

8. The sequence $\{c_n\}_{n=1}^{\infty}$ is defined recursively as

$$c_1 = 3, \quad c_2 = -9, \qquad c_n = 7c_{n-1} - 10c_{n-2}, \quad \text{for } n \geq 3.$$

Use induction to show that $c_n = 4 \cdot 2^n - 5^n$ for all integers $n \geq 1$.

9. The sequence $\{d_n\}_{n=1}^{\infty}$ is defined recursively as

$$d_1 = 2, \quad d_2 = 56, \qquad d_n = d_{n-1} + 6d_{n-2}, \quad \text{for } n \geq 3.$$

Use induction to show that $d_n = 5(-2)^n + 4 \cdot 3^n$ for all integers $n \geq 1$.

10. The sequence $\{a_n\}_{n=1}^{\infty}$ is defined recursively as

$$a_1 = 2, \quad a_2 = 4, \qquad a_n = 2a_{n-1} + 3a_{n-2}, \quad \text{for } n \geq 3.$$

Use induction to show that $a_n > \left(\frac{5}{2}\right)^n$ for any integer $n \geq 4$.

Chapter 4

Sets

4.1 An Introduction

A **set** is a collection of objects. The objects in a set are called its **elements** or **members**. The elements in a set can be any types of objects, including sets! The members of a set do not even have to be of the same type. For example, although it may not have any meaningful application, a set can consist of numbers and names.

We usually use capital letters such as A, B, C, S, and T to represent sets, and denote their generic elements by their corresponding lowercase letters a, b, c, s, and t, respectively. To indicate that b is an element of the set B, we adopt the notation $b \in B$, which means "b belongs to B" or "b is an element of B." We also write $B \ni b$, and say "B contains b (as an element)."

We designate these notations for some special sets of numbers:

$$
\begin{aligned}
\mathbb{R} &= \text{the set of real numbers,} \\
\mathbb{Q} &= \text{the set of rational numbers,} \\
\mathbb{Z} &= \text{the set of integers,} \\
\mathbb{N} &= \text{the set of natural numbers (positive integers).}
\end{aligned}
$$

All these are infinite sets, because they all contain infinitely many elements. In contrast, finite sets contain finitely many elements.

We can use the **roster method** to describe a set if it has only a small number of elements. We list all its elements explicitly, as in

$$A = \text{the set of natural numbers not exceeding } 7 = \{1, 2, 3, 4, 5, 6, 7\}.$$

For sets with more elements, show the first few entries to display a pattern, and use an ellipsis to indicate "and so on." For example,

$$\{1, 2, 3, \ldots, 20\}$$

represents the set of the first 20 positive integers. The repeating pattern can be extended indefinitely, as in

$$
\begin{aligned}
\mathbb{N} &= \{1, 2, 3, \ldots\} \\
\mathbb{Z} &= \{\ldots, -2, -1, 0, 1, 2, \ldots\}
\end{aligned}
$$

There are three kinds of integers: positive, negative, and the signless integer zero. In regards to parity, an integer is either even or odd. An integer is even if and only if it is divisible by two. Therefore, the set of even integers can be described as $\{\ldots, -4, -2, 0, 2, 4, \ldots\}$.

We can use a **set-builder notation** to describe a set. For example, the set of natural numbers is defined as

$$\mathbb{N} = \{x \in \mathbb{Z} \mid x > 0\}.$$

Here, the vertical bar | is read as "such that" or "for which." Hence, the right-hand side of the equation is pronounced as "the set of x belonging to the set of integers such that $x > 0$," or simply "the set of integers x such that $x > 0$." In general, this descriptive method appears in the format

$$\{\,\text{membership} \mid \text{properties}\,\}.$$

The notation | means "such that" or "for which" only when it is used in the set notation. It may mean something else in a different context. Therefore, *do not* write "let x be a real number | $x^2 > 3$" if you want to say " let x be a real number such that $x^2 > 3$." It is considered improper to use a mathematical notation as an abbreviation.

Example 4.1.1   Write these two sets

$$\{x \in \mathbb{Z} \mid x^2 \le 1\} \quad \text{and} \quad \{x \in \mathbb{N} \mid x^2 \le 1\}$$

by listing their elements explicitly.

Solution: The first set has three elements, and equals $\{-1, 0, 1\}$. The second set is a singleton set; it is equal to $\{1\}$.   ▲

Hands-On Exercise 4.1.1   Use the roster method to describe the sets $\{x \in \mathbb{Z} \mid x^2 \le 20\}$ and $\{x \in \mathbb{N} \mid x^2 \le 20\}$.

△

Hands-On Exercise 4.1.2   Use the roster method to describe the set

$$\{x \in \mathbb{N} \mid x \le 20 \text{ and } x = n^2 \text{ for some integer } n\}.$$

△

There is a slightly different format for the set-builder notation. Before the vertical bar, we describe the form the elements assume, and after the vertical bar, we indicate from where we are going to pick these elements:

$$\{\,\text{pattern} \mid \text{membership}\,\}.$$

Here the vertical bar | means "where." For example,

$$\{x^2 \mid x \in \mathbb{Z}\}$$

is the set of x^2 where $x \in \mathbb{Z}$. It represents the set of squares: $\{0, 1, 4, 9, 16, 25, \ldots\}$.

Example 4.1.2   The set

$$\{2n \mid n \in \mathbb{Z}\}$$

describes the set of even numbers. We can also write the set as $2\mathbb{Z}$.   ▲

Hands-On Exercise 4.1.3   Describe the set $\{2n + 1 \mid n \in \mathbb{Z}\}$ with the roster method.

$\triangle$

Hands-On Exercise 4.1.4   Use the roster method to describe the set $\{3n \mid n \in \mathbb{Z}\}$.

$\triangle$

An interval is a set of real numbers, all of which lie between two real numbers. Should the endpoints be included or excluded depends on whether the interval is **open**, **closed**, or **half-open**. We adopt the following **interval notation** to describe them:

$$(a, b) = \{x \in \mathbb{R} \mid a < x < b\},$$
$$[a, b] = \{x \in \mathbb{R} \mid a \leq x \leq b\},$$
$$[a, b) = \{x \in \mathbb{R} \mid a \leq x < b\},$$
$$(a, b] = \{x \in \mathbb{R} \mid a < x \leq b\}.$$

It is understood that a must be less than or equal to b. Hence, the notation $(5, 3)$ does not make much sense. How about $[3, 3]$? Is it a legitimate notation?

An interval contains not just integers, but all the numbers between the two endpoints. By numbers, we mean whole numbers *and* decimal numbers. For instance, $(1, 5) \neq \{2, 3, 4\}$ because the interval $(1, 5)$ also includes decimal numbers such at 1.276, $\sqrt{2}$, and π. *The interval (a, b) includes decimal numbers.*

We can use $\pm\infty$ in the interval notation:

$$(a, \infty) = \{x \in \mathbb{R} \mid a < x\},$$
$$(-\infty, a) = \{x \in \mathbb{R} \mid x < a\}.$$

However, we cannot write $(a, \infty]$ or $[-\infty, a)$, because $\pm\infty$ are *not* numbers. It is nonsense to say $x \leq \infty$ or $-\infty \leq x$. For the same reason, we can write $[a, \infty)$ and $(-\infty, a]$, but *not* $[a, \infty]$ or $[-\infty, a]$. *∞ is not a number, neither is $-\infty$*

Example 4.1.3   Write the intervals $(2, 3)$, $[2, 3]$, and $(2, 3]$ in the descriptive form.

Solution: According to the definition of an interval, we find

$$(2, 3) = \{x \in \mathbb{R} \mid 2 < x < 3\},$$
$$[2, 3] = \{x \in \mathbb{R} \mid 2 \leq x \leq 3\},$$
$$(2, 3] = \{x \in \mathbb{R} \mid 2 < x \leq 3\}.$$

What would you say about $[2, 3)$? ▲

Example 4.1.4   Write these sets

$$\{x \in \mathbb{R} \mid -2 \leq x < 5\} \quad \text{and} \quad \{x \in \mathbb{R} \mid x^2 \leq 1\}$$

in the interval form.

Solution: The answers are $[-2, 5)$ and $[-1, 1]$, respectively. The membership of x affects the answers. If we change the second set to $\{x \in \mathbb{Z} \mid x^2 \leq 1\}$, the answer would have been $\{-1, 0, 1\}$. Can you explain why $\{-1, 0, 1\} \neq [-1, 1]$? ▲

Example 4.1.5 Be sure you are using the right types of numbers. Compare these two sets

$$S = \{x \in \mathbb{Z} \mid x^2 \leq 5\},$$
$$T = \{x \in \mathbb{R} \mid x^2 \leq 5\}.$$

One consists of integers only, while the other contains real numbers. Thus, $S = \{-2, -1, 0, 1, 2\}$, and $T = \left[-\sqrt{5}, \sqrt{5}\right]$. ▲

Hands-On Exercise 4.1.5 Which of the following sets

$$\{x \in \mathbb{Z} \mid 1 < x < 7\} \quad \text{and} \quad \{x \in \mathbb{R} \mid 1 < x < 7\}$$

can be represented by the interval notation $(1, 7)$? Explain.

△

Hands-On Exercise 4.1.6 Explain why $[2, 7] \neq \{2, 3, 4, 5, 6, 7\}$.

△

Hands-On Exercise 4.1.7 True or false: $(-2, 3) = \{-1, 0, 1, 2\}$? Explain.

△

Let S be a set of numbers; we define

$$S^+ = \{x \in S \mid x > 0\},$$
$$S^- = \{x \in S \mid x < 0\},$$
$$S^* = \{x \in S \mid x \neq 0\}.$$

In plain English, S^+ is the subset of S containing only those elements that are positive, S^- contains only the negative elements of S, and S^* contains only the nonzero elements of S.

Example 4.1.6 It should be obvious that $\mathbb{N} = \mathbb{Z}^+$. ▲

Hands-On Exercise 4.1.8 What is the notation for the set of negative integers?

△

See Example 2.1.8.   Some mathematicians also adopt these notations:

$$bS = \{bx \mid x \in S\},$$
$$a + bS = \{a + bx \mid x \in S\}.$$

Accordingly, we can write the set of even integers as $2\mathbb{Z}$, and the set of odd integers can be represented by $1 + 2\mathbb{Z}$.

An **empty set** is a set that does not contain any element. Both

$$\{x \in \mathbb{R} \mid x > 0 \text{ and } x < 0\} \qquad \text{and} \qquad \{x \in \mathbb{R} \mid x^2 < 0\}$$

are examples of empty sets. The second example illustrates a typical application of an empty set. It provides a convenient way of declaring that a problem has no solution: we say that the solution set is an empty set. We denote an empty set with the notation $\emptyset$ or $\{\ \}$. For example, can you explain why $(3,3) = \emptyset$?

Hands-On Exercise 4.1.9 What does the notation $[7,7]$ mean? How would you describe the sets $(7,7)$, $(7,7]$ and $[7,7]$?

$\triangle$

Example 4.1.7 Determine which of these statements are true.

$$\begin{aligned}
\{x \in \mathbb{R} \mid (x^2 + 2)(x^2 + 3) = 0\} &= \emptyset, \\
\{x \in \mathbb{Z} \mid (x^2 - 2)(x^2 + 3) = 0\} &= \emptyset, \\
\{x \in \mathbb{R} \mid (x^2 - 2)(x^2 + 3) = 0\} &= \emptyset, \\
\{x \in \mathbb{R} \mid (x^2 - 2)(x^2 + 3) \geq 0\} &= \emptyset.
\end{aligned}$$

Solution: The answers are: true, true, false, and false, respectively. ▲

Example 4.1.8 When we write $3, 4, 5, \ldots, n$, we are referring to a list of integers between 3 and n, inclusive. It is understood that $n \geq 3$. Consequently, the set

$$\{3, 4, 5, \ldots, n\}$$

is empty when $n = 2$. ▲

Two sets A and B are said to be **equal** if they contain the same collection of elements. More rigorously, we define

$$A = B \Leftrightarrow \forall x \, (x \in A \Leftrightarrow x \in B).$$

Since the elements of a set can themselves be sets, exercise caution and use proper notation when you compare the contents of two sets.

Example 4.1.9 Explain why $\{0, \{1\}\} \neq \{0, 1\}$.

Solution: The set $\{0, \{1\}\}$ consists of two elements: the integer 0 and the set $\{1\}$. The set $\{0, 1\}$ also consists of two elements, both of them integers; namely, 0 and 1.

A set may contain another set as an element.

You may find the following analogy helpful. Imagine a set being a box. You open a box to look at its contents. The box itself can be compared to the curly braces $\{$ and $\}$. What it holds is exactly what we call the elements of the set it represents. The contents of the two sets $\{0, \{1\}\}$ and $\{0, 1\}$ are depicted in the boxes shown in Figure 4.1.

When you open the first box, you find two items. One of them is the number 0; the other is another box that contains the number 1. The second box also contains two items that are both numbers. What you find in these two boxes is not the same. Hence, the sets they represent are different. ▲

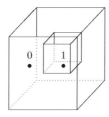 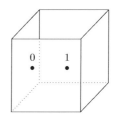

Figure 4.1: The two sets $\{0, \{1\}\}$ and $\{0, 1\}$.

Hands-On Exercise 4.1.10   Name some differences between the sets $\{0, \{1\}\}$ and $\{\{0\}, \{1\}\}$.

$\triangle$

Example 4.1.10   True or false: $\mathbb{Z} = \{\{\dots, -3, -2, -1\}, 0, \{1, 2, 3, \dots\}\}$?

Solution: The set on the left is $\mathbb{Z}$, and

$$\mathbb{Z} = \{\dots, -3, -2, -1, 0, 1, 2, 3, \dots\}.$$

Pay attention to the details.

It is an infinite set. The set on the right consists of only three elements:

(i)   the set $\{\dots, -3, -2, -1\}$, which is the set of negative integers,
(ii) the integer 0, and
(iii) the set $\{1, 2, 3, \dots\}$, which is the set of positive integers.

Hence, they are not equal. Notice that

$$\mathbb{Z} \neq \{\{\dots, -3, -2, -1\}, \{0\}, \{1, 2, 3, \dots\}\}$$

either, because the set on the right is a set of three sets, while the set on the left is a set of integers. One has three elements; the other has infinitely many elements.   ▲

To reduce confusion, instead of saying a set of sets, we could say a **collection of sets** or a **family of sets**. For example,

$$\{\{1, 3, 5, \dots, \}, \{2, 4, 6, \dots\}\}$$

is a family of two sets, one of which is the set of positive odd integers; the other is the set of positive even integers.

Definition.   A set is said to be **finite** if it has a finite number of elements. The number of elements in a finite set A is called its **cardinality**, and is denoted by $|A|$. Hence, $|A|$ is always nonnegative. If A is an infinite set, some authors would write $|A| = \infty$. $\diamond$

$|A|$ is nonnegative.

Example 4.1.11   While it is trivial that $|\{1, 4, 7, 8\}| = 4$, and $|\{0, 1\}| = 2$, it may not be obvious that

$$|\{0, \{1\}\}| = 2,$$

and

$$|\{\{\dots, -3, -2, -1\}, 0, \{1, 2, 3, \dots\}\}| = 3.$$

What matters is the number of entries in a set, which can be compared to how many items you can find when you open a box. Here is another example:

$$|\{x \in \mathbb{R} \mid x^2 = 9\}| = 2$$

because the equation $x^2 = 9$ has two real solutions. What is $|\{x \in \mathbb{N} \mid x^2 = 9\}|$?   ▲

Hands-On Exercise 4.1.11   Determine these cardinalities:

(a) $|\{x \in \mathbb{Z} \mid x^2 - 7x - 6 = 0\}|$

(b) $|\{x \in \mathbb{R} \mid x^2 - x - 12 < 0\}|$

(c) $|\{x \in \mathbb{Z} \mid x \text{ is prime and } x \text{ is even}\}|$

Recall that your answers should be nonnegative.   △

Hands-On Exercise 4.1.12   Explain why it is incorrect to say $|\emptyset| = \emptyset$. In fact, it is nonsense to say $|\emptyset| = \emptyset$. Explain. What should be the value of $|\emptyset|$?

$|\emptyset|$ *is an integer.*

△

We close this section with an important remark about sets. It follows from the definition of equality of sets that we do not count repeated elements as separate elements. For example, suppose a small student club has three officers:

$$\begin{array}{ll} \text{chair:} & \text{Mary,} \\ \text{vice chair:} & \text{John,} \\ \text{secretary:} & \text{John;} \end{array}$$

and let A represent the set of its officers, and B the set of positions in its executive board, then $|A| = 2$ and $|B| = 3$, because

$$A = \{\text{Mary}, \text{John}\},$$

and

$$B = \{\text{chair}, \text{vice chair}, \text{secretary}\}.$$

Example 4.1.12   Find the errors in the following statement:

$$|\{-2, 2\}| = \{|-2|, |2|\} = \{2\} = 2,$$

and correct them.

Solution: This statement contains several errors. The first mistake is assuming that we can distribute the "absolute value" symbols $|\ \ |$ over the contents of a set:

$$|\{-2, 2\}| \neq \{|-2|, |2|\}.$$

After all, the two vertical bars do not mean absolute value in this case. Instead, it means the cardinality of the set $\{-2, 2\}$. Hence, $|\{-2, 2\}| = 2$.

The second equality $\{|-2|, |2|\} = \{2\}$ is correct. After taking absolute values, both entries become 2. However, we do not write $\{|-2|, |2|\} = \{2, 2\}$, because a set should not contain repetition. Therefore, it is correct to say $\{|-2|, |2|\} = \{2\}$.

The last equality $\{2\} = 2$ is wrong. We cannot compare a set to a number. Imagine the set $\{2\}$ as a box containing only one object, and that object is the number 2. In contrast, 2 on the right-hand side is left in the open air without any containment. It is clear that $\{2\} \neq 2$.

The entire statement contains multiple mistakes; some of them are syntactical errors while some are conceptual. Nevertheless, we do have $|\{-2, 2\}| = 2$. Although the final answer is correct, the argument used to obtain it is not.   ▲

In some situations, we do want to count repeated elements as separate elements, as in $S = \{1, 2, 2, 2, 3, 3, 4, 4\}$. We call such a collection a ***multiset*** instead of an ordinary set. In this case, $|S| = 8$.

Summary and Review

- A set is a collection of objects (without repetitions).
- To describe a set, either list all its elements explicitly, or use a descriptive method.
- Intervals are sets of real numbers.
- The elements in a set can be any type of object, including sets.
- We can even have a set containing dissimilar elements. In particular, we can mix elements and sets inside a set.
- If a set A is finite, its cardinality $|A|$ is the number of elements it contains. Consequently, $|A|$ is always nonnegative.

Exercises 4.1

1. Write each of these sets by listing its elements explicitly (that is, using the roster method).

   (a) $\{n \in \mathbb{Z} \mid -6 < n < 4\}$ (b) $\{n \in \mathbb{N} \mid -6 < n < 4\}$

   (c) $\{x \in \mathbb{Q} \mid x^3 - x^2 - 6x = 0\}$ (d) $\{x \in \mathbb{Q} \mid x^4 - 11x^2 + 18 = 0\}$.

2. Use the roster method to describe these sets:

   (a) $\{x \in \mathbb{N} \mid x < 20 \text{ and } x \text{ is a multiple of } 3\}$
   (b) $\{x \in \mathbb{Z} \mid |x| < 20 \text{ and } x \text{ is a multiple of } 3 \text{ or a multiple of } 5\}$
   (c) $\{x \in \mathbb{Z} \mid |x| < 20 \text{ and } x \text{ is a multiple of } 3 \text{ and a multiple of } 5\}$
   (d) $\{x \in \mathbb{N} \mid x < 20 \text{ and } x \text{ is a multiple of } 3 \text{ but not a multiple of } 5\}$

3. Write each of the following sets in the form $\{n \in \mathbb{Z} \mid p(n)\}$ with a logical statement $p(n)$ describing the property of n.

   (a) $\{\ldots, -3, -2, -1\}$ (b) $\{\ldots, -27, -8, -1, 0, 1, 8, 27, \ldots\}$

   (c) $\{0, 1, 4, 9, 16, \ldots\}$ (d) $\{\ldots, -15, -10, -5, 0, 5, 10, 15, \ldots\}$

   (e) $\{0, 4, 8, 12, \ldots\}$ (f) $\{\ldots, -14, -8, -2, 4, 10, 16, \ldots\}$

4. Repeat Problem 3, but write the sets in the form $\{f(n) \mid n \in S\}$, where $f(n)$ is a formula that describes the pattern of the elements, and S is an appropriate set of numbers.

5. Whenever possible, express the sets in Problem 3 in the form S^+, S^-, bS, or $a + bS$ for some appropriate set S.

6. Determine whether the following sets are empty, finite sets, or infinite sets:

   (a) $\{2n + 1 \mid n \in \mathbb{N}\}$ (b) $\{x \in \mathbb{R} \mid x^2 < 0\}$

   (c) $\{x \in \mathbb{Q} \mid x \geq 0 \text{ and } x \leq 0\}$ (d) $\{x \in \mathbb{N} \mid x < 0 \text{ or } x > 0\}$

7. Write each of these sets in the interval notation.

    (a) $\{x \in \mathbb{R} \mid -4 < x < 7\}$

    (c) $\{x \in \mathbb{R}^+ \mid -4 < x \leq 7\}$

    (e) $\{x \in \mathbb{R} \mid x \leq 6\}$

    (b) $\{x \in \mathbb{R} \mid -4 < x \leq 7\}$

    (d) $\{x \in \mathbb{R} \mid -4 < x\}$

    (f) $\{x \in \mathbb{R}^- \mid 0 \leq x \leq 6\}$

8. Is $[-\infty, \infty]$ a legitimate or correct notation? Explain.

9. Evaluate the following expressions.

    (a) $|\{x \in \mathbb{Z} \mid -4 < x < 7\}|$

    (c) $|\{x \in \mathbb{N} \mid -4 < x \leq 7\}|$

    (e) $|\{-3, -2, 2, 3\}|$

    (b) $|\{x \in \mathbb{Z} \mid -4 < x \leq 7\}|$

    (d) $|\{x \in \mathbb{R} \mid x^4 - 2x^3 - 35x^2 = 0\}|$

    (f) $|\{x \in \mathbb{Q} \mid x^2 = 3\}|$

10. Determine which of the following statements are true, and which are false.

    (a) $a \in \{a\}$

    (c) $\emptyset \in \emptyset$

    (e) $\{\ \} = \emptyset$

    (b) $\{3, 5\} = \{5, 3\}$

    (d) $\emptyset = \{\emptyset\}$

    (f) $\emptyset \in \{\emptyset\}$

11. Determine which of the following statements are true, and which are false.

    (a) $2 \in (2, 7)$

    (c) $\left(\sqrt{5}\right)^2 \in \mathbb{Q}$

    (b) $\sqrt{2} \in (1, 3)$

    (d) $-5 \in \mathbb{N}$

12. Give examples of sets A, B and C such that:

    (a) $A \in B$ and $B \in C$, and $A \notin C$

    (b) $A \in B$ and $B \in C$, and $A \in C$

13. Determine whether the following statements are correct or incorrect *syntactically*. For those that are syntactically correct, determine their truth values; for those that are syntactically incorrect, suggest ways to fix them.

    (a) $(3, 7] = 3 < x \leq 7$.

    (b) $\{x \in \mathbb{R} \mid x^2 < 0\} \equiv \emptyset$.

14. Determine whether the following statements are correct or incorrect *syntactically*. For those that are syntactically correct, determine their truth values; for those that are syntactically incorrect, suggest ways to fix them.

    (a) $\frac{7}{4} \in [2, \sqrt{7})$.

    (b) There does not exist x such that $x \in \mathbb{R}^+$ and $\mathbb{R}^-$.

    (c) If $(0, \infty)$, then x is positive.

4.2   Subsets and Power Sets

We usually consider sets containing elements of similar types. The collection of all the objects under consideration is called the ***universal set***, and is denoted $\mathcal{U}$. For example, for numbers, the universal set is $\mathbb{R}$.

Example 4.2.1   Venn diagrams are useful in demonstrating set relationship. Let

$$\begin{aligned}
\mathcal{U} &= \text{set of geometric figures,} \\
S &= \text{set of squares,} \\
P &= \text{set of parallelogram,} \\
R &= \text{set of rhombuses,} \\
L &= \text{set of rectangles,} \\
C &= \text{set of circles.}
\end{aligned}$$

Their relationship is displayed in Figure 4.2.   ▲

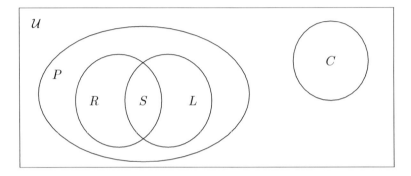

Figure 4.2: The relationship among various sets of geometric figures.

The pictorial representation in Figure 4.2 is called a ***Venn diagram***. We use a rectangle to represent the universal set, and circles or ovals to represent the sets inside the universal set. The relative positions of these circles and ovals indicate the relationship of the respective sets. For example, having R, S, and L inside P means that rhombuses, squares, and rectangles are parallelograms. In contrast, circles are incomparable to parallelograms.

A set A is a subset of another set B, denoted by $A \subseteq B$, if every element of A is also an element of B. See Figure 4.3. We also call B a ***superset*** of A, and write $B \supseteq A$, which is similar to $y \geq x$.

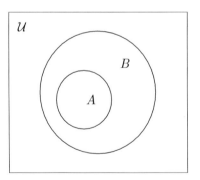

Figure 4.3: The Venn diagram for $A \subseteq B$.

Example 4.2.2   It is clear that $\mathbb{N} \subseteq \mathbb{Z}$ and $\mathbb{Z} \subseteq \mathbb{R}$. We can nest these two relationships into one, and write $\mathbb{N} \subseteq \mathbb{Z} \subseteq \mathbb{R}$. More generally, we have

$$\mathbb{N} \subseteq \mathbb{Z} \subseteq \mathbb{Q} \subseteq \mathbb{R}.$$

Compare this to $x \leq y \leq z \leq w$. We shall discover many similarities between $\subseteq$ and $\leq$.   ▲

Example 4.2.3   It is obvious that

$$\{1,2,7\} \subseteq \{1,2,3,6,7,9\}$$

because all three elements 1, 2, and 7 from the set on the left also appear as elements in the set on the right. Meanwhile,

$$\{1,2,7\} \nsubseteq \{1,2,3,6,8,9\}$$

because 7 belongs to the first set but not the second.   ▲

Example 4.2.4   The following statements are true:

(a) $\{1,2,3\} \subseteq \mathbb{N}$.
(b) $\{x \in \mathbb{R} \mid x^2 = 1\} \subseteq \mathbb{Z}$.

Be sure you can explain clearly why these subset relationships hold.   ▲

Hands-On Exercise 4.2.1   Are these statements true or false?

(a) $\{-1,2\} \nsubseteq \mathbb{N}$, and $\{-1,2\} \subseteq \mathbb{Z}$.

(b) $\{x \in \mathbb{Z} \mid x^2 \leq 1\} \subseteq \mathbb{R}$.   △

Example 4.2.5   Do not assume that if $A \nsubseteq B$ then we must have $B \subseteq A$. For instance, if $A = \{1,5,7\}$ and $B = \{3,8\}$, then $A \nsubseteq B$; but we also have $B \nsubseteq A$.   ▲

The last example demonstrates that $A \nsubseteq B$ is more complicated than just changing the subset notation like we do with inequalities. We need a more precise definition of the subset relationship:

The definition of $A \subseteq B$.

$$\boxed{A \subseteq B \Leftrightarrow \forall x \in \mathcal{U}\,(x \in A \Rightarrow x \in B).}$$

It follows that

$$A \nsubseteq B \Leftrightarrow \exists x \in \mathcal{U}\,(x \in A \wedge x \notin B).$$

Hence, to show that A is not a subset of B, we need to find an element x that belongs to A but not B. There are three possibilities; their Venn diagrams are depicted in Figure 4.4.

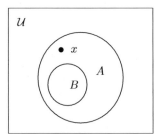 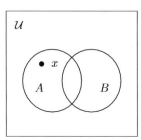 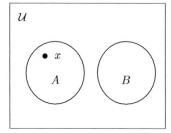

Figure 4.4: Three cases of $A \nsubseteq B$.

Example 4.2.6   We have $[3,6] \subseteq [2,7)$, and $[3,6] \nsubseteq [4,7)$. We also have $(3,4) \subseteq [3,4]$.   ▲

Hands-On Exercise 4.2.2   True or false: $[3,4) \subseteq (3,4)$? Explain.

△

With the notion of universal set, we can now refine the definition for set equality:

$$A = B \Leftrightarrow \forall x \in \mathcal{U}\,(x \in A \Leftrightarrow x \in B).$$

Logically, $x \in A \Leftrightarrow x \in B$ is equivalent to

$$(x \in A \Rightarrow x \in B) \wedge (x \in B \Rightarrow x \in A).$$

Therefore, we can also define the equality of sets via subset relationship:

$$A = B \Leftrightarrow (A \subseteq B) \wedge (B \subseteq A),$$

which can be compared to

$$x = y \Leftrightarrow (x \leq y) \wedge (y \leq x)$$

for real numbers x and y.

This new definition of set equality suggests that in order to prove that $A = B$, we could use this two-step argument:

A way to prove
$A = B$.

1. Show that $A \subseteq B$.
2. Show that $B \subseteq A$.

This technique is useful when it is impossible or impractical to list the elements of A and B for comparison. This is particularly true when A and B are defined abstractly. We will apply this technique in the coming sections.

The two relationship $\subseteq$ and $\leq$ share many common properties. The ***transitive property*** is another example.

Compare this to
$(x \leq y) \wedge (y \leq z)$
$\Rightarrow x \leq z$.

Theorem 4.2.1 *Let A, B, and C be sets. If $A \subseteq B$ and $B \subseteq C$, then $A \subseteq C$.*

Discussion. The theorem statement is in the form of an implication. To prove $p \Rightarrow q$, we start with the assumption p, and use it to show that q must also be true. In this case, these two steps become

(i) Assume that $A \subseteq B$ and $B \subseteq C$.
(ii) Show that $A \subseteq C$.

How can we prove that $A \subseteq C$? We know that $A \subseteq C$ means

$$\forall x \in \mathcal{U}\,(x \in A \Rightarrow x \in C).$$

So we have to start with $x \in A$, and attempt to show that $x \in C$ as well. How can we show that $x \in C$? We need to use the assumption $A \subseteq B$ and $B \subseteq C$. $\Diamond$

Proof: Assume $A \subseteq B$ and $B \subseteq C$. Let $x \in A$. Since $A \subseteq B$, we also have $x \in B$. Likewise, $B \subseteq C$ implies that $x \in C$. Since every element x in A is also an element of C, we conclude that $A \subseteq C$.   ∎

The proof relies on the definition of the subset relationship. Many proofs in mathematics are rather simple if you know the underlying definitions.

Example 4.2.7   Prove that $x \in A \Leftrightarrow \{x\} \subseteq A$, for any element $x \in \mathcal{U}$.

Discussion. We call $p \Leftrightarrow q$ a biconditional statement because it consists of two implications $p \Rightarrow q$ and $p \Leftarrow q$. Hence, we need to prove it in two steps:

1. Show that $p \Rightarrow q$.
2. Show that $q \Rightarrow p$.

We call these two implications the ***necessity*** and ***sufficiency*** of the biconditional statement, and denote them $(\Rightarrow)$ and $(\Leftarrow)$, respectively. In this problem,

- $(\Rightarrow)$ means "$x \in A \Rightarrow \{x\} \subseteq A$".
- $(\Leftarrow)$ means "$\{x\} \subseteq A \Rightarrow x \in A$".

This is how the proof may look:

$(\Rightarrow)$	Assume $x \in A$. $\quad$ ...	Therefore $\{x\} \subseteq A$.
$(\Leftarrow)$	Assume $\{x\} \subseteq A$. $\quad$ ...	Therefore $x \in A$.

We now proceed to finish the proof. $\qquad \diamond$

Solution: $(\Rightarrow)$ $\quad$ Assume $x \in A$. The set $\{x\}$ contains only one element x, which is also an element of A. Thus, every element of $\{x\}$ is also an element of A. By definition, $\{x\} \subseteq A$.

$(\Leftarrow)$ $\quad$ Assume $\{x\} \subseteq A$. The definition of the subset relationship asserts that every element of $\{x\}$ is also an element of A. In particular, x is an element of $\{x\}$, so it is also an element of A. Thus, $x \in A$. $\qquad \blacktriangle$

Definition. The set A is a ***proper subset*** of B, denoted $A \subsetneq B$ or $A \subset B$, if A is a subset of B, and $A \neq B$. Symbolically, $A \subset B \Leftrightarrow (A \subseteq B) \wedge (A \neq B)$. Equivalently,

$$A \subset B \Leftrightarrow (A \subseteq B) \wedge \exists x \in \mathcal{U} \, (x \in B \wedge x \notin A).$$

See the Venn diagram in Figure 4.5. $\qquad \diamond$

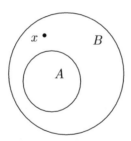

Figure 4.5: The definition of a proper subset.

Example 4.2.8 $\quad$ It is clear that $[0, 5] \subset \mathbb{R}$. We also have

$$\mathbb{N} \subset \mathbb{Z} \subset \mathbb{Q} \subset \mathbb{R}.$$

Note the similarities between $\subset$ and $<$. Compare the last expression to

$$x < y < z < w.$$

Here is another similarity between $\subset$ and $<$. For numbers, $x < y$ and $y < z$ together imply that $x < z$. We call this the transitive property. In a similar fashion, for sets, if $A \subset B$ and $B \subset C$, then $A \subset C$; see Theorem 4.2.1. $\qquad \blacktriangle$

Hands-On Exercise 4.2.3 $\quad$ True or false: $(3, 4) \subset [3, 4]$? How about $(3, 4) \subset (3, 4)$?

$\qquad \triangle$

Theorem 4.2.2 *For any set A, we have $\emptyset \subseteq A$ and $A \subseteq A$. In particular, $\emptyset \subseteq \emptyset$.*

Proof: Since every element of A also appears in A, it follows immediately that $A \subseteq A$. To show that $\emptyset \subseteq A$, we need to verify the implication

$$x \in \emptyset \Rightarrow x \in A$$

An implication is always true if its hypothesis is false.

for any arbitrary $x \in \mathcal{U}$. Since $\emptyset$ is empty, $x \in \emptyset$ is always false; hence, the implication is always true. Consequently, $\emptyset \subseteq A$ for any set A. In particular, when $A = \emptyset$, we obtain $\emptyset \subseteq \emptyset$.   ∎

Example 4.2.9   Determine the truth values of these expressions.

(a) $\emptyset \in \emptyset$ (b) $1 \subseteq \{1\}$ (c) $\emptyset \in \{\emptyset\}$

Solution: (a) By definition, an empty set contains no element. Consequently, the statement $\emptyset \in \emptyset$ is false.

(b) A subset relation only exists between two sets. To the left of the symbol $\subseteq$, we have only a number, which is not a set. Hence, the statement is false. In fact, this expression is syntactically incorrect.

(c) The set $\{\emptyset\}$ contains one element, which happens to be an empty set. Compare this to an empty box inside another box. The outer box is described by the pair of set brackets $\{\ldots\}$, and the (empty) box inside is $\emptyset$. It follows that $\emptyset \in \{\emptyset\}$ is a true statement.   ▲

Hands-On Exercise 4.2.4   Determine the truth values of these expressions.

(a) $\emptyset \subseteq \{\emptyset\}$ (b) $\{1\} \subseteq \{1, \{1,2\}\}$ (c) $\{1\} \subseteq \{\{1\}, \{1,2\}\}$

△

Definition.   The set of all subsets of A is called the ***power set*** of A, denoted $\wp(A)$.   ◇

Every element in $\wp(A)$ is a stand-alone set; more precisely, it is a subset of A.

Since a power set itself is a set, we need to use a pair of left and right curly braces (set brackets) to enclose all its elements. Its elements are themselves sets, each of which requires its own pair of left and right curly braces. Consequently, we need at least two levels of set brackets to describe a power set.

Example 4.2.10   Let $A = \{1, 2\}$ and $B = \{1\}$. The subsets of A are $\emptyset$, $\{1\}$, $\{2\}$ and $\{1, 2\}$. Therefore,

$$\wp(A) = \big\{\emptyset, \{1\}, \{2\}, \{1, 2\}\big\}.$$

In a similar manner, we find

$$\wp(B) = \big\{\emptyset, \{1\}\big\}.$$

We can write directly

$$\wp(\{1, 2\}) = \big\{\emptyset, \{1\}, \{2\}, \{1, 2\}\big\}, \quad \text{and} \quad \wp(\{1\}) = \big\{\emptyset, \{1\}\big\}$$

without introducing letters to represent the sets involved.   ▲

Hands-On Exercise 4.2.5   Let us evaluate $\wp(\{1,2,3,4\})$. To ensure that no subset is missed, we list these subsets according to their sizes. Since $\emptyset$ is the subset of any set, $\emptyset$ is always an element in the power set. This is the subset of size 0. Next, list the singleton subsets (subsets with only one element). Then the doubleton subsets, and so forth. Complete the following table.

size	subsets
0	$\emptyset$
1	$\{1\}, \{2\}, \ldots$
2	$\{1,2\}, \{1,3\}, \ldots$
3	$\{1,2,3\}, \ldots$
4	$\ldots$

Since $\emptyset \subseteq A$ for any set A, we always have $\emptyset \in \wp(A)$.

Since $A \subseteq A$ for any set A, the power set $\wp(A)$ always contains A itself. As a result, the last subset in the list should be A itself.

We are now ready to put them together to form the power set. All you need is to put all the subsets inside a pair of bigger curly braces (a power set is itself a set; hence, it needs a pair of curly braces in its description). Put your final answer in the space below.

Check to make sure that the left and right braces match perfectly. $\triangle$

Example 4.2.11   Since A is a subset of A, it belongs to $\wp(A)$. Nonetheless, it is improper to say $A \subseteq \wp(A)$. Can you explain why? What should be the correct notation?

Solution: The power set $\wp(A)$ is the collection of all the subsets of A. Thus, the elements in $\wp(A)$ are subsets of A. One of these subsets is the set A itself. Hence, A itself appears as an *element* in $\wp(A)$, and we write $A \in \wp(A)$ to describe this *membership*.

This is different from saying that $A \subseteq \wp(A)$. In order to have the *subset* relationship $A \subseteq \wp(A)$, every element in A must also appear as an element in $\wp(A)$. The elements of $\wp(A)$ are sets (they are subsets of A, and subsets are sets). An element of A is not the same as a subset of A. Therefore, although $A \subseteq \wp(A)$ is syntactically correct, its truth value is false.   ▲

Hands-On Exercise 4.2.6   Explain the difference between $\emptyset$ and $\{\emptyset\}$. How many elements are there in $\emptyset$ and $\{\emptyset\}$? Is it true that $\wp(\emptyset) = \{\emptyset\}$?

$\triangle$

Theorem 4.2.3 *If A is an n-element set, then $\wp(A)$ has 2^n elements. In other words, an n-element set has 2^n distinct subsets.*

Proof: How many subsets of A can we construct? To form a subset, we go through each of the n elements and ask ourselves if we want to include this particular element or not. Since there are two choices (yes or no) for each of the n elements in A, we have found $\underbrace{2 \cdot 2 \cdots 2}_{n \text{ times}} = 2^n$ subsets.   ■

Hands-On Exercise 4.2.7   How many elements are there in $\wp(\{\alpha, \beta, \gamma\})$? What are they?

△

Hands-On Exercise 4.2.8   What is the cardinality of $\emptyset$? How about $\wp(\emptyset)$? Describe $\wp(\emptyset)$.

△

Hands-On Exercise 4.2.9   Is it correct to write $|\wp(A)| = 2^{|A|}$? How about $|\wp(A)| = 2^A$? Explain.

△

Example 4.2.12   When a set contains sets as elements, its power set could become rather complicated. Here are two examples.

$$\wp(\{\{a\},\{1\}\}) = \Big\{\emptyset, \{\{a\}\}, \{\{1\}\}, \{\{a\},\{1\}\}\Big\},$$

$$\wp(\{\emptyset,\{1\}\}) = \Big\{\emptyset, \{\emptyset\}, \{\{1\}\}, \{\emptyset,\{1\}\}\Big\}.$$

Be sure you understand the notations used in these examples. In particular, examine the number of levels of set brackets used in each example.   ▲

Summary and Review

- A set S is a subset of another set T if and only if every element in S can be found in T.
- In symbols, $S \subseteq T \Leftrightarrow \forall x \in \mathcal{U} \, (x \in S \Rightarrow x \in T)$.
- Consequently, to show that $S \subseteq T$, we have to start with an arbitrary element x in S, and show that x also belongs to T.
- The definition of subset relationship implies that for any set S, we always have $\emptyset \subseteq S$ and $S \subseteq S$.
- The power set of a set S, denoted $\wp(S)$, contains all the subsets of S.
- If $|S| = n$, then $|\wp(S)| = 2^n$. Hence, an n-element set has 2^n subsets.
- To construct $\wp(S)$, list the subsets of S according to their sizes. Be sure to use a pair of curly braces for each subset, and enclose all of them within a pair of outer curly braces.

Exercises 4.2

1. Determine which of the following statements are true and which are false.

   (a) $\{1, 2, 3\} \subseteq \{0, 1, 2, 3, 4\}$ (b) $\{1, 2, 3\} \subseteq \mathbb{N}$
   (c) $\{1, 2\} \subset [1, 2]$ (d) $[2, 4] \subseteq (0, 6)$
   (e) $[2, 4) \subset [2, 4]$ (f) $[2, 4) \subseteq (2, 4]$

2. Determine which of the following statements are true and which are false.

   (a) $a \subseteq \{a\}$ (b) $\{a\} \subseteq \{a, b\}$
   (c) $\emptyset \subseteq \emptyset$ (d) $\emptyset \subseteq \{\emptyset\}$
   (e) $\emptyset \subset \{\emptyset\}$ (f) $\{a\} \subseteq \wp(\{\{a\}, \{b\}\})$

3. Explain why $\mathbb{Z} \subseteq \mathbb{Q}$. In particular, explain how to express an integer as a rational number.

4. True or false: $\mathbb{N} \subseteq 6\mathbb{N}$? Explain.

5. If $A \subseteq B$, $B \subseteq C$, and $C \subseteq D$, is it true that $A \subseteq D$? What do you call this property?

6. Determine whether the following statements are true or false:

   (a) The empty set $\emptyset$ is a subset of $\{1, 2, 3\}$.
   (b) If $A = \{1, 2, 3\}$, then $\{1\}$ is a subset of $\wp(A)$.

7. Find the power set of the following sets.

   (a) $\{a, b\}$ (b) $\{4, 7\}$ (c) $\{x, y, z, w\}$
   (d) $\{\{a\}\}$ (e) $\{a, \{b\}\}$ (f) $\{\{x\}, \{y\}\}$

8. Evaluate the following sets.

   (a) $\wp(\{\emptyset\})$ (b) $\wp(\wp(\{a, b\}))$ (c) $\wp(\wp(\wp(\emptyset)))$

9. We have learned that $A \subseteq A$ for any set A. Then, should we write $A \in \wp(A)$ or $A \subseteq \wp(A)$? Explain.

10. Prove that $X \in \wp(A)$ if and only if $X \subseteq A$.

11. Determine which of the following statements are true, and which are false. Explain!

   (a) $\{a\} \in \{a, b, c\}$ (b) $\{a\} \subseteq \{\{a\}, b, c\}$ (c) $\{a\} \in \wp(\{\{a\}, b, c\})$

12. Determine which of the following statements are true, and which are false. Explain!

   (a) $\{a\} \subseteq \{a, b, c\}$ (b) $\{a\} \subseteq \{\{a, b\}, c\}$ (c) $\{a\} \subseteq \wp(\{\{a\}, b, c\})$

4.3   Unions and Intersections

We can form a new set from existing sets by carrying out a set operation.

Definition.   Given two sets A and B, define their ***intersection*** to be the set

$$A \cap B = \{x \in \mathcal{U} \mid x \in A \wedge x \in B\}.$$

Note the similarity between the symbols $\cap$ and $\wedge$.

Loosely speaking, $A \cap B$ contains elements common to both A and B. $\diamond$

Definition.   The ***union*** of A and B is defined as

$$A \cup B = \{x \in \mathcal{U} \mid x \in A \vee x \in B\}.$$

Note the similarity between the symbols $\cup$ and $\vee$.

Thus $A \cup B$ is, as the name suggests, the set combining all the elements from A and B. $\diamond$

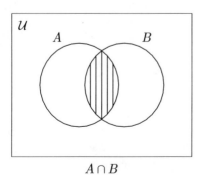

$A \cap B$

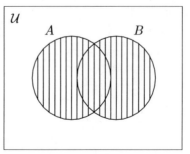

$A \cup B$

$x \in A - B$ means x belongs to A but not to B.

Definition.   The *set difference* $A - B$, sometimes written as $A \setminus B$, is defined as

$$A - B = \{x \in \mathcal{U} \mid x \in A \wedge x \notin B\}.$$

In words, $A - B$ contains elements that can only be found in A but not in B. Operationally speaking, $A - B$ is the set obtained from A by removing the elements that also belong to B. Therefore, the set difference $A - B$ is also called the *relative complement* of B in A. In particular, $\mathcal{U} - A$ is called the *complement* of A, and is denoted by $\overline{A}$, A' or A^c. $\diamond$

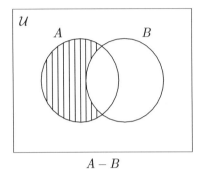

$A - B$

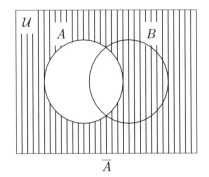

$\overline{A}$

Remark.   We would like to remind the readers that it is not uncommon among authors to adopt different notations for the same mathematical concept. Likewise, the same notation could mean something different in another textbook or even another branch of mathematics. It is important to develop the habit of examining the context and making sure that you understand the meaning of the notations when you start reading a mathematical exposition. $\diamond$

Example 4.3.1   Let $\mathcal{U} = \{1, 2, 3, 4, 5\}$, $A = \{1, 2, 3\}$, and $B = \{3, 4\}$. Find $A \cap B$, $A \cup B$, $A - B$, $B - A$, $\overline{A}$, and $\overline{B}$.

Solution: We have

$$
\begin{aligned}
A \cap B &= \{3\}, \\
A \cup B &= \{1, 2, 3, 4\}, \\
A - B &= \{1, 2\}, \\
B - A &= \{4\}.
\end{aligned}
$$

We also find $\overline{A} = \{4, 5\}$, and $\overline{B} = \{1, 2, 5\}$.   ▲

Hands-On Exercise 4.3.1   Let $\mathcal{U} = \{\text{John}, \text{Mary}, \text{Dave}, \text{Lucy}, \text{Peter}, \text{Larry}\}$,

$$A = \{\text{John}, \text{Mary}, \text{Dave}\}, \quad \text{and} \quad B = \{\text{John}, \text{Larry}, \text{Lucy}\}.$$

Find $A \cap B$, $A \cup B$, $A - B$, $B - A$, $\overline{A}$, and $\overline{B}$.

$\triangle$

Hands-On Exercise 4.3.2   If $A \subseteq B$, what would be $A - B$?

$\triangle$

Example 4.3.2   The set of integers can be written as the

$$\mathbb{Z} = \{-1, -2, -3, \ldots\} \cup \{0\} \cup \{1, 2, 3, \ldots\}.$$

Can we replace $\{0\}$ with 0? Explain.   ▲

Hands-On Exercise 4.3.3   Explain why the following expressions are syntactically incorrect.

(a) $\mathbb{Z} = \{-1, -2, -3, \ldots\} \cup 0 \cup \{1, 2, 3, \ldots\}$.
(b) $\mathbb{Z} = \ldots, -3, -2, -1 \cup 0 \cup 1, 2, 3, \ldots$
(c) $\mathbb{Z} = \ldots, -3, -2, -1 + 0 + 1, 2, 3, \ldots$
(d) $\mathbb{Z} = \mathbb{Z}^- \cup 0 \cup \mathbb{Z}^+$

How would you fix the errors in these expressions?

△

Example 4.3.3   For any set A, what are $A \cap \emptyset$, $A \cup \emptyset$, $A - \emptyset$, $\emptyset - A$ and $\overline{\overline{A}}$?

Solution: It is clear that

$$A \cap \emptyset = \emptyset, \qquad A \cup \emptyset = A, \qquad \text{and} \qquad A - \emptyset = A.$$

From the definition of set difference, we find $\emptyset - A = \emptyset$. Finally, $\overline{\overline{A}} = A$.   ▲

Example 4.3.4   Write, in interval notation, $[5, 8) \cup (6, 9]$ and $[5, 8) \cap (6, 9]$.

Solution: The answers are

$$[5, 8) \cup (6, 9] = [5, 9], \qquad \text{and} \qquad [5, 8) \cap (6, 9] = (6, 8).$$

They are obtained by comparing the location of the two intervals on the real number line.   ▲

Hands-On Exercise 4.3.4   Write, in interval notation, $(0, 3) \cup [-1, 2)$ and $(0, 3) \cap [-1, 2)$.

△

Example 4.3.5   We are now able to describe the following set

$$\{x \in \mathbb{R} \mid (x < 5) \vee (x > 7)\}$$

in the interval notation. It can be written as either $(-\infty, 5) \cup (7, \infty)$ or, using complement, $\mathbb{R} - [5, 7]$. Consequently, saying $x \notin [5, 7]$ is the same as saying $x \in (-\infty, 5) \cup (7, \infty)$, or equivalently, $x \in \mathbb{R} - [5, 7]$.   ▲

Theorem 4.3.1 *The following properties hold for any sets A, B, and C in a universal set $\mathcal{U}$.*

1. **Commutative properties**: $A \cup B = B \cup A$,
$$A \cap B = B \cap A.$$

2. **Associative properties**: $(A \cup B) \cup C = A \cup (B \cup C)$,
$$(A \cap B) \cap C = A \cap (B \cap C).$$

3. **Distributive laws**: $A \cup (B \cap C) = (A \cup B) \cap (A \cup C)$,
$$A \cap (B \cup C) = (A \cap B) \cup (A \cap C).$$

4. **Idempotent laws**: $A \cup A = A$,
$$A \cap A = A.$$

5. **De Morgan's laws**: $\overline{A \cup B} = \overline{A} \cap \overline{B}$,
$$\overline{A \cap B} = \overline{A} \cup \overline{B}.$$

6. **Laws of the excluded middle**, *or* **inverse laws**: $A \cup \overline{A} = \mathcal{U}$,
$$A \cap \overline{A} = \emptyset.$$

As an illustration, we shall prove the distributive law

$$A \cup (B \cap C) = (A \cup B) \cap (A \cup C).$$

We need to show that

$$\forall x \in \mathcal{U} \left[x \in A \cup (B \cap C) \Leftrightarrow x \in (A \cup B) \cap (A \cup C) \right].$$

Equivalently, we need to show that

$$A \cup (B \cap C) \subseteq (A \cup B) \cap (A \cup C), \quad \text{and} \quad (A \cup B) \cap (A \cup C) \subseteq A \cup (B \cap C).$$

Either way, we need to establish the equality in two steps.

We now present two proofs of the distributive law $A \cup (B \cap C) = (A \cup B) \cap (A \cup C)$.

Proof 1:　Let $x \in A \cup (B \cap C)$. Then $x \in A$, or $x \in B \cap C$. We know that $x \in B \cap C$ implies that $x \in B$ and $x \in C$. So we have

(i) $x \in A$ or $x \in B$, and
(ii) $x \in A$ or $x \in C$;

equivalently,

(i) $x \in A \cup B$, and
(ii) $x \in A \cup C$.

Thus, $x \in (A \cup B) \cap (A \cup C)$. We have proved that $A \cup (B \cap C) \subseteq (A \cup B) \cap (A \cup C)$.

Now let $x \in (A \cup B) \cap (A \cup C)$. Then $x \in A \cup B$ and $x \in A \cup C$. From the definition of union, we find

(i) $x \in A$ or $x \in B$, and
(ii) $x \in A$ or $x \in C$.

Both conditions require $x \in A$, so we can rewrite them as

(i) $x \in A$, or
(ii) $x \in B$ and $x \in C$;

equivalently,

   (i) $x \in A$, or

  (ii) $x \in B \cap C$.

Thus, $x \in A \cup (B \cap C)$. This proves that $(A \cup B) \cap (A \cup C) \subseteq A \cup (B \cap C)$. Together with $A \cup (B \cap C) \subseteq (A \cup B) \cap (A \cup C)$, we conclude that $A \cup (B \cap C) = (A \cup B) \cap (A \cup C)$.   ■

Below is an alternate proof. This type of argument is shorter, but is more symbolic; hence, it is more difficult to follow.

Proof 2:   Since

$$
\begin{aligned}
x \in A \cup (B \cap C) &\Leftrightarrow x \in A \vee x \in (B \cap C) && \text{(defn. of union)} \\
&\Leftrightarrow x \in A \vee (x \in B \wedge x \in C) && \text{(defn. of intersection)} \\
&\Leftrightarrow (x \in A \vee x \in B) \wedge (x \in A \vee x \in C) && \text{(distributive law)} \\
&\Leftrightarrow (x \in A \cup B) \wedge (x \in A \cup C) && \text{(defn. of union)} \\
&\Leftrightarrow x \in (A \cup B) \cap (A \cup C) && \text{(defn. of intersection)}
\end{aligned}
$$

it follows that $A \cup (B \cap C) = (A \cup B) \cap (A \cup C)$.   ■

Hands-On Exercise 4.3.5   Prove that $A \cap (B \cup C) = (A \cap B) \cup (A \cap C)$.

△

Hands-On Exercise 4.3.6   Prove that if $A \subseteq B$ and $A \subseteq C$, then $A \subseteq B \cap C$.

Discussion.   Let us start with a draft. The statement we want to prove takes the form of

$$(A \subseteq B) \wedge (A \subseteq C) \Rightarrow A \subseteq B \cap C.$$

Hence, what do we assume and what do we want to prove?

    Assume:

    Want to Prove:

Did you put down we assume $A \subseteq B$ and $A \subseteq C$, and we want to prove $A \subseteq B \cap C$? Great! Now, what does it mean by $A \subseteq B$? How about $A \subseteq C$? What is the meaning of $A \subseteq B \cap C$?

$A \subseteq B$ means: For any $x \in \mathcal{U}$, if $x \in A$, then $x \in B$ as well.

$A \subseteq C$ means:

$A \subseteq B \cap C$ means:

How can you use the first two pieces of information to obtain what we need to establish?

Now it is time to put everything together, and polish it into a final version. Remember three things:

  (i) the outline of the proof,
 (ii) the reason in each step of the main argument, and
(iii) the introduction and the conclusion.

Put the complete proof in the space below.

$\triangle$

Here are two results involving complements.

Theorem 4.3.2 *For any two sets A and B, we have $A \subseteq B \Leftrightarrow \overline{B} \subseteq \overline{A}$.*

Theorem 4.3.3 (Generalized De Morgan's Laws) *For any sets A, B and C,*

$$\begin{aligned}
A - (B \cup C) &= (A - B) \cap (A - C), \\
A - (B \cap C) &= (A - B) \cup (A - C),
\end{aligned}$$

Summary and Review

- Memorize the definitions of intersection, union, and set difference. We rely on them to prove or derive new results.
- The intersection of two sets A and B, denoted $A \cap B$, is the set of elements common to both A and B. In symbols, $\forall x \in \mathcal{U} \left[x \in A \cap B \Leftrightarrow (x \in A \wedge x \in B) \right]$.
- The union of two sets A and B, denoted $A \cup B$, is the set that combines all the elements in A and B. In symbols, $\forall x \in \mathcal{U} \left[x \in A \cap B \Leftrightarrow (x \in A \vee x \in B) \right]$.
- The set difference between two sets A and B, denoted by $A - B$, is the set of elements that can only be found in A but not in B. In symbol, it means $\forall x \in \mathcal{U} \left[x \in A - B \Leftrightarrow (x \in A \wedge x \notin B) \right]$.
- Know the properties of intersection, union, and set differences listed in Theorem 4.3.1.

Exercises 4.3

1. Write each of the following sets by listing its elements explicitly.

   (a) $[-4, 4] \cap \mathbb{Z}$ (b) $(-4, 4] \cap \mathbb{Z}$ (c) $(-4, \infty) \cap \mathbb{Z}$

   (d) $(-\infty, 4] \cap \mathbb{N}$ (e) $(-4, \infty) \cap \mathbb{Z}^-$ (f) $(4, 5) \cap \mathbb{Z}$

2. Assume $\mathcal{U} = \mathbb{Z}$, and let

$$
\begin{aligned}
A &= \{\ldots, -6, -4, -2, 0, 2, 4, 6, \ldots\} &&= 2\mathbb{Z}, \\
B &= \{\ldots, -9, -6, -3, 0, 3, 6, 9, \ldots\} &&= 3\mathbb{Z}, \\
C &= \{\ldots, -12, -8, -4, 0, 4, 8, 12, \ldots\} &&= 4\mathbb{Z}.
\end{aligned}
$$

Describe the following sets by listing their elements explicitly.

(a) $A \cap B$

(b) $C - A$

(c) $A - B$

(d) $A \cap \overline{B}$

(e) $B - A$

(f) $B \cup C$

(g) $(A \cup B) \cap C$

(h) $(A \cup B) - C$

3. Are these statements true or false?

(a) $[1, 2] \cap [2, 3] = \emptyset$

(b) $[1, 2) \cup (2, 3] = [2, 3]$

4. Let the universal set $\mathcal{U}$ be the set of people who voted in the 2012 U.S. presidential election. Define the subsets D, B, and W of $\mathcal{U}$ as follows:

$$
\begin{aligned}
D &= \{x \in \mathcal{U} \mid x \text{ registered as a Democrat}\}, \\
B &= \{x \in \mathcal{U} \mid x \text{ voted for Barack Obama}\}, \\
W &= \{x \in \mathcal{U} \mid x \text{ belonged to a union}\}.
\end{aligned}
$$

Express the following subsets of $\mathcal{U}$ in terms of D, B, and W.

(a) People who did not vote for Barack Obama.

(b) Union members who voted for Barack Obama.

(c) Registered Democrats who voted for Barack Obama but did not belong to a union.

(d) Union members who either were not registered as Democrats or voted for Barack Obama.

(e) People who voted for Barack Obama but were not registered as Democrats and were not union members.

(f) People who were either registered as Democrats and were union members, or did not vote for Barack Obama.

5. An insurance company classifies its set $\mathcal{U}$ of policy holders by the following sets:

$$
\begin{aligned}
A &= \{x \mid x \text{ drives a subcompact car}\}, \\
B &= \{x \mid x \text{ drives a car older than 5 years}\}, \\
C &= \{x \mid x \text{ is married}\}, \\
D &= \{x \mid x \text{ is over 21 years old}\}, \\
E &= \{x \mid x \text{ is a male}\}.
\end{aligned}
$$

Describe each of the following subsets of $\mathcal{U}$ in terms of A, B, C, D, and E.

(a) Male policy holders over 21 years old.

(b) Policy holders who are either female or drive cars more than 5 years old.

(c) Female policy holders over 21 years old who drive subcompact cars.

(d) Male policy holders who are either married or over 21 years old and do not drive subcompact cars.

6. Let A and B be arbitrary sets. Complete the following statements.

(a) $A \subseteq B \Leftrightarrow A \cap B = $ _____ .

(b) $A \subseteq B \Leftrightarrow A \cup B = $ _____ .

(c) $A \subseteq B \Leftrightarrow A - B = $ _____ .

(d) $A \subset B \Leftrightarrow (A - B = $ _____ $\wedge \; B - A \neq $ _____ $)$.

(e) $A \subset B \Leftrightarrow (A \cap B = $ _____ $\wedge \; A \cap B \neq $ _____ $)$.

(f) $A - B = B - A \Leftrightarrow $ _____ .

7. Give examples of sets A and B such that $A \in B$ and $A \subset B$.

8. Prove the De Morgan's laws.

9. Let A, B, and C be any three sets. Prove that if $A \subseteq C$ and $B \subseteq C$, then $A \cup B \subseteq C$.

10. Prove Theorem 4.3.2

11. Prove Theorem 4.3.3

12. Let A, B, and C be any three sets. Prove that

(a) $A - B = A \cap \overline{B}$

(b) $A = (A - B) \cup (A \cap B)$

(c) $A - (B - C) = A \cap (\overline{B} \cup C)$

(d) $(A - B) - C = A - (B \cup C)$

13. Comment on the following statements. Are they syntactically correct?

(a) $x \in A \cap x \in B \equiv x \in A \cap B$

(b) $x \in A \wedge B \Rightarrow x \in A \cap B$

14. Prove or disprove each of the following statements about arbitrary sets A and B. If you think a statement is true, prove it; if you think it is false, provide a counterexample.

(a) $\wp(A \cap B) = \wp(A) \cap \wp(B)$

(b) $\wp(A \cup B) = \wp(A) \cup \wp(B)$

(c) $\wp(A - B) = \wp(A) - \wp(B)$

Remark. To show that two sets U and V are equal, we usually want to prove that $x \in U \Leftrightarrow x \in V$. In this problem, the element x is actually a set. Since we usually use uppercase letters to denote sets, we should start the proof of (a) with "Let $S \in \wp(A \cap B)$." If you prefer to use the alternate approach, it looks like the following:

$$
\begin{aligned}
S \in \wp(A \cap B) \quad &\Leftrightarrow \quad \ldots \\
&\Leftrightarrow \quad \ldots \\
&\;\;\vdots \\
&\Leftrightarrow \quad S \in \wp(A) \cap \wp(B).
\end{aligned}
$$

These remarks also apply to (b) and (c). $\Diamond$

4.4   Cartesian Products

Another way to obtain a new set from two given sets A and B is to form ordered pairs. An **ordered pair** (x, y) consists of two values x and y. Their order of appearance is important, so we call them first and second elements respectively. Consequently, $(a, b) \neq (b, a)$ unless $a = b$. In general, $(a, b) = (c, d)$ if and only if $a = c$ and $b = d$.

Definition. The **Cartesian product** of A and B is the set

$$A \times B = \{(a,b) \mid a \in A \wedge b \in B\}.$$

*Enclose ordered pairs in parentheses. Write them as (x,y), and **not** as $\{x,y\}$.*

Thus, $A \times B$ (read as "A cross B") contains all the ordered pairs in which the first elements are selected from A, and the second elements are selected from B.   ◇

Example 4.4.1   Let $A = \{\text{John}, \text{Jim}, \text{Dave}\}$ and $B = \{\text{Mary}, \text{Lucy}\}$. Determine $A \times B$ and $B \times A$.

Solution: We find

$A \times B = \{(\text{John}, \text{Mary}), (\text{John}, \text{Lucy}), (\text{Jim}, \text{Mary}), (\text{Jim}, \text{Lucy}), (\text{Dave}, \text{Mary}), (\text{Dave}, \text{Lucy})\}$,
$B \times A = \{(\text{Mary}, \text{John}), (\text{Mary}, \text{Jim}), (\text{Mary}, \text{Dave}), (\text{Lucy}, \text{John}), (\text{Lucy}, \text{Jim}), (\text{Lucy}, \text{Dave})\}$.

In general, $A \times B \neq B \times A$.   ▲

Example 4.4.2   Determine $A \times B$ and $A \times A$:

(a) $A = \{1,2\}$ and $B = \{2,5,6\}$.

(b) $A = \{5\}$ and $B = \{0,7\}$.

Solution: (a) We find

$$\begin{aligned} A \times B &= \{(1,2),(1,5),(1,6),(2,2),(2,5),(2,6)\}, \\ A \times A &= \{(1,1),(1,2),(2,1),(2,2)\}. \end{aligned}$$

(b) The answers are $A \times B = \{(5,0),(5,7)\}$, and $A \times A = \{(5,5)\}$.   ▲

Hands-On Exercise 4.4.1   Let $A = \{a,b,c,d\}$ and $B = \{r,s,t\}$. Find $A \times B$, $B \times A$, and $B \times B$.

△

Example 4.4.3   Determine $\wp(\{1,2\}) \times \{3,7\}$. Be sure to use correct notation.

Solution: For a complicated problem, divide it into smaller tasks and solve each one separately. Then assemble them to form the final answer. In this problem, we first evaluate

Divide and conquer!

$$\wp(\{1,2\}) = \{\emptyset, \{1\}, \{2\}, \{1,2\}\}.$$

This leads to

$$\begin{aligned} \wp(\{1,2\}) \times \{3,7\} &= \{\emptyset, \{1\}, \{2\}, \{1,2\}\} \times \{3,7\} \\ &= \{(\emptyset,3), (\emptyset,7), (\{1\},3), (\{1\},7), (\{2\},3), (\{2\},7), (\{1,2\},3), (\{1,2\},7)\}. \end{aligned}$$

Check to make sure that we have matching left and right parentheses, and matching left and right curly braces.   ▲

Hands-On Exercise 4.4.2   Find $\{a, b, c\} \times \wp(\{d\})$.

$\triangle$

Example 4.4.4   How could we describe the contents of the Cartesian product $[1, 3] \times \{2, 4\}$? Since $[1, 3]$ is an infinite set, it is impossible to list all the ordered pairs. We need to use the set-builder notation:

$$[1, 3] \times \{2, 4\} = \{(x, y) \mid 1 \le x \le 3, y = 2, 4\}.$$

We can also write $[1, 3] \times \{2, 4\} = \{(x, 2), (x, 4) \mid 1 \le x \le 3\}$.   ▲

Hands-On Exercise 4.4.3   Describe, using the set-builder notation, the Cartesian product $[1, 3] \times [2, 4]$.

$\triangle$

Cartesian products can be extended to more than two sets. Instead of ordered pairs, we need **ordered n-tuples**. The n-**fold Cartesian product** of n sets $A_1, A_2, \ldots, A_n$ is the set

$$\boxed{A_1 \times A_2 \times \cdots \times A_n = \{(a_1, a_2, \ldots, a_n) \mid a_i \in A_i \text{ for each } i, 1 \le i \le n\}.}$$

In particular, when $A_i = A$ for all i, we abbreviate the Cartesian product as A^n.

Example 4.4.5   The n-dimensional space is denoted $\mathbb{R}^n$. It is the n-fold Cartesian product of $\mathbb{R}$. In special cases, $\mathbb{R}^2$ is the xy-plane, and $\mathbb{R}^3$ is the xyz-space.   ▲

Hands-On Exercise 4.4.4   Let $A = \{1, 2\}$, $B = \{a, b\}$, and $C = \{r, s, t\}$. Find $A \times B \times C$.

$\triangle$

$(A \times B) \times C$, $A \times (B \times C)$ and $A \times B \times C$ are three different sets.

Example 4.4.6   From a technical standpoint, $(A \times B) \times C$ is different from $A \times B \times C$. Can you explain why? Can you discuss the difference, if any, between $(A \times B) \times C$ and $A \times (B \times C)$? For instance, give some specific examples of the elements in $(A \times B) \times C$ and $A \times (B \times C)$ to illustrate their differences.

Solution: The elements of $(A \times B) \times C$ are ordered pairs in which the first coordinates are themselves ordered pairs. A typical element in $(A \times B) \times C$ takes the form of

$$((a, b), c).$$

The elements in $A \times B \times C$ are ordered triples of the form

$$(a, b, c).$$

Since their elements look different, it is clear that $(A \times B) \times C \neq A \times B \times C$. Likewise, a typical element in $A \times (B \times C)$ looks like

$$\big(a, (b, c)\big).$$

Therefore, $(A \times B) \times C \neq A \times (B \times C)$, and $A \times (B \times C) \neq A \times B \times C$.   ▲

Theorem 4.4.1 *For any sets A, B, and C, we have*

$$
\begin{aligned}
A \times (B \cup C) &= (A \times B) \cup (A \times C), \\
A \times (B \cap C) &= (A \times B) \cap (A \times C), \\
A \times (B - C) &= (A \times B) - (A \times C).
\end{aligned}
$$

Remark.   How would we show that the two sets S and T are equal? We need to show that

$$x \in S \Leftrightarrow x \in T.$$

The complication in this problem is that both S and T are Cartesian products, so x takes on a special form, namely, that of an ordered pair. Consider the first identity as an example; we need to show that

$$(u, v) \in A \times (B \cup C) \Leftrightarrow (u, v) \in (A \times B) \cup (A \times C).$$

We prove this in two steps: first showing $\Rightarrow$, then $\Leftarrow$, which is equivalent to first showing $\subseteq$, then $\supseteq$. Alternatively, we can use $\Leftrightarrow$ throughout the argument.

Proof 1:   Let $(u, v) \in A \times (B \cup C)$. Then $u \in A$, and $v \in B \cup C$. The definition of union implies that $v \in B$ or $v \in C$. Thus far, we have found

(i) $u \in A$ and $v \in B$, or
(ii) $u \in A$ and $v \in C$.

This is equivalent to

(i) $(u, v) \in A \times B$, or
(ii) $(u, v) \in A \times C$.

Thus, $(u, v) \in (A \times B) \cup (A \times C)$. This proves that $A \times (B \cup C) \subseteq (A \times B) \cup (A \times C)$.

Next, let $(u, v) \in (A \times B) \cup (A \times C)$. Then $(u, v) \in A \times B$, or $(u, v) \in A \times C$. This means

(i) $u \in A$ and $v \in B$, or
(ii) $u \in A$ and $v \in C$.

Both conditions require $u \in A$, so we can rewrite them as

(i) $u \in A$, and
(ii) $v \in B$ or $v \in C$;

which is equivalent to

(i) $u \in A$, and
(ii) $v \in B \cup C$.

Thus, $(u, v) \in A \times (B \cup C)$. We have proved that $(A \times B) \cup (A \times C) \subseteq A \times (B \cup C)$. Together with $A \times (B \cup C) \subseteq (A \times B) \cup (A \times C)$ that we have proved earlier, we conclude that $A \times (B \cup C) = (A \times B) \cup (A \times C)$.   ■

Proof 2:   We shall only prove the first equality. Since

$$
\begin{aligned}
(u, v) \in A \times (B \cup C) &\Leftrightarrow u \in A \wedge v \in (B \cup C) &&\text{(defn. of Cartesian product)} \\
&\Leftrightarrow u \in A \wedge (v \in B \vee v \in C) &&\text{(defn. of union)} \\
&\Leftrightarrow (u \in A \wedge v \in B) \vee (u \in A \wedge v \in C) &&\text{(distributive law)} \\
&\Leftrightarrow (u, v) \in A \times B \vee (u, v) \in A \times C &&\text{(defn. of Cartesian product)} \\
&\Leftrightarrow (u, v) \in (A \times B) \cup (A \times C) &&\text{(defn. of union)}
\end{aligned}
$$

we conclude that $A \times (B \cup C) = (A \times B) \cup (A \times C)$.   ■

Theorem 4.4.2 *If A and B are finite sets, with $|A| = m$ and $|B| = n$, then $|A \times B| = mn$.*

Proof: The elements of $A \times B$ are ordered pairs of the form (a, b), where $a \in A$, and $b \in B$. There are m choices of a. For each fixed a, we can form the ordered pair (a, b) in n ways, because there are n choices for b. Together, the ordered pairs (a, b) can be formed in mn ways. ■

The argument we used in the proof is called ***multiplication principle***. We shall study it again in Chapter 8. In brief, it says that if a job can be completed in several steps, then the number of ways to finish the job is the product of the number of ways to finish each step.

Corollary 4.4.3 *If $A_1, A_2, \ldots, A_n$ are finite sets, then $|A_1 \times A_2 \times \cdots \times A_n| = |A_1| \cdot |A_2| \cdots |A_n|$.*

Corollary 4.4.4 *If A is a finite set with $|A| = n$, then $|\wp(A)| = 2^n$.*

Proof: Let the elements of A be $a_1, a_2, \ldots, a_n$. The elements of $\wp(A)$ are subsets of A. Each subset of A contains some elements from A. Associate to each subset S of A an ordered n-tuple $(b_1, b_2, \ldots, b_n)$ from $\{0, 1\}^n$ such that

$$b_i = \begin{cases} 0 & \text{if } a_i \notin S, \\ 1 & \text{if } a_i \in S. \end{cases}$$

The value of the ith element in this ordered n-tuple indicates whether the subset S contains the element a_i. It is clear that the subsets of A are in one-to-one correspondence with the n-tuples. This means the power set $\wp(A)$ and the Cartesian product $\{0, 1\}^n$ have the same cardinality. Since there are 2^n ordered n-tuples, we conclude that there are 2^n subsets as well. ■

This idea of one-to-one correspondence is a very important concept in mathematics. We shall study it again in Chapter 6.

Summary and Review

- The Cartesian product of two sets A and B, denoted $A \times B$, consists of ordered pairs of the form (a, b), where a comes from A, and b comes from B.
- Since ordered pairs are involved, $A \times B$ usually is not equal to $B \times A$.
- The notion of ordered pairs can be extended analogously to ordered n-tuples, thereby yielding an n-fold Cartesian product.
- If A and B are finite sets, then $|A \times B| = |A| \cdot |B|$.

Exercises 4.4

1. Let $X = \{-2, 2\}$, $Y = \{0, 4\}$ and $Z = \{-3, 0, 3\}$. Evaluate the following Cartesian products.

    (a) $X \times Y$ (b) $X \times Z$ (c) $Z \times Y \times Y$

2. Consider the sets X, Y and Z defined in Problem 1. Evaluate the following Cartesian products.

    (a) $X \times Y \times Z$ (b) $(X \times Y) \times Z$ (c) $X \times (Y \times Z)$

3. Without listing all the elements of $X \times Y \times X \times Z$, where X, Y, and Z are defined in Problem 1, determine $|X \times Y \times X \times Z|$.

4. Determine $|\wp(\wp(\wp(\{1, 2\})))|$.

5. Consider the set $X = \{-2, 2\}$. Evaluate the following Cartesian products.

    (a) $X \times \wp(X)$ (b) $\wp(X) \times \wp(X)$ (c) $\wp(X \times X)$

6. Let A and B be arbitrary nonempty sets.

    (a) Under what condition does $A \times B = B \times A$?

    (b) Under what condition is $(A \times B) \cap (B \times A)$ empty?

7. Let A, B, and C be any three sets. Prove that

    (a) $A \times (B \cap C) = (A \times B) \cap (A \times C)$

    (b) $A \times (B - C) = (A \times B) - (A \times C)$

8. Let A, B, and C be any three sets. Prove that if $A \subseteq B$, then $A \times C \subseteq B \times C$.

4.5 Index Sets

The notion of union can be extended to three sets:

$$A \cup B \cup C = \{x \in \mathcal{U} \mid (x \in A) \vee (x \in B) \vee (x \in C)\}.$$

It is obvious how to generalize it to the union of any number of sets. We use a notation that resembles the summation notation to describe such a union:

$$\bigcup_{i=1}^{n} A_i = A_1 \cup A_2 \cup \cdots \cup A_n.$$

We define

$$\bigcup_{i=1}^{n} A_i = \{x \in \mathcal{U} \mid (x \in A_1) \vee (x \in A_2) \vee \cdots \vee (x \in A_n)\}.$$

It looks messy! Here is a better alternative:

$$\boxed{\bigcup_{i=1}^{n} A_i = \{x \in \mathcal{U} \mid x \in A_i \text{ for } some\ i, \text{where } 1 \leq i \leq n\}.}$$

In a similar manner, $\bigcap_{i=1}^{n} A_i = A_1 \cap A_2 \cap \cdots \cap A_n$, and we define

$$\boxed{\bigcap_{i=1}^{n} A_i = \{x \in \mathcal{U} \mid x \in A_i \text{ for } all\ i, \text{where } 1 \leq i \leq n\}.}$$

In plain English, $\bigcup_{i=1}^{n} A_i$ is the collection of all elements in the A_i's, and $\bigcap_{i=1}^{n} A_n$ is the collection of all elements *common* to all A_i's.

Example 4.5.1   For $i = 1, 2, 3, \ldots$, let $A_i = [-i, i]$. First, construct several A_i for comparison, because it may help us detect any specific pattern. See Figure 4.6. It is clear that $A_1 \subset A_2 \subset \cdots$. Thus, $\bigcup_{i=1}^{n} A_i = [-n, n] = A_n$, and $\bigcap_{i=1}^{n} A_i = [-1, 1] = A_1$.   ▲

Hands-On Exercise 4.5.1   Evaluate $\bigcup_{i=1}^{n} B_i$ and $\bigcap_{i=1}^{n} B_i$, where $B_i = [0, 2i)$.

△

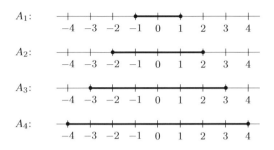

Figure 4.6: Comparing intervals to find their union and intersection.

It is obvious that we can also extend the upper bound to infinity.

$$\bigcup_{i=1}^{\infty} A_i = A_1 \cup A_2 \cup \cdots = \{x \in \mathcal{U} \mid x \in A_i \text{ for } some \ i \in \mathbb{N}\},$$

$$\bigcap_{i=1}^{\infty} A_i = A_1 \cap A_2 \cap \cdots = \{x \in \mathcal{U} \mid x \in A_i \text{ for } all \ i \in \mathbb{N}\}.$$

In some situations, we may borrow the idea of partial sums from calculus. We first find the union or intersection of the first n sets, then take the limit as n approaches infinity. Thus, if the limit is well-defined, then

$$\bigcup_{i=1}^{\infty} A_i = \lim_{n \to \infty} \bigcup_{i=1}^{n} A_i, \quad \text{and} \quad \bigcap_{i=1}^{\infty} A_i = \lim_{n \to \infty} \bigcap_{i=1}^{n} A_i.$$

Inclusion or exclusion of endpoints may change when we take limit.

Example 4.5.2   Let $A_i = [-i, i]$. We have learned from the last example that $\bigcup_{i=1}^{n} A_i = [-n, n]$ and $\bigcap_{i=1}^{n} A_i = [-1, 1]$. Hence,

$$\bigcup_{i=1}^{\infty} A_i = \lim_{n \to \infty} [-n, n] = (-\infty, \infty), \quad \text{and} \quad \bigcap_{i=1}^{\infty} A_i = [-1, 1].$$

Recall that we write $(-\infty, \infty)$ instead of $[-\infty, \infty]$ because $\pm\infty$ are *not* numbers, they are merely symbols representing infinitely large values.   ▲

Hands-On Exercise 4.5.2   Evaluate $\bigcup_{i=1}^{\infty} B_i$ and $\bigcap_{i=1}^{\infty} B_i$, where $B_i = [0, 2i)$.

△

Example 4.5.3   Let $B_i = \left(0, 1 - \frac{1}{2i}\right]$. Determine $\bigcup_{i=1}^{\infty} B_i$ and $\bigcap_{i=1}^{\infty} B_i$.

First take finite union and intersection.

Solution: Once again, we have $B_1 \subset B_2 \subset \cdots$. It is easy to check that

$$\bigcup_{i=1}^{n} B_i = B_n = \left(0, 1 - \frac{1}{2n}\right], \quad \text{and} \quad \bigcap_{i=1}^{n} B_i = B_1 = \left(0, \frac{1}{2}\right].$$

Then take limit.

It follows that

$$\bigcup_{i=1}^{\infty} B_i = \lim_{n \to \infty} \left(0, 1 - \frac{1}{2n}\right] = (0, 1), \quad \text{and} \quad \bigcap_{i=1}^{\infty} B_i = \left(0, \frac{1}{2}\right].$$

The last step: check the endpoints.

Note that $\lim_{n \to \infty}\left(0, 1 - \frac{1}{2n}\right] \neq (0, 1]$ because the endpoint 1 does not belong to any B_i.   ▲

Hands-On Exercise 4.5.3   Let $C_i = \left[0, 1 - \frac{1}{i}\right]$. Determine $\bigcup_{i=1}^{\infty} C_i$ and $\bigcap_{i=1}^{\infty} C_i$.

$\triangle$

Example 4.5.4   Let $D_i = \left(1 - \frac{1}{i}, 1 + \frac{1}{i}\right)$. Determine $\bigcup_{i=1}^{\infty} D_i$ and $\bigcap_{i=1}^{\infty} D_i$.

Solution: As the value of i increases, the value of $\frac{1}{i}$ decreases. Hence, the left endpoint $1 - \frac{1}{i}$ increases, and the right endpoint $1 + \frac{1}{i}$ decreases.

i	$D_i = \left(1 - \frac{1}{i}, 1 + \frac{1}{i}\right)$
1	$(0, 2)$
2	$\left(\frac{1}{2}, \frac{3}{2}\right)$
3	$\left(\frac{2}{3}, \frac{4}{3}\right)$
4	$\left(\frac{3}{4}, \frac{5}{4}\right)$

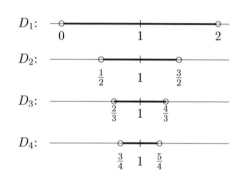

It is clear that $D_1 \supseteq D_2 \supseteq D_3 \supseteq \cdots$. Thus, $\bigcup_{i=1}^{\infty} D_i = D_1 = (0, 2)$, and $\bigcap_{i=1}^{\infty} D_i = \{1\}$.   ▲

Hands-On Exercise 4.5.4   Let $E_i = \left[-i, 1 + \frac{1}{i}\right)$. Determine $\bigcup_{i=1}^{\infty} E_i$ and $\bigcap_{i=1}^{\infty} E_i$.

$\triangle$

Hands-On Exercise 4.5.5   For each positive integer i, define $F_i = \{i, i + 1, i + 2, \ldots, 3i\}$. Determine $\bigcup_{i=1}^{\infty} F_i$ and $\bigcap_{i=1}^{\infty} F_i$.

$\triangle$

The next two results are obvious.

Theorem 4.5.1   *If* $A_1 \subseteq A_2 \subseteq A_3 \subseteq \cdots$, *then* $\bigcap_{i=1}^{\infty} A_i = A_1$.

Theorem 4.5.2 *If $A_1 \supseteq A_2 \supseteq A_3 \supseteq \cdots$, then $\bigcup_{i=1}^{\infty} A_i = A_1$.*

How could we describe the union $A_2 \cup A_4 \cup A_6 \cup \cdots$? Well, we can write

$$\bigcup_{i \text{ even}} A_i,$$

which means that union of A_i, where i is even. Since the set of even positive integers is denoted by $2\mathbb{N}$, another way to describe the same union is

$$\bigcup_{i \in 2\mathbb{N}} A_i.$$

It means the union all A_i, where i is taken out from the set $2\mathbb{N}$. Accordingly,

$$\bigcup_{i=0}^{\infty} A_i = \bigcup_{i \in \mathbb{N}} A_i, \qquad \text{and} \qquad \bigcap_{i=0}^{\infty} A_i = \bigcap_{i \in \mathbb{N}} A_i.$$

We can even go one step further, by allowing i to be taken from any set of integers, or any set of real numbers, or even any set of objects. The only restriction is that A_i must exist, and its content must somehow depend on i.

In general, given a nonempty set I, if we could associate with each $i \in I$ a set A_i, we define the ***indexed family of sets*** $\mathcal{A}$ as

$$\mathcal{A} = \{A_i \mid i \in I\}.$$

We call I the ***index set***, and define

$$\bigcup_{i \in I} A_i = \{x \mid x \in A_i \text{ for } some \ i \in I\},$$

$$\bigcap_{i \in I} A_i = \{x \mid x \in A_i \text{ for } all \ i \in I\}.$$

Let us look at a few examples.

Example 4.5.5   To describe the union

$$A_1 \cup A_3 \cup A_7 \cup A_{11} \cup A_{23},$$

we first define the index set to be $I = \{1, 3, 7, 11, 23\}$, which is the set of all the subscripts used in the union. Now the union can be conveniently described as $\bigcup_{i \in I} A_i$.   ▲

Example 4.5.6   Consider five sets

$$
\begin{aligned}
A_1 &= \{1, 4, 23\}, \\
A_2 &= \{7, 11, 23\}, \\
A_3 &= \{3, 6, 9\}, \\
A_4 &= \{5, 17, 22\}, \\
A_5 &= \{3, 6, 23\}.
\end{aligned}
$$

Let $I = \{2, 5\}$, then

$$\bigcup_{i \in I} A_i = A_2 \cup A_5 = \{7, 11, 23\} \cup \{3, 6, 23\} = \{3, 6, 7, 11, 23\}.$$

Likewise, $\bigcap_{i \in I} A_i = A_2 \cap A_5 = \{7, 11, 23\} \cap \{3, 6, 23\} = \{23\}$.   ▲

Hands-On Exercise 4.5.6   Let $J = \{1, 4, 5\}$. Evaluate $\bigcup_{i \in J} A_i$ and $\bigcap_{i \in J} A_i$, where A_is are defined in the last example.

$\triangle$

Hands-On Exercise 4.5.7   An index set could be a set of any objects. For instance, the sets of numbers in the last example could be the favorite Lotto numbers of five different students. We could index these sets according to the names of the students:

$$
\begin{aligned}
A_{\text{John}} &= \{1, 4, 23\}, \\
A_{\text{Mary}} &= \{7, 11, 23\}, \\
A_{\text{Joe}} &= \{3, 6, 9\}, \\
A_{\text{Pete}} &= \{5, 17, 22\}, \\
A_{\text{Lucy}} &= \{3, 6, 23\}.
\end{aligned}
$$

If $I = \{\text{Mary}, \text{Joe}, \text{Lucy}\}$, what is $\bigcup_{i \in I}$? How would you interpret its physical meaning?

$\triangle$

Example 4.5.7   Let $I = \{x \mid x \text{ is a living human being}\}$, and define

$$
\begin{aligned}
B_i &= \{x \in I \mid x \text{ is a child of } i\}, \\
A_i &= \{i\} \cup B_i
\end{aligned}
$$

for each $i \in I$. Then

$$
\bigcap_{i \in I} A_i = \emptyset, \qquad \bigcup_{i \in I} A_i = I, \qquad \bigcap_{i \in I} B_i = \emptyset,
$$

and

$$
\bigcup_{i \in I} B_i = I - \{x \mid x\text{'s parents are both deceased}\}.
$$

We leave it as an exercise to verify these unions and intersections. ▲

Hands-On Exercise 4.5.8   Verify the intersection and union in the last example.

$\triangle$

Hands-On Exercise 4.5.9   If I represents a set of students, and A_i represents the set of friends of student i, interpret the meaning of $\bigcup_{i \in I} A_i$ and $\bigcap_{i \in I} A_i$.

$\triangle$

We close this section with yet another generalization of De Morgan's laws.

Theorem 4.5.3 (Extended De Morgan's Laws) *For any nonempty index set I, we have*

$$\overline{\bigcup_{i \in I} A_i} = \bigcap_{i \in I} \overline{A_i}, \qquad \text{and} \qquad \overline{\bigcap_{i \in I} A_i} = \bigcup_{i \in I} \overline{A_i}.$$

Proof 1:   Let $x \in \overline{\bigcup_{i \in I} A_i}$, then

$$x \notin \bigcup_{i \in I} A_i = \{x \mid x \in A_i \text{ for } some \ i \in I\}.$$

This means $x \notin A_i$ for every $i \in I$. Hence, $x \in \overline{A_i}$ for each $i \in I$. Consequently,

$$x \in \bigcap_{i \in I} \overline{A_i}.$$

This proves that $\overline{\bigcup_{i \in I} A_i} \subseteq \bigcap_{i \in I} \overline{A_i}$.

Next, let $x \in \bigcap_{i \in I} \overline{A_i}$. Then $x \in \overline{A_i}$ for each $i \in I$. This means $x \notin A_i$ for each $i \in I$. Then

$$x \notin \{x \mid x \in A_i \text{ for } some \ i \in I\} = \bigcup_{i \in I} A_i.$$

Thus, $x \in \overline{\bigcup_{i \in I} A_i}$, proving that $\bigcap_{i \in I} \overline{A_i} \subseteq \overline{\bigcup_{i \in I} A_i}$. We proved earlier that $\overline{\bigcup_{i \in I} A_i} \subseteq \bigcap_{i \in I} \overline{A_i}$. Therefore, the two sets must be equal.

The proof of $\overline{\bigcap_{i \in I} A_i} = \bigcup_{i \in I} \overline{A_i}$ proceeds in a similar manner, and is left as an exercise. $\blacksquare$

Proof 2:   We shall prove $\overline{\bigcup_{i \in I} A_i} = \bigcap_{i \in I} \overline{A_i}$. We leave out the explanations for you to fill in:

$$
\begin{aligned}
x \in \overline{\bigcup_{i \in I} A_i} \quad &\Leftrightarrow \quad \overline{x \in \bigcup_{i \in I} A_i} \\
&\Leftrightarrow \quad \overline{x \in A_i \text{ for some } i} \\
&\Leftrightarrow \quad x \notin A_i \text{ for all } i \\
&\Leftrightarrow \quad x \in \overline{A_i} \text{ for all } i \\
&\Leftrightarrow \quad x \in \bigcap_{i \in I} \overline{A_i}.
\end{aligned}
$$

The proof of $\overline{\bigcap_{i \in I} A_i} = \bigcup_{i \in I} \overline{A_i}$ is left as an exercise. $\blacksquare$

Summary and Review

- When dealing with arbitrary intersection or union of intervals, first identify the endpoints, then analyze the sets involved in the operation to determine whether an endpoint should be included or excluded.
- Intersection and union can be performed on a group of similar sets identified by subscripts belonging to an index set.
- Consequently, intersection or union can be formed by naming a specific index set.

Exercises 4.5

1. For each $n \in \mathbb{Z}^+$, define $A_n = \left(-\frac{1}{n}, 2n\right)$. Find $\bigcap_{n=1}^{\infty} A_n$ and $\bigcup_{n=1}^{\infty} A_n$.

2. For each $n \in \mathbb{Z}^+$, define $B_n = \{m \in \mathbb{Z} \mid -\frac{n}{2} \leq m \leq 3n\}$. Evaluate $\bigcap_{n=1}^{\infty} B_n$ and $\bigcup_{n=1}^{\infty} B_n$.

3. Define $C_n = \{n, n+1, n+2, \ldots, 2n+1\}$ for each integer $n \geq 0$. Evaluate $\bigcap_{n=0}^{\infty} C_n$ and $\bigcup_{n=0}^{\infty} C_n$.

4. For each $n \in I = \{1, 2, 3, \ldots, 100\}$, define $D_n = [-n, 2n] \cap \mathbb{Z}$. Evaluate $\bigcap_{n \in I} D_n$ and $\bigcup_{n \in I} D_n$.

5. For each $n \in \mathbb{N}$, define $E_n = \{-n, -n+1, -n+2, \ldots, n^2\}$. Evaluate $\bigcap_{n \in \mathbb{N}} E_n$ and $\bigcup_{n \in \mathbb{N}} E_n$.

6. For each $n \in \mathbb{N}$, define $F_n = \left\{\frac{m}{n} \mid m \in \mathbb{Z}\right\}$. Evaluate $\bigcap_{n \in \mathbb{N}} F_n$ and $\bigcup_{n \in \mathbb{N}} F_n$.

7. Let $I = (0, 1)$, and define $A_i = \left[1, \frac{1}{i}\right]$ for each $i \in I$. For instance $A_{0.5} = [1, 2]$ and $A_{\frac{\pi}{4}} = \left[1, \frac{4}{\pi}\right]$. Evaluate $\bigcup_{i \in I} A_i$ and $\bigcap_{i \in I} A_i$.

8. Define $I = (0, 1)$, and for each $i \in I$, let $B_i = \left(-i, \frac{1}{i}\right)$. Evaluate $\bigcup_{i \in I} B_i = (-1, \infty)$ and $\bigcap_{i \in I} B_i$.

9. Evaluate $\bigcap_{x \in (1,2)} (1 - 2x, x^2)$ and $\bigcup_{x \in (1,2)} (1 - 2x, x^2)$.

10. Evaluate $\bigcap_{x \in (0,1)} \left(x, \frac{1}{x}\right)$ and $\bigcup_{x \in (0,1)} \left(x, \frac{1}{x}\right)$.

11. Let the universal set be $\mathbb{R}^2$. For each $r \in (0, \infty)$, define
$$A_r = \{(x, y) \mid y = rx^2\};$$
that is, A_r is the set of points on the parabola $y = rx^2$, where $r > 0$. Evaluate $\bigcap_{r \in (0,\infty)} A_r$ and $\bigcup_{r \in (0,\infty)} A_r$.

12. Prove that $\overline{\bigcap_{i \in I} A_i} = \bigcup_{i \in I} \overline{A_i}$ for any nonempty index set I.

Chapter 5

Basic Number Theory

5.1 The Principle of Well-Ordering

Number theory studies the properties of integers. Some basic results in number theory rely on the existence of a certain number. The next theorem can be used to show that such a number exists.

Theorem 5.1.1 (Principle of Well-Ordering) *Every nonempty subset of $\mathbb{N}$ has a smallest element.*

The idea is rather simple. Start with the integer 1. If it belongs to S, we are done. If not, consider the next integer 2, and then 3, and so on, until we find the first element in S. However, like the principle of mathematical induction, it is unclear why "and so on" is possible. In fact, we cannot prove the principle of well-ordering with just the familiar properties that the natural numbers satisfy under addition and multiplication. Hence, we shall regard the principle of well-ordering as an axiom. Interestingly though, it turns out that the principle of mathematical induction and the principle of well-ordering are logically equivalent.

Theorem 5.1.2 *The principle of mathematical induction holds if and only if the principle of well-ordering holds.*

Proof: ($\Rightarrow$) Suppose S is a nonempty set of natural numbers that has no smallest element. Let

$$R = \{x \in \mathbb{N} \mid x \leq s \text{ for every } s \in S\}.$$

Since S does not have a smallest element, it is clear that $R \cap S = \emptyset$. It is also obvious that $1 \in R$. Assume $k \in R$. Then any natural number less than or equal to k must also be less than or equal to s for every $s \in S$. Hence $1, 2, \ldots, k \in R$. Because $R \cap S = \emptyset$, we find $1, 2, \ldots, k \notin S$. If $k + 1 \in S$, then $k + 1$ would have been the smallest element of S. This contradiction shows that $k + 1 \in R$. Therefore, the principle of mathematical induction would have implied that $R = \mathbb{N}$. That would make S an empty set, which contradicts the assumption that S is nonempty. Therefore, any nonempty set of natural numbers must have a smallest element.

($\Leftarrow$) Let S be a set of natural numbers such that

(i) $1 \in S$,
(ii) For any $k \geq 1$, if $k \in S$, then $k + 1 \in S$.

Suppose $S \neq \mathbb{N}$. Then $\overline{S} = \mathbb{N} - S \neq \emptyset$. The principle of well-ordering states that $\overline{S}$ has a smallest element z. Since $1 \in S$, we deduce that $z \geq 2$, which makes $z - 1 \geq 1$. The minimality of z implies that $z - 1 \notin \overline{S}$. Hence, $z - 1 \in S$. Condition (ii) implies that $z \in S$, which is a contradiction. Therefore, $S = \mathbb{N}$. ∎

The principle of well-ordering is an existence theorem. It does not tell us which element is the smallest integer, nor does it tell us how to find the smallest element.

Example 5.1.1   Consider the sets

$$
\begin{aligned}
A &= \{n \in \mathbb{N} \mid n \text{ is a multiple of } 3\}, \\
B &= \{n \in \mathbb{N} \mid n = -11 + 7m \text{ for some } m \in \mathbb{Z}\}, \\
C &= \{n \in \mathbb{N} \mid n = x^2 - 8x + 12 \text{ for some } x \in \mathbb{Z}\}.
\end{aligned}
$$

It is easy to check that all three sets are nonempty, and since they contain only positive integers, the principle of well-ordering guarantees that each of them has a smallest element.

These smallest elements may not be easy to find. It is obvious that the smallest element in A is 3. To find the smallest element in B, we need $-11 + 7m > 0$, which means $m > 11/7 \approx 1.57$. Since m has to be an integer, we need $m \geq 2$. Since $-11 + 7m$ is an increasing function in m, its smallest value occurs when $m = 2$. The smallest element in B is $-11 + 7 \cdot 2 = 3$.

To determine the smallest element in C, we need to solve the inequality $x^2 - 8x + 12 > 0$. Factorization leads to $x^2 - 8x + 12 = (x - 2)(x - 6) > 0$, so we need $x < 2$ or $x > 6$. Because $x \in \mathbb{Z}$, we determine that the minimum value of $x^2 - 8x + 12$ occurs at $x = 1$ or $x = 7$. Since

$$
1^2 - 8 \cdot 1 + 12 = 7^2 - 8 \cdot 7 + 12 = 5,
$$

The smallest element in C is 5.   ▲

Example 5.1.2   The principle of well-ordering may not be true over real numbers or negative integers. In general, not every set of integers or real numbers must have a smallest element. Here are two examples:

Two sets that do not have a smallest element.

- The set $\mathbb{Z}$.
- The open interval $(0, 1)$.

The set $\mathbb{Z}$ has no smallest element because given any integer x, it is clear that $x - 1 < x$, and this argument can be repeated indefinitely. Hence, $\mathbb{Z}$ does not have a smallest element.

A similar problem occurs in the open interval $(0, 1)$. If x lies between 0 and 1, then so is $\frac{x}{2}$, and $\frac{x}{2}$ lies between 0 and x, such that

$$
0 < x < 1 \quad \Rightarrow \quad 0 < \frac{x}{2} < x < 1.
$$

This process can be repeated indefinitely, yielding

$$
0 < \cdots < \frac{x}{2^n} < \cdots < \frac{x}{2^3} < \frac{x}{2^2} < \frac{x}{2} < x < 1.
$$

We keep getting smaller and smaller numbers. All of them are positive and less than 1. There is no end in sight, hence the interval $(0, 1)$ does not have a smallest element.   ▲

The idea behind the principle of well-ordering can be extended to cover numbers other than positive integers.

Definition.   A set T of real numbers is said to be ***well-ordered*** if every nonempty subset of T has a smallest element.   ◇

Therefore, according to the principle of well-ordering, $\mathbb{N}$ is well-ordered.

Example 5.1.3   Show that $\mathbb{Q}$ is not well-ordered.

A proof by contradiction.

Solution: Suppose x is the smallest element in $\mathbb{Q}$. Then $x - 1$ is a rational number that is smaller than x, which contradicts the minimality of x. This shows that $\mathbb{Q}$ does not have a smallest element. Therefore $\mathbb{Q}$ is not well-ordered. ▲

Hands-On Exercise 5.1.1 Show that the interval $[0,1]$ is not well-ordered by finding a subset that does not have a smallest element.

△

Summary and Review

- A set of real numbers (which could be decimal numbers) is said to be well-ordered if every nonempty subset in it has a smallest element.
- A well-ordered set must be nonempty and have a smallest element.
- Having a smallest element does not guarantee that a set of real numbers is well-ordered.
- A well-ordered set can be finite or infinite, but a finite set is always well-ordered.

Exercises 5.1

1. Find the smallest element in each of these subsets of $\mathbb{N}$.

   (a) $\{n \in \mathbb{N} \mid n = m^2 - 10m + 28 \text{ for some integer } m\}$
   (b) $\{n \in \mathbb{N} \mid n = 5q + 3 \text{ for some integer } q\}$
   (c) $\{n \in \mathbb{N} \mid n = -150 - 17d \text{ for some integer } d\}$
   (d) $\{n \in \mathbb{N} \mid n = 4s + 9t \text{ for some integers } s \text{ and } t\}$

2. Determine which of the following subsets of $\mathbb{R}$ are well-ordered:

   (a) $\{\ \}$
   (b) $\{-9, -7, -3, 5, 11\}$
   (c) $\{0\} \cup \mathbb{Q}^+$
   (d) $2\mathbb{Z}$
   (e) $5\mathbb{N}$
   (f) $\{-6, -5, -4, \dots\}$

3. Show that the interval $[3, 5]$ is not well-ordered.

   Hint: Find a subset of $[3, 5]$ that does not have a smallest element.

4. Assume $\emptyset \neq T_1 \subseteq T_2 \subseteq \mathbb{R}$. Show that if T_2 is well-ordered, then T_1 is also well-ordered.

   Hint: Let S be a nonempty subset of T_1. We want to show that S has a smallest element. To achieve this goal, note that $T_1 \subseteq T_2$.

5. Prove that $2\mathbb{N}$ is well-ordered.

   Hint: Use Problem 4

6. Assume $\emptyset \neq T_1 \subseteq T_2 \subseteq \mathbb{R}$. Prove that if T_1 does not have a smallest element, then T_2 is not well-ordered.

5.2 Division Algorithm

When we divide a positive integer (the dividend) by another positive integer (the divisor), we obtain a quotient. We multiply the quotient to the divisor, and subtract the product from the dividend to obtain the remainder. Such a division produces two results: a quotient and a remainder.

This is how we normally divide 23 by 4:

$$
\begin{array}{r}
5 \\
4\overline{)\;23} \\
20 \\
\hline
3
\end{array}
$$

In general, the division $b \div a$ takes the form

$$
\begin{array}{r}
q \\
a\overline{)\;b} \\
aq \\
\hline
r
\end{array}
$$

so that $r = b - aq$, or equivalently, $b = aq + r$. Of course, both q and r are integers. Yet, the following "divisions"

$$
\begin{array}{r}
4 \\
4\overline{)\;23} \\
16 \\
\hline
7
\end{array}
\qquad
\begin{array}{r}
2 \\
4\overline{)\;23} \\
8 \\
\hline
15
\end{array}
\qquad
\begin{array}{r}
6 \\
4\overline{)\;23} \\
24 \\
\hline
-1
\end{array}
\qquad
\begin{array}{r}
7 \\
4\overline{)\;23} \\
28 \\
\hline
-5
\end{array}
$$

also satisfy the requirement $b = aq + r$, but that is not what we normally do. This means having $b = aq + r$ alone is not enough to define what quotient and remainder are. We need a more rigid definition.

Theorem 5.2.1 (Division Algorithm) *Given any integers a and b, where $a > 0$, there exist integers q and r such that*

$$b = aq + r,$$

where $0 \leq r < a$. Furthermore, q and r are uniquely determined by a and b.

The integers b, a, q, and r are called the **dividend**, **divisor**, **quotient**, and **remainder**, respectively. Notice that b is a multiple of a if and only if $r = 0$.

The division algorithm describes what happens in long division. Strictly speaking, it is not an algorithm. An algorithm describes a procedure for solving a problem. The theorem does not tell us *how* to find the quotient and the remainder. Some mathematicians prefer to call it the division theorem. Here, we follow the tradition and call it the division algorithm.

Remark.   This is the outline of the proof:

1. Describe how to find the integers q and r such that $b = aq + r$.
2. Show that our choice of r satisfies $0 \leq r < a$.
3. Establish the uniqueness of q and r.

Regarding the last part of the proof: to show that a certain number x is uniquely determined, a typical approach is to assume that x' is another choice that satisfies the given condition, and show that we must have $x = x'$.   ◇

Step 1: Show that there exist $q, r \in \mathbb{Z}$ such that $b = aq + r$.

Proof: We first show the existence of q and r. Let

$$S = \{b - ax \mid x \in \mathbb{Z} \text{ and } b - ax \geq 0\}.$$

Clearly, S is a set of nonnegative integers. To be able to apply the principle of well-ordering, we need to show that S is nonempty. Here is a constructive proof.

- Case 1. If $b \geq 0$, we can set $x = 0$. Then $b - ax = b \geq 0$.

- Case 2. If $b < 0$, set $x = b$. Since $a \geq 1$, we have $1 - a \leq 0$. Then

$$b - ax = b - ab = b(1 - a) \geq 0.$$

Since S is nonempty, it follows from the principle of well-ordering that S has a smallest element. Call it r. From the definition of S, there exists some integer q such that $b - aq = r$.

Next, we show that $0 \leq r < a$. The definition of S tells us immediately that $r \geq 0$, so we only need to show that $r < a$. Suppose, on the contrary, $r \geq a$. Then $r = a + t$ for some integer $t \geq 0$. Now $b - aq = r = a + t$ implies that

Step 2: Show that r satisfies the criterion $0 \leq r < a$.

$$0 \leq t = b - aq - a = b - a(q + 1).$$

So $t \in S$. Now $t = r - a < r$ suggests that we have found another element in S which is even smaller than r. This contradicts the minimality of r. Therefore $r < a$.

Finally, we have to establish the uniqueness of both q and r. Let q' and r' be integers such that

Step 3: Establish the uniqueness of q and r.

$$b = aq' + r', \qquad 0 \leq r' < a.$$

From $aq + r = b = aq' + r'$, we find $a(q - q') = r' - r$. Hence

$$a \, |q - q'| = |r' - r|.$$

Since $|r' - r|$ is an integer, if $|r' - r| \neq 0$, we would have $a \leq |r' - r|$. From $0 \leq r, r' < a$, we deduce that $|r' - r| < a$, which clearly contradicts our observation that $a \leq |r' - r|$. Hence, $|r' - r| = 0$. Then $r' = r$. It follows that $q' = q$. So the quotient q and the remainder r are unique. ∎

You should not have any problem dividing a positive integer by another positive integer. This is the kind of long division that we normally perform. It is more challenging to divide a negative integer by a positive integer. When b is negative, the quotient q will be negative as well, but the remainder r must be *nonnegative*. In a way, r is the deciding factor: we choose q such that the remainder r satisfies the condition $0 \leq r < a$.

In general, for any integer b, dividing b by a produces a decimal number. If the result is not an integer, round it *down* to the next smaller integer (see Example 6.1.3). It is the quotient q that we want, and the remainder r is obtained from the subtraction $r = b - aq$. For example,

$$\frac{-22}{7} = -3.1428\ldots\,.$$

Rounding it down produces the quotient $q = -4$, and the remainder is $r = -22 - 7(-4) = 6$; and we do have $-22 = 7 \cdot (-4) + 6$.

Hands-On Exercise 5.2.1   Compute the quotients q and the remainders r when b is divided by a:

(a) $b = 128$, $a = 7$ (b) $b = -128$, $a = 7$ (c) $b = -389$, $a = 16$

Be sure to verify that $b = aq + r$.

△

The division algorithm can be generalized to any nonzero integer a.

Corollary 5.2.2 *Given any integers a and b with $a \neq 0$, there exist uniquely determined integers q and r such that $b = aq + r$, where $0 \leq r < |a|$.*

Proof: We only have to consider the case of $a < 0$. Since $-a > 0$, the original Euclidean Algorithm assures that there exist uniquely determined integers q' and r such that

$$b = (-a) \cdot q' + r,$$

where $0 \leq r < -a = |a|$. Therefore, we can set $q = -q'$. ∎

Example 5.2.1 Not every calculator or computer program computes q and r the way we want them done in mathematics. The safest solution is to compute $|b| \div |a|$ in the usual way, inspect the remainder to see if it fits the criterion $0 \leq r < |a|$. If necessary, adjust the value of q so that the remainder r satisfies the requirement $0 \leq r < |a|$. Here are some examples:

Remember: what really matters is the choice of r; it must satisfy $0 \leq r < |a|$.

b	a	$b = aq + r$	q	r
14	4	$14 = 4 \cdot 3 + 2$	3	2
-14	4	$-14 = 4 \cdot (-4) + 2$	-4	2
-17	-3	$-17 = (-3) \cdot 6 + 1$	6	1
17	-3	$17 = (-3) \cdot (-5) + 2$	-5	2

The quotient q can be positive or negative, and the remainder r is always nonnegative. ▲

Definition. Given integers a and b, with $a \neq 0$, let q and r denote the unique integers such that $b = aq + r$, where $0 \leq r < |a|$. Define the *binary* operators div and mod as follows:

$$\begin{aligned} b \text{ div } a &= q, \\ b \bmod a &= r. \end{aligned}$$

Therefore, b div a gives the quotient, and b mod a yields the remainder of the integer division $b \div a$. Recall that b div a can be positive, negative, or even zero. But b mod a *is always a nonnegative integer less than $|a|$.* ◇

Example 5.2.2 From the last example, we have

 (a) 14 div 4 = 3, and 14 mod 4 = 2.
 (b) -14 div 4 = -4, and -14 mod 4 = 2.
 (c) -17 div -3 = 6, and -17 mod -3 = 1.
 (d) 17 div -3 = -5, and 17 mod -3 = 2.

Do not forget to check the computations, and remember that a need not be positive. ▲

Hands-On Exercise 5.2.2 Complete the following table:

b	a	b div a	b mod a
334	15		
334	-15		
-334	15		
-334	-15		

Do not forget: b mod a is always nonnegative. △

Example 5.2.3 Let n be an integer such that

$$n \text{ div } 6 = q, \qquad \text{and} \qquad n \bmod 6 = 4.$$

Determine the values of $(2n + 5)$ div 6, and $(2n + 5)$ mod 6.

Solution: The given information implies that $n = 6q + 4$. Then

$$2n + 5 = 2(6q + 4) + 5 = 12q + 13 = 6(2q + 2) + 1.$$

Therefore, $(2n + 5) \text{ div } 6 = 2q + 2$, and $(2n + 5) \text{ mod } 6 = 1$. ▲

Hands-On Exercise 5.2.3 Let n be an integer such that

$$n \text{ div } 11 = q, \qquad \text{and} \qquad n \text{ mod } 11 = 5.$$

Compute the values of $(6n - 4) \text{ div } 11$ and $(6n - 4) \text{ mod } 11$.

△

Example 5.2.4 Suppose today is Wednesday. Which day of the week is it a year from now?

Solution: Denote Sunday, Monday, ... , Saturday as Day 0, 1, ... 6, respectively. Today is Day 3. A year (assuming 365 days in a year) from today will be Day 368. Since

$$368 = 7 \cdot 52 + 4,$$

it will be Day 4 of the week. Therefore, a year from today will be Thursday. ▲

Hands-On Exercise 5.2.4 Suppose today is Friday. Which day of the week is it 1000 days from today?

△

Any integer divided by 7 will produce a remainder between 0 and 6, inclusive. Define

$$A_i = \{x \in \mathbb{Z} \mid x \text{ mod } 7 = i\} \quad \text{for } 0 \le i \le 6,$$

we find

$$\mathbb{Z} = A_0 \cup A_1 \cup A_2 \cup A_3 \cup A_4 \cup A_5 \cup A_6,$$

where the sets A_i are **pairwise disjoint**. The collection of sets

$$\{A_0, A_1, A_2, A_3, A_4, A_5, A_6\}$$

is called a **partition** of $\mathbb{Z}$, because every integer belongs to one and only one of these seven subsets. We also say that $\mathbb{Z}$ is a **disjoint union** of $A_0, A_1, \ldots, A_6$. The same argument also applies to the division by any integer $n \ge 2$.

In general, a collection or family of finite sets $\{S_1, S_2, \ldots, S_n\}$ is called a partition of the set S if S is the disjoint union of $S_1, S_2, \ldots S_n$. Partition is a very important concept, because it divides the elements of S into n classes $S_1, S_2, \ldots, S_n$ such that every element of S belongs to a unique class. We shall revisit partition again when we study relations in Chapter 7.

Summary and Review

- The division of integers can be extended to negative integers.
- Given any integer b, and any nonzero integer a, there exist uniquely determined integers q and r such that $b = aq + r$, where $0 \le r < |a|$.
- We call q the quotient, and r the remainder.
- The reason we have unique choices for q and r is the criterion we place on r. It has to satisfy the requirement $0 \le r < |a|$.
- In fact, the criterion $0 \le r < |a|$ is the single most important deciding factor in our choice of q and r.
- We define two binary operations on integers. The div operation yields the quotient, and the mod operation produces the remainder, of the integer division $b \div a$. In other words, $b \text{ div } a = q$, and $b \text{ mod } a = r$.

Exercises 5.2

1. Find $b \text{ div } a$ and $b \text{ mod } a$, where

    (a) $a = 13$, $b = 300$ (b) $a = 11$, $b = -120$ (c) $a = -22$, $b = 145$

2. Find $b \text{ div } a$ and $b \text{ mod } a$, where

    (a) $a = 19$, $b = 79$ (b) $a = 59$, $b = 18$ (c) $a = 16$, $b = -823$

    (d) $a = -16$, $b = 172$ (e) $a = -8$, $b = -67$ (f) $a = -12$, $b = -134$

3. Prove that
$$b \text{ mod } a \in \{0, 1, 2, \ldots, |a| - 1\}$$
   for any integers a and b, where $a \ne 0$.

4. Prove that among any three consecutive integers, one of them is a multiple of 3.

   Hint: Let the three consecutive integers be n, $n + 1$, and $n + 2$. What are the possible values of $n \text{ mod } 3$? What does this translate into, according to the division algorithm? In each case, what would n, $n + 1$, and $n + 2$ look like?

5. Prove that $n^3 - n$ is always a multiple of 3 for any integer n by

   (a) A case-by-case analysis.

   (b) Factoring $n^3 - n$.

6. Prove that the set $\{n, n + 4, n + 8, n + 12, n + 16\}$ contains a multiple of 5 for any positive integer n.

7. Let m and n be integers such that

$$m \text{ div } 5 = s, \qquad m \text{ mod } 5 = 1, \qquad n \text{ div } 5 = t, \qquad n \text{ mod } 5 = 3.$$

   Determine

   (a) $(m + n) \text{ div } 5$ (b) $(m + n) \text{ mod } 5$

   (c) $(mn) \text{ div } 5$ (d) $(mn) \text{ mod } 5$

8. Let m and n be integers such that

$$m \text{ div } 8 = s, \qquad m \text{ mod } 8 = 3, \qquad n \text{ div } 8 = t, \qquad n \text{ mod } 8 = 6.$$

   Determine

(a) $(m + 2)$ div 8   (b) $(m + 2)$ mod 8

(c) $(3mn)$ div 8   (d) $(3mn)$ mod 8

(e) $(5m + 2n)$ div 8   (f) $(5m + 2n)$ mod 8

(g) $(3m - 2n)$ div 8   (h) $(3m - 2n)$ mod 8

5.3   Divisibility

In this section, we shall study the concept of divisibility. Let a and b be two integers such that $a \neq 0$. The following statements are equivalent:

- a **divides** b,
- a is a **divisor** of b,
- a is a **factor** of b,
- b is a **multiple** of a, and
- b is **divisible by** a.

They all mean

$$\boxed{\text{There exists an integer } q \text{ such that } b = aq.}$$

Memorize this definition!

In terms of division, we say that a divides b if and only if the remainder is zero when b is divided by a. We adopt the notation

$$a \mid b \qquad [\text{pronounced as ``}a \text{ divides } b\text{''}]$$

Do not use a forward slash / or a backward slash \ in the notation. To say that a does not divide b, we add a slash across the vertical bar, as in

*Write $a \mid b$, **not** a/b or $a\backslash b$.*

$$a \nmid b \qquad [\text{pronounced as ``}a \text{ does not divide } b\text{''}]$$

Do not confuse the notation $a \mid b$ with $\frac{a}{b}$. The notation $\frac{a}{b}$ represents a fraction. It is also written as a/b with a (forward) slash. It uses floating-point (that is, real or decimal) division. For example, $\frac{11}{4} = 2.75$.

The definition of divisibility is very important. Many students fail to finish very simple proofs because they cannot recall the definition. So here we go again:

Memorize this definition.

$$\boxed{a \mid b \Leftrightarrow b = aq \text{ for some integer } q.}$$

Both integers a and b can be positive or negative, and b could even be 0. The only restriction is $a \neq 0$. In addition, q must be an integer. For instance, $3 = 2 \cdot \frac{3}{2}$, but it is certainly absurd to say that 2 divides 3.

Example 5.3.1   Since $14 = (-2) \cdot (-7)$, it is clear that $-2 \mid 14$.   ▲

Hands-On Exercise 5.3.1   Verify that

$$5 \mid 35, \quad 8 \nmid 35, \quad 25 \nmid 35, \quad 7 \mid 14, \quad 2 \mid -14, \quad \text{and} \quad 14 \mid 14,$$

by finding the quotient q and the remainder r such that $b = aq + r$, and $r = 0$ if $a \mid b$.

△

Example 5.3.2   An integer is **even** if and only if it is divisible by 2, and it is **odd** if and only if it is not divisible by 2.   ▲

Hands-On Exercise 5.3.2   What is the remainder when an odd integer is divided by 2? Complete the following sentences:

The definition of even and odd integers.

- If n is even, then $n =$ _____ for some integer ____ .

- If n is odd, then $n =$ _____ for _____ .

Memorize them well, as you will use them frequently in this course.   △

Hands-On Exercise 5.3.3   Complete the following sentence:

- If n is not divisible by 3, then $n =$ _____ , or $n =$ _____ , for some integer ____ .

Compare this to the div and mod operations. What are the possible values of $n \bmod 3$?   △

0 is divisible by any nonzero integer.

Example 5.3.3   Given any integer $a \neq 0$, we always have $a \mid 0$ because $0 = a \cdot 0$. In particular, 0 is divisible by 2, hence, it is considered an even integer.   ▲

Example 5.3.4   Similarly, ± 1 and $\pm b$ divide b for any nonzero integer b. They are called the **trivial divisors** of a. A divisor of b that is not a trivial divisor is called a **nontrivial divisor** of b.

For example, the integer 15 has eight divisors: $\pm 1, \pm 3, \pm 5, \pm 15$. Its trivial divisors are ± 1 and ± 15, and the nontrivial divisors are ± 3 and ± 5.   ▲

Definition.   A positive integer a is a **proper divisor** of b if $a \mid b$ and $a < |b|$. If a is a proper divisor of b, we say that a **divides** b **properly**.   ◇

Remark.   Some number theorists include negative numbers as proper divisors. In this convention, a is a proper divisor of b if $a \mid b$, and $|a| < |b|$. To add to the confusion, some number theorists exclude ± 1 as proper divisors. Use caution when you encounter these terms.   ◇

Example 5.3.5   It is clear that 12 divides 132 properly, and 2 divides -14 properly as well. The integer 11 has no proper divisor.   ▲

Hands-On Exercise 5.3.4   What are the proper divisors of 132?

△

Definition.   An integer $p > 1$ is a **prime** if its positive divisors are 1 and p itself. Any integer greater than 1 that is not a prime is called **composite**.   ◇

Remark.   A positive integer n is composite if it has a divisor d that satisfies $1 < d < n$. Also, according to the definition, the integer 1 is neither prime nor composite.   ◇

Example 5.3.6   The integers $2, 3, 5, 7, 11, 13, 17, 19, 23, \ldots$ are primes.   ▲

Hands-On Exercise 5.3.5   What are the next five primes after 23?

△

Theorem 5.3.1 *There are infinitely many primes.*

Proof: We postpone its proof to a later section, after we prove a fundamental result in number theory.   ■

Theorem 5.3.2 *For all integers a, b, and c where $a \neq 0$, we have*

(1) *If $a \mid b$, then $a \mid xb$ for any integer x.*

(2) *If $a \mid b$ and $b \mid c$, then $a \mid c$.   (This is called the **transitive property** of divisibility.)*

(3) *If $a \mid b$ and $a \mid c$, then $a \mid (sb + tc)$ for any integers x and y.   (The expression $sb + tc$ is called a **linear combination** of b and c.)*

(4) *If $b \neq 0$ and $a \mid b$ and $b \mid a$, then $a = \pm b$.*

(5) *If $a \mid b$ and $a, b > 0$, then $a \leq b$.*

Proof: We shall only prove (1), (4), and (5), and leave the proofs of (2) and (3) as exercises.

Proof of (1). Assume $a \mid b$, then there exists an integer q such that $b = aq$. For any integer x, we have
$$xb = x \cdot aq = a \cdot xq,$$
where xq is an integer. Hence, $a \mid xb$.

Proof of (4). Assume $a \mid b$, and $b \mid a$. Then there exist integers q and q' such that $b = aq$, and $a = bq'$. It follows that
$$a = bq' = aq \cdot q'.$$
This implies that $qq' = 1$. Both q and q' are integers. Thus, each of them must be either 1 or -1, which makes $b = \pm a$.

Proof of (5). Assume $a \mid b$ and $a, b > 0$. Then $b = aq$ for some integer q. Since $a, b > 0$, we also have $q > 0$. Being an integer, we must have $q \geq 1$. Then $b = aq \geq a \cdot 1 = a$.   ■

Example 5.3.7   Use the definition of divisibility to show that given any integers a, b, and c, where $a \neq 0$, if $a \mid b$ and $a \mid c$, then $a \mid (sb^2 + tc^2)$ for any integers s and t.

Solution: We try to prove it from first principles, that is, using only the definition of divisibility. Here is the complete proof.

Assume $a \mid b$ and $a \mid c$. There exist integers x and y such that $b = ax$ and $c = ay$. Then
$$sb^2 + tc^2 = s(ax)^2 + t(ay)^2 = a(sax^2 + tay^2),$$
where $sax^2 + tay^2$ is an integer. Hence $a \mid (sb^2 + tc^2)$.

The key step is substituting $b = ax$ and $c = ay$ into the expression $sb^2 + tc^2$. You may ask, how can we know this is the right thing to do?

  Here is the reason. We want to show that $a \mid (sb^2 + tc^2)$. This means we need to find an integer which, when multiplied by a, yields $sb^2 + tc^2$. This calls for writing $sb^2 + tc^2$ as a product of a and another integer that is yet to be determined. Since s and t bear no relationship to a, our only hope lies in b and c. We do know that $b = ax$ and $c = ay$, therefore, we should substitute them into $sb^2 + tc^2$.   ▲

Hands-On Exercise 5.3.6   Let a, b, and c be integers such that $a \neq 0$. Prove that if $a \mid b$ or $a \mid c$, then $a \mid bc$.

$\triangle$

Summary and Review

- An integer b is divisible by a nonzero integer a if and only if there exists an integer q such that $b = aq$.
- An integer $n > 1$ is said to be prime if its only divisors are ± 1 and $\pm n$; otherwise, we say that n is composite.
- If a positive integer n is composite, it has a proper divisor d that satisfies the inequality $1 < d < n$.

Exercises 5.3

1. Let a, b, and c be integers such that $a \neq 0$. Use the definition of divisibility to prove that if $a \mid b$ and $c \mid (-a)$, then $(-c) \mid b$. Use only the definition of divisibility to prove these implications.

2. Let a, b, c, and d be integers with $a, c \neq 0$. Prove that

   (a) If $a \mid b$ and $c \mid d$, then $ac \mid bd$.

   (b) If $ac \mid bc$, then $a \mid b$.

3. Let a, b, and c be integers such that $a, b \neq 0$. Prove that if $a \mid b$ and $b \mid c$, then $a \mid c$.

4. Let a, b, and c be integers such that $a \neq 0$. Prove that if $a \mid b$ and $a \mid c$, then $a \mid (sb + tc)$ for any integers s and t.

5. Prove that if n is an odd integer, then $n^2 - 1$ is divisible by 4.

6. Use the result from Problem 5 to show that none of the numbers 11, 111, 1111, and 11111 is a perfect square. Generalize, and prove your conjecture.

   Hint: Let x be one of these numbers. Suppose x is a perfect square, then $x = n^2$ for some integer n. How can you apply the result from Problem 5?

7. Prove that the square of any integer is of the form $3k$ or $3k + 1$.

8. Use Problem 7 to prove that $3m^2 - 1$ is not a perfect square for any integer m.

9. Use induction to prove that $3 \mid (2^{2n} - 1)$ for all integers $n \geq 1$.

10. Use induction to prove that $8 \mid (5^{2n} + 7)$ for all integers $n \geq 1$.

11. Use induction to prove that $5 \mid (n^5 - n)$ for all integers $n \geq 1$.

12. Use induction to prove that $5 \mid (3^{3n+1} + 2^{n+1})$ for all integers $n \geq 1$.

5.4 Greatest Common Divisors

Given any two integers a and b, an integer $c \neq 0$ is a **common divisor** or **common factor** of a and b if c divides both a and b. If, in addition, a and b are not both equal to zero, then the **greatest common divisor**, denoted by $\gcd(a, b)$, is defined as the largest common divisor of a and b. Greatest common divisors are also called highest common factors. It should be clear that $\gcd(a, b)$ must be positive.

$\gcd(a, b)$ is always positive.

Example 5.4.1   The common divisors of 24 and 42 are ± 1, ± 2, ± 3, and ± 6. Among them, 6 is the largest. Therefore, $\gcd(24, 42) = 6$. The common divisors of 12 and 32 are ± 1, ± 2 and ± 4, it follows that $\gcd(12, 32) = 4$.

Hands-On Exercise 5.4.1   Verify that

$$\gcd(5, 35) = 5, \quad \gcd(-5, 10) = 5, \quad \gcd(20, -10) = 10, \quad \text{and} \quad \gcd(20, 70) = 10.$$

Explain why $\gcd(3, 5) = 1$.

$\triangle$

Example 5.4.2   Can you explain why $\gcd(0, 3) = 3$? How about $\gcd(0, -3) = 3$?

Solution: Recall that 0 is divisible by any nonzero integer. Hence, all the divisors of 3 are also divisors of 0. Obviously, 3 itself is the largest divisor of 3. Therefore, $\gcd(0, 3) = 3$.   ▲

Hands-On Exercise 5.4.2   Explain why $\gcd(0, -8) = 8$.

$\triangle$

Theorem 5.4.1 *For any nonzero integer b, we have $\gcd(0, b) = |b|$.*

If $b \neq 0$, then $\gcd(0, b) = |b|$.

Proof: The largest positive divisor of b is $|b|$. Since $|b|$ also divides 0, we conclude that $\gcd(0, b) = |b|$.   ■

Theorem 5.4.1 tells us that $\gcd(0, b) = |b|$ if b is nonzero. From the definition of common divisor and greatest common divisor, it is clear that $\gcd(a, b) = \gcd(b, a)$, and $\gcd(a, b) = \gcd(\pm a, \pm b)$. So we may assume $1 \leq a \leq b$.

Assume $1 \leq a \leq b$.

Theorem 5.4.2 *Let a and b be integers such that $1 \leq a \leq b$. If $b = aq + r$, where $0 \leq r < a$, then $\gcd(b, a) = \gcd(a, r)$.*

The main theorem.

Proof: To facilitate our argument, let $d = \gcd(b, a)$ and $e = \gcd(a, r)$. By definition, d is a divisor of both b and a. Therefore, $b = dx$ and $a = dy$ for some integers x and y. Then

$$r = b - aq = dx - dy \cdot q = d(x - yq),$$

where $x - yq$ is an integer. Hence, $d \mid r$. This makes d a common divisor of both r and a. Since e is the greatest common divisor of a and r, we determine that $d \leq e$.

Similarly, $e = \gcd(a, r)$ is a divisor of both a and r. Thus, $a = eu$ and $r = ev$ for some integers u and v. Then

$$b = aq + r = a \cdot eu + ev = e(au + v),$$

where $au + v$ is an integer. Hence, $e \mid b$. This makes e a common divisor of both b and a. Since d is the greatest common divisor of b and a, we deduce that $e \leq d$. Together with $d \leq e$, we conclude that $d = e$.   ∎

Example 5.4.3   From $997 = 996 \cdot 1 + 1$, we obtain $\gcd(997, 996) = \gcd(996, 1) = 1$.   ▲

The theorem assures that $\gcd(b, a) = \gcd(a, r)$. We can apply the theorem again to $\gcd(a, r)$. Dividing a by r produces a new quotient and a new remainder. If necessary, repeat the process until the remainder becomes zero. If we denote $b = r_0$ and $a = r_1$, then

$$
\begin{aligned}
r_0 &= r_1 q_1 + r_2, & 0 &\leq r_2 < r_1, \\
r_1 &= r_2 q_2 + r_3, & 0 &\leq r_3 < r_2, \\
r_2 &= r_3 q_3 + r_4, & 0 &\leq r_4 < r_3, \\
&\ \ \vdots \quad\ \ \vdots & & \\
r_{k-1} &= r_k q_k + r_{k+1}, & 0 &\leq r_{k+1} < r_k, \\
&\ \ \vdots \quad\ \ \vdots & & \\
r_{n-3} &= r_{n-2} q_{n-2} + r_{n-1}, & 0 &\leq r_{n-1} < r_{n-2}, \\
r_{n-2} &= r_{n-1} q_{n-1} + r_n, & r_n &= 0.
\end{aligned}
$$

It follows that

$$\gcd(b, a) = \gcd(r_0, r_1) = \gcd(r_1, r_2) = \cdots = \gcd(r_{n-1}, r_n) = \gcd(r_{n-1}, 0) = r_{n-1}.$$

The last nonzero remainder is $\gcd(a, b)$. This method for finding the greatest common divisor is called **Euclidean algorithm**.

Example 5.4.4   Find $\gcd(426, 246)$.

Solution: By applying the theorem repeatedly, we find

$$
\begin{aligned}
426 &= 246 \cdot 1 + 180, & \gcd(426, 246) &= \gcd(246, 180) \\
246 &= 180 \cdot 1 + 66, & \gcd(246, 180) &= \gcd(180, 66) \\
180 &= 66 \cdot 2 + 48, & \gcd(180, 66) &= \gcd(66, 48) \\
66 &= 48 \cdot 1 + 18, & \gcd(66, 48) &= \gcd(48, 18) \\
48 &= 18 \cdot 2 + 12, & \gcd(48, 18) &= \gcd(18, 12) \\
18 &= 12 \cdot 1 + 6, & \gcd(18, 12) &= \gcd(12, 6) \\
12 &= 6 \cdot 2 + 0, & \gcd(12, 6) &= \gcd(6, 0) = 6.
\end{aligned}
$$

Therefore, $\gcd(426, 246) = 6$.   ▲

Hands-On Exercise 5.4.3   Determine $\gcd(732, 153)$.

△

Hands-On Exercise 5.4.4   Determine gcd(6958, 2478).

△

By hand, it is more efficient to use a two-column format. First, put the two numbers 426 and 246 in two separate columns, with the larger number on the left. Perform a short division, and write the quotient on the left:

$$
\begin{array}{c|c|c}
1 & 426 & 246 \\
\cline{2-2}
 & 246 & \\
\cline{2-2}
 & 180 & \\
\end{array}
$$

In the next round, perform another short division on the two numbers 246 and 180 at the bottom. Since the larger number is now on the right column, leave the quotient to its right:

$$
\begin{array}{c|c|c|c}
1 & 426 & 246 & 1 \\
\cline{2-3}
 & 246 & 180 & \\
\cline{2-3}
 & 180 & 66 & \\
\end{array}
$$

Continue in this manner until the remainder becomes 0. The last nonzero entry at the bottom is the greatest common divisor. We can also leave all the quotients on the left:

$$
\begin{array}{c|c|c|c}
1 & 426 & 246 & 1 \\
 & 246 & 180 & \\
2 & 180 & 66 & 1 \\
 & 132 & 48 & \\
2 & 48 & 18 & 1 \\
 & 36 & 12 & \\
2 & 12 & 6 & \\
 & 12 & & \\
 & 0 & & \\
\end{array}
\qquad \text{or} \qquad
\begin{array}{c|c|c}
1 & 426 & 246 \\
1 & 246 & 180 \\
2 & 180 & 66 \\
1 & 132 & 48 \\
2 & 48 & 18 \\
1 & 36 & 12 \\
2 & 12 & 6 \\
 & 12 & \\
 & 0 & \\
\end{array}
$$

Hands-On Exercise 5.4.5   Use the two-column format to compute gcd(153, 732).

△

Hands-On Exercise 5.4.6   Use the two-column format to compute $\gcd(6958, 2478)$.

$\triangle$

Given any integers m and n, the numbers of the form $ms + nt$, where s, t are integers, are called the **linear combinations** of m and n. They play an important role in the study of $\gcd(m, n)$, as indicated in the next theorem.

Theorem 5.4.3 *For any nonzero integers a and b, there exist integers s and t such that $\gcd(a, b) = as + bt$.*

Proof: The proof of this theorem is lengthy and complicated. We leave it, along with other related results, many of which are rather technical, to the next section.   ■

Theorem 5.4.4 *Every linear combination of a and b is a multiple of $\gcd(a, b)$.*

Corollary 5.4.5 *The greatest common divisor of two nonzero integers a and b is the smallest positive integer among all their linear combinations.*

It is important to understand what these three results say. Finding a linear combination of a and b only gives us a multiple of $\gcd(a, b)$. Only a special linear combination will produce the exact value of $\gcd(a, b)$.

Example 5.4.5   Let n and $n + 1$ be two consecutive positive integers. Then

$$n \cdot (-1) + (n + 1) \cdot 1 = 1$$

implies that 1 is a multiple of the greatest common divisor of n and $n + 1$. This means the greatest common divisor must be 1. Therefore, $\gcd(n, n + 1) = 1$ for all integers n.   ▲

Definition.   Two integers a and b are said to be **relatively prime** if $\gcd(a, b) = 1$. Therefore, a and b are relatively prime if they have no common divisors except ± 1.   ◇

Example 5.4.6   Prove that if $\gcd(a, b) = 1$, then $\gcd(a + b, a - b)$ equals to 1 or 2.

Solution: From the linear combinations

A linear combination is only a multiple of the gcd.

$$\begin{aligned} (a + b) \cdot 1 + (a - b) \cdot 1 &= 2a, \\ (a + b) \cdot 1 + (a - b) \cdot (-1) &= 2b, \end{aligned}$$

we know that $\gcd(a + b, a - b)$ divides both $2a$ and $2b$. Since $\gcd(a, b) = 1$, we conclude that $\gcd(a + b, a - b)$ divides 2. Consequently, $\gcd(a + b, a - b)$ is either 1 or 2.   ▲

Example 5.4.7   Show that if $\gcd(a, b) = 1$, then $\gcd(2a + b, a + 2b)$ equals to either 1 or 3.

Solution: From the linear combinations

$$(2a + b) \cdot 2 + (a + 2b) \cdot (-1) = 3a,$$
$$(2a + b) \cdot (-1) + (a + 2b) \cdot 2 = 3b,$$

we know that $\gcd(2a + b, a + 2b)$ divides both $3a$ and $3b$. Since $\gcd(a, b) = 1$, we conclude that $\gcd(2a + b, a + 2b)$ divides 3. Thus, $\gcd(a + b, a - b)$ is 1 or 3. ▲

Hands-On Exercise 5.4.7 What are the possible values of $\gcd(5m + 7n, 7m + 5n)$ if the two positive integers m and n are relatively prime?

△

Example 5.4.8 Find the integers s and t such that $6 = \gcd(426, 246) = 246s + 426t$.

Solution: Earlier, we studied how to find $\gcd(426, 246) = 6$. In each division, we want to express the remainder as a linear combination of 246 and 426. This is how the computation proceeds:

$$426 = 246 \cdot 1 + 180, \qquad 180 = 246 \cdot (-1) + 426 \cdot 1$$

$$246 = 180 \cdot 1 + 66, \qquad \begin{aligned} 66 &= 246 \cdot 1 + 180 \cdot (-1) \\ &= 246 \cdot 1 + [246 \cdot (-1) + 426 \cdot 1] \cdot (-1) \\ &= 246 \cdot 2 + 426 \cdot (-1) \end{aligned}$$

$$180 = 66 \cdot 2 + 48, \qquad \begin{aligned} 48 &= 180 \cdot 1 + 66 \cdot (-2) \\ &= [246 \cdot (-1) + 426 \cdot 1] \cdot 1 + [246 \cdot 2 + 426 \cdot (-1)] \cdot (-2) \\ &= 246(-5) + 426 \cdot 3 \end{aligned}$$

$$66 = 48 \cdot 1 + 18, \qquad \begin{aligned} 18 &= 66 \cdot 1 + 48 \cdot (-1) \\ &= [246 \cdot 2 + 426 \cdot (-1)] \cdot 1 + [246(-5) + 426 \cdot 3] \cdot (-1) \\ &= 246 \cdot 7 + 426 \cdot (-4) \end{aligned}$$

$$48 = 18 \cdot 2 + 12, \qquad \begin{aligned} 12 &= 48 \cdot 1 + 18 \cdot (-2) \\ &= [246(-5) + 426 \cdot 3] \cdot 1 + [246 \cdot 7 + 426 \cdot (-4)] \cdot (-2) \\ &= 246 \cdot (-19) + 426 \cdot 11 \end{aligned}$$

$$18 = 12 \cdot 1 + 6, \qquad \begin{aligned} 6 &= 18 \cdot 1 + 12 \cdot (-1) \\ &= [246 \cdot 7 + 426 \cdot (-4)] \cdot 1 + [246 \cdot (-19) + 426 \cdot 11] \cdot (-1) \\ &= 246 \cdot 26 + 426 \cdot (-15) \end{aligned}$$

The answer is $6 = 246 \cdot 26 + 426 \cdot (-15)$. ▲

The computation is tedious! The ***extended Euclidean algorithm*** provides a relief. It keeps track of two sequences of integers s_k and t_k alongside with r_k, such that

$$r_k = as_k + bt_k.$$

This expresses every remainder as a linear combination of a and b. Since the last nonzero remainder is $\gcd(a, b)$, the corresponding linear combination will be the answer we are looking for.

The values of s_k and t_k for the last example are summarized below:

k	r_k	s_k	t_k
2	180	-1	1
3	60	2	-1
4	48	-5	3
5	18	7	-4
6	12	-19	11
7	6	26	-15

The main issue is: how can we compute these values efficiently?

The table above starts with $k = 2$. How about $k = 0$ and $k = 1$? From

$$b = r_0 = as_0 + bt_0,$$

we determine that $s_0 = 0$ and $t_0 = 1$. Similarly,

$$a = r_1 = as_1 + bt_1$$

implies that $s_1 = 1$ and $t_1 = 0$. Hence, the list of values of s_k and t_k start with the following:

k	s_k	t_k
0	0	1
1	1	0

In general, before we carry out the division $r_{k-1} \div r_k$, we should have already generated s_0 through s_k, and t_0 through t_k. After the division, we obtain q_k and r_{k+1} as in

$$r_{k-1} = r_k q_k + r_{k+1}.$$

Next, we compute s_{k+1} and t_{k+1} before moving on to the next division. We find

$$
\begin{aligned}
r_{k+1} &= r_{k-1} - r_k q_k \\
&= (as_{k-1} + bt_{k-1}) - (as_k + bt_k)q_k \\
&= a(s_{k-1} - s_k q_k) + b(t_{k-1} - t_k q_k).
\end{aligned}
$$

Therefore, we need

$$
\begin{aligned}
s_{k+1} &= s_{k-1} - s_k q_k, \\
t_{k+1} &= t_{k-1} - t_k q_k.
\end{aligned}
$$

In words:

next s-value = previous-previous s-value $-$ previous s-value $\times$ corresponding q,

next t-value = previous-previous t-value $-$ previous t-value $\times$ corresponding q.

For example, assume at a certain stage, the values of s, t, and q are as follow:

k	s_k	t_k	q_k
0	0	1	
1	1	0	1
2	-1	1	1
3	2	-1	2
			1
			2
			1
			2

Then

$$\text{next } s\text{-value} = -1 - 2 \cdot 2 = -5,$$
$$\text{next } t\text{-value} = 1 - (-1) \cdot 2 = 3.$$

Now the list becomes

k	s_k	t_k	q_k
0	0	1	
1	1	0	1
2	−1	1	1
3	2	−1	2
4	−5	3	1
			2
			1
			2

The entire computation can be carried out in a modified two-column format.

Example 5.4.9   Find integers s and t such that $\gcd(246, 426) = 246s + 426t$.

Solution: First, copy the quotients from the right-most column and insert them between those quotients in the left-most column:

1	426	246	1				1	426	246	1
	246	180					1	246	180	
2	180	66	1				2	180	66	1
	132	48					1	132	48	
2	48	18	1	becomes			2	48	18	1
	36	12					1	36	12	
2	12	6					2	12	6	
	12							12		
	0							0		

Next, compute s_k and t_k alongside these quotients (we do not need to record the values of k):

s_k	t_k	q_k			
0	1				
1	0	1	426	246	1
−1	1	1	246	180	
2	−1	2	180	66	1
−5	3	1	132	48	
7	−4	2	48	18	1
−19	11	1	36	12	
26	−15	2	12	6	
			12		
			0		

The last nonzero remainder is the greatest common divisor, and the last linear combination gives the desired answer. We find $\gcd(246, 426) = 6 = 26 \cdot 246 - 15 \cdot 426$.   ▲

Observe that, starting with $k = 2$, the signs of s_k and t_k alternate. This provides a quick check of their signs. In addition, the signs of s_k and t_k are opposite for each $k \geq 2$.

Hands-On Exercise 5.4.8   Use the two-column format to find the linear combination that produces $\gcd(153, 732)$.

$\triangle$

Hands-On Exercise 5.4.9   Use the two-column format to find the linear combination that produces $\gcd(2478, 6958)$.

$\triangle$

Summary and Review

- The greatest common divisor of two integers, not both zero, is the largest (hence it must be positive) integer that divides both.
- Use Euclidean algorithm to find the greatest common divisor. It can be implemented in a two-column format.
- Using an extended version with two additional columns for computing s_k and t_k, we can find the special linear combination of two integers that produces their greatest common divisor.
- In general, a linear combination of two integers only gives a multiple of their greatest common divisor.

Exercises 5.4

1. For each of the following pairs of integers, find the linear combination that equals to their greatest common divisor.

   (a) 27, 81   (b) 24, 84   (c) 1380, 3020

2. For each of the following pairs of integers, find the linear combination that equals to their greatest common divisor.

   (a) 120, 615   (b) 412, 936   (c) 1122, 3672

3. What are the possible values of $\gcd(2a + 5b, 5a - 2b)$ if the two positive integers a and b are relatively prime?

4. Prove that any consecutive odd positive integers are relatively prime.

5. Let m and n be positive integers. Prove that $\gcd(m, m+n) \mid n$.

6. Let a and b be integers such that $1 < a < b$ and $\gcd(a, b) = 1$. Prove that $\gcd(a+b, ab) = 1$.

7. What are the possible values of $\gcd(3m - 5n, 5m + 3n)$ if the two positive integers m and n are relatively prime?

8. What are the possible values of $\gcd(4p + 7q, 7p - 4q)$ if the two positive integers p and q are relatively prime?

5.5 More on GCD

In this section, we shall discuss a few technical results about $\gcd(a, b)$.

Theorem 5.5.1 *Let $d = \gcd(a, b)$, where $a, b \in \mathbb{N}$. Then*

$$\{as + bt \mid s, t \in \mathbb{Z}\} = \{nd \mid n \in \mathbb{Z}\}.$$

Hence, every linear combination of a and b is a multiple of $\gcd(a, b)$, and vice versa, every multiple of $\gcd(a, b)$ is expressible as a linear combination of a and b.

Proof: For brevity, let

$$S = \{as + bt \mid s, t \in \mathbb{Z}\}, \qquad \text{and} \qquad T = \{nd \mid n \in \mathbb{Z}\}.$$

Name the two sets, and give a brief outline of the proof.

We shall show that $S = T$ by proving that $S \subseteq T$ and $T \subseteq S$.

Let $x \in S$. To prove that $S \subseteq T$, we want to show that $x \in T$ as well. Being in S means $x = as + bt$ for some integers s and t. Since $d = \gcd(a, b)$, we know that $d \mid a$ and $d \mid b$. Hence, $a = da'$ and $b = db'$ for some integers a' and b'. Then

Part 1: $S \subseteq T$.

$$x = as + bt = da's + db't = d(a's + b't),$$

where $a's + b't$ is an integer. This shows that x is a multiple of d. Hence, $x \in T$.

To show that $T \subseteq S$, it suffices to show that $d \in S$. The reason is, if $d = as + bt$ for some integers s and t, then $nd = n(as + bt) = a(ns) + b(nt)$ implies that $nd \in S$.

Part 2: $T \subseteq S$. First, reduce it to a simpler problem.

To prove that $d \in S$, consider S^+. Since $a = a \cdot 1 + b \cdot 0$, we have $a \in S^+$. Hence, S^+ is a nonempty set of positive integers. The principle of well-ordering implies that S^+ has a smallest element. Call it e. Then

$$e = as^* + bt^*$$

PWO states that S^+ has a smallest element e.

for some integers s^* and t^*. We already know that $a \in S^+$. Being the smallest element in S^+, we must have $e \leq a$. Then $a = eq + r$ for some integers q and r, where $0 \leq r < e$. If $r > 0$, then

$$r = a - eq = a - (as^* + bt^*)q = a(1 - s^*q) + b(-t^*q).$$

This makes r a linear combination of a and b. Since $r > 0$, we find $r \in S^+$. Since $r < e$ would contradict the minimality of e, we must have $r = 0$. Consequently, $a = eq$, thus $e \mid a$. Similarly, since $b = a \cdot 0 + b \cdot 1 \in S^+$, we can apply the same argument to show that $e \mid b$. We conclude that e is a common divisor of a and b.

This e is a common divisor of a and b.

Let f be any common divisor of a and b. Then $f \mid a$ and $f \mid b$. It follows that $f \mid (ax + by)$ for any integers x and y. In particular, $f \mid (as^* + bt^*) = e$. Hence, $f \leq e$. Since e is itself a common divisor of a and b, and we have just proved that e is larger than any other common divisor of a and b, the integer e itself must be the greatest common divisor. It follows that $d = \gcd(a, b) = e \in S^+$. The proof is now complete. ∎

But e is larger than the other common divisors, hence, it must be the gcd.

Corollary 5.5.2 *The greatest common divisor of two nonzero integers a and b is the smallest positive integer among all their linear combinations. In other words, $\gcd(a,b)$ is the smallest positive element in the set $\{as + bt \mid s, t \in \mathbb{Z}\}$.*

Corollary 5.5.3 *For any nonzero integers a and b, there exist integers s and t such that $\gcd(a,b) = as + bt$.*

Proof: Theorem 5.5.1 maintains that the set of all the linear combinations of a and b equals to the set of all the multiples of $\gcd(a,b)$. Since $\gcd(a,b)$ is a multiple of itself, it must equal to one of those linear combinations. Thus, $\gcd(a,b) = sa + tb$ for some integers s and t. ■

Theorem 5.5.4 *Two nonzero integers a and b are relatively prime if and only if $as + bt = 1$ for some integers s and t.*

Proof: The result is a direct consequence of the definition that a and b are said to be relatively prime if $\gcd(a,b) = 1$. ■

Example 5.5.1   It is clear that 5 and 7 are relatively prime, so are 14 and 27. Find the linear combination of these two pairs of numbers that equals to 1.

Solution: By inspection, or using the extended Euclidean algorithm, we find $3 \cdot 5 - 2 \cdot 7 = 1$, and $2 \cdot 14 - 1 \cdot 27 = 1$. ▲

Hands-On Exercise 5.5.1   Show that $\gcd(133, 143) = 1$ by finding an appropriate linear combination.

△

Hands-On Exercise 5.5.2   Show that 757 and 1215 are relatively prime by finding an appropriate linear combination.

△

Example 5.5.2   It follows from

$$(-1) \cdot n + 1 \cdot (n + 1) = 1$$

that $\gcd(n, n+1) = 1$. Thus, any pair of consecutive positive integers is relatively prime. ▲

Theorem 5.5.5 (Euclid's Lemma) *Let $a, b, c \in \mathbb{Z}$. If $\gcd(a,c) = 1$ and $c \mid ab$, then $c \mid b$.*

Discussion: Let us write down what we know and what we want to show (WTS):

$$\begin{aligned} \text{Know}: \quad & as + ct = 1 \text{ for some integers } s \text{ and } t, \\ & ab = cx \text{ for some integer } x, \\ \text{WTS}: \quad & b = cq \text{ for some integer } q. \end{aligned}$$

To be able to show that $b = cq$ for some integer q, we have to come up with some information about b. This information must come from the two equations $as + ct = 1$ and $ab = cx$. Since $b = b \cdot 1$, we can multiply b to both sides of $as + ct = 1$. By convention, we cannot write

$$(as + ct = 1) \cdot b.$$

WRONG notation!

This notation is unacceptable! The reason is: we cannot multiply an equation by a number. Rather, we have to multiply *both sides* of an equation by the number:

$$b = 1 \cdot b = (as + ct) \cdot b = asb + ctb.$$

Obviously, ctb is a multiple of c; we are one step closer to our goal. Since $asb = ab \cdot s$, and we do know that ab is indeed a multiple of c, so the proof can be completed. We are now ready to tie up the loose ends, and polish up the proof.   ◇

Proof: Assume $\gcd(a, c) = 1$, and $c \mid ab$. There exist integers s and t such that

$$as + ct = 1.$$

This leads to

$$b = 1 \cdot b = (as + ct) \cdot b = asb + ctb.$$

Since $c \mid ab$, there exists an integer x such that $ab = cx$. Then

$$b = ab \cdot s + ctb = cx \cdot s + ctb = c(xs + tb),$$

where $xc + tb \in \mathbb{Z}$. Therefore, $c \mid b$.   ∎

Corollary 5.5.6 *If $a, b \in \mathbb{Z}$ and p is a prime such that $p \mid ab$, then either $p \mid a$ or $p \mid b$.*

Proof: If $p \mid a$, we are done with the proof. If $p \nmid a$, then $\gcd(p, a) = 1$, and Euclid's lemma implies that $p \mid b$.   ∎

We cannot apply the corollary if p is composite. For instance, $6 \mid 4 \cdot 15$, but $6 \nmid 4$ and $6 \nmid 15$. On the other hand, when $p \mid ab$, where p is a prime, it is possible to have both $p \mid a$ and $p \mid b$. For instance, $5 \mid 15 \cdot 25$, yet we have both $5 \mid 15$ and $5 \mid 25$.

Corollary 5.5.7 *If $a_1, a_2, \ldots, a_n \in \mathbb{Z}$ and p is a prime such that $p \mid a_1 a_2 \cdots a_n$, then $p \mid a_i$ for some i, where $1 \leq i \leq n$. Consequently, if a prime p divides a product of n factors, then p must divide at least one of these n factors.*

Proof: We leave the proof to you as an exercise.   ∎

Example 5.5.3   Prove that $\sqrt{2}$ is irrational.

Remark.   We proved previously that $\sqrt{2}$ is irrational in a hands-on exercise. The solution we presented has a minor flaw. A key step in that proof claims that

The integer 2 divides m^2, therefore 2 divides m.

This claim is false in general. For example, 4 divides 6^2, but 4 does not divide 6. Therefore, we have to justify why this claim is valid for 2.   ◇

Solution: Suppose $\sqrt{2}$ is rational, then we can write

$$\sqrt{2} = \frac{m}{n}$$

for some positive integers m and n that do not share any common divisor except 1. Squaring both sides and cross-multiplying gives

$$2n^2 = m^2.$$

Thus 2 divides m^2. Since 2 is prime, Euclid's lemma implies that 2 must also divide m. Then we can write $m = 2s$ for some integer s. The equation above becomes

$$2n^2 = m^2 = (2s)^2 = 4s^2.$$

Hence,

$$n^2 = 2s^2,$$

which implies that 2 divides n^2. Again, since 2 is prime, Euclid's lemma implies that 2 also divides n. We have proved that both m and n are divisible by 2. This contradicts the assumption that m and n do not share any common divisor. Hence, $\sqrt{2}$ must be irrational.   ▲

Hands-On Exercise 5.5.3   Prove that $\sqrt{7}$ is irrational.

△

We close this section with a truly fascinating result.

Theorem 5.5.8 *For any positive integers m and n, $\gcd(F_m, F_n) = F_{\gcd(m,n)}$.*

Corollary 5.5.9 *For any positive integer n, $3 \mid F_n \Leftrightarrow 4 \mid n$.*

To prove a biconditional statement, we need to prove both necessity and sufficiency.

Proof: ($\Rightarrow$) If $3 \mid F_n$, then, because $F_3 = 4$, we have

$$3 = \gcd(3, F_n) = \gcd(F_4, F_n) = F_{\gcd(4,n)}.$$

It follows that $\gcd(4, n) = 4$, which in turn implies that $4 \mid n$.

($\Leftarrow$) If $4 \mid n$, then $\gcd(4, n) = 4$, and

$$\gcd(3, F_n) = \gcd(F_4, F_n) = F_{\gcd(4,n)} = F_4 = 3;$$

therefore, $3 \mid F_n$.   ■

Summary and Review

- Given any two nonzero integers, there is only one special linear combination that would equal to their greatest common divisor.
- All other linear combinations are only multiples of their greatest common divisor.
- If a and c are relatively prime, then Euclid's lemma asserts that if c divides ab, then c must divide b.
- In particular, if p is prime, and if $p \mid ab$, then either $p \mid a$ or $p \mid b$.

Exercises 5.5

1. Given any arbitrary positive integer n, prove that $2n + 1$ and $3n + 2$ are relatively prime.

2. Use induction to prove that for any integer $n \geq 2$, if $a_1, a_2, \ldots, a_n \in \mathbb{Z}$ and p is a prime such that $p \mid a_1 a_2 \cdots a_n$, then $p \mid a_i$ for some i, where $1 \leq i \leq n$.

3. Prove that $\sqrt{p}$ is irrational for any prime number p.

4. Prove that $\sqrt[3]{2}$ is irrational.

5. Given any arbitrary positive integers a, b, and c, show that if $a \mid c$, $b \mid c$, and $\gcd(a, b) = 1$, then $ab \mid c$.

   Remark. This result is very important. Remember it!

6. Given any arbitrary positive integers a, b, and c, show that if $a \mid c$, and $b \mid c$, then $ab \mid cd$, where $d = \gcd(a, b)$.

7. Use induction to prove that $3 \mid (2^{4n} - 1)$ and $5 \mid (2^{4n} - 1)$ for any integer $n \geq 1$. Use these results to prove that $15 \mid (2^{4n} - 1)$ for any integer $n \geq 1$.

8. Prove that $2 \mid F_n \Leftrightarrow 3 \mid n$ for any positive integer n.

5.6   Fundamental Theorem of Arithmetic

Primes are positive integers that do not have any proper divisor except 1. Primes can be regarded as the building blocks of all integers with respect to multiplication.

Theorem 5.6.1 (Fundamental Theorem of Arithmetic) *Given any integer $n \geq 2$, there exist primes $p_1 \leq p_2 \leq \cdots \leq p_s$ such that $n = p_1 p_2 \ldots p_s$. Furthermore, this factorization is unique, in the sense that if $n = q_1 q_2 \ldots q_t$ for some primes $q_1 \leq q_2 \leq \cdots \leq q_t$, then $s = t$ and $p_i = q_i$ for each i, $1 \leq i \leq s$.*

Proof: We first prove the existence of the factorization. Let S be the set of integers $n \geq 2$ that are *not* expressible as the product of primes. Since a product may contain as little as just one prime, S does not contain any prime. Suppose $S \neq \emptyset$, then the principle of well-ordering implies that S has a smallest element d. Since S does not contain any prime, d is composite, so $d = xy$ for some integers x and y, where $2 \leq x, y < d$. The minimality of d implies that $x, y \notin S$. So both x and y can be expressed as products of primes, then $d = xy$ is also a product of primes, which is a contradiction, because d belongs to S. Therefore, $S = \emptyset$, which means every integer $n \geq 2$ can be expressed as a product of primes.

Next, we prove that the factorization is unique. Assume there are two ways to factor n, say $n = p_1 p_2 \ldots p_s = q_1 q_2 \ldots q_t$. Without loss of generality, we may assume $s \leq t$. Suppose there exists a smallest i, where $1 \leq i \leq s$, such that $p_i \neq q_i$. Then

$$p_1 = q_1, \quad p_2 = q_2, \quad \cdots \quad p_{i-1} = q_{i-1}, \quad \text{but} \quad p_i \neq q_i.$$

It follows that

$$p_i p_{i+1} \cdots p_s = q_i q_{i+1} \cdots q_t,$$

in which both sides have at least two factors (why?). Without loss of generality, we may assume $p_i < q_i$. Since $p_i \mid q_i q_{i+1} \cdots q_t$, and p_i is prime, Euclid's lemma implies that $p_i \mid q_j$ for some j, where $i < j \leq t$. Since q_j is prime, we must have $p_i = q_j \geq q_i$, which contradicts the assumption that $p_i < q_i$. Therefore, there does not exist any i for which $p_i \neq q_i$. This means $p_i = q_i$ for each i, and as a consequence, we must have have $s = t$. ∎

Interestingly, we can use the strong form of induction to prove the existence part of the Fundamental Theorem of Arithmetic.

Proof 2:   (Existence) Induct on n. The claim obviously holds for $n = 2$. Assume it holds for $n = 2, 3, \ldots, k$ for some integer $k \geq 2$. We want to show that it also holds for $k + 1$. If $k + 1$ is a prime, we are done. Otherwise, $k + 1 = \alpha\beta$ for some integers α and β, both less than $k + 1$. Since $2 \leq \alpha, \beta \leq k$, both α and β can be expressed as a product of primes. Putting these primes together, and relabeling and rearranging them if necessary, we see that $k + 1$ is also expressible as a product of primes in the form we desire. This completes the induction. ∎

The next result is one of the oldest theorems in mathematics, numerous proofs can be found in the literature.

Theorem 5.6.2 *There are infinitely many primes.*

Proof: Suppose there are only a finite number of primes $p_1, p_2, \ldots, p_n$. Consider the integer

$$x = 1 + p_1 p_2 \cdots p_n.$$

It is obvious that $x \neq p_i$ for any i. Since $p_1, p_2, \ldots, p_n$ are assumed to be the only primes, the integer x must be composite, hence can be factored into a product of primes. Let p_k be one of these prime factors, so that $x = p_k q$ for some integer q. Then

$$
\begin{aligned}
1 &= x - p_1 p_2 \cdots p_n \\
&= p_k q - p_1 p_2 \cdots p_n \\
&= p_k (q - p_1 p_2 \cdots p_{k-1} p_{k+1} \cdots p_n),
\end{aligned}
$$

which is impossible. This contradiction proves that there are infinitely many primes. ∎

Some of the primes listed in the Fundamental Theorem of Arithmetic can be identical. If we group the identical primes together, we obtain the **canonical factorization** or **prime-power factorization** of an integer.

Theorem 5.6.3 *All integers $n \geq 2$ can be uniquely expressed in the form $n = p_1^{e_1} p_2^{e_2} \cdots p_t^{e_t}$ for some distinct primes p_i and positive integers e_i.*

Once we find the prime-power factorization of two integers, their greatest common divisor can be obtained easily.

Example 5.6.1   From the factorizations $246 = 2 \cdot 3 \cdot 41$ and $426 = 2 \cdot 3 \cdot 79$, it is clear that $\gcd(246, 426) = 2 \cdot 3 = 6$. ▲

Hands-On Exercise 5.6.1   Find the factorizations of 153 and 732, and use them to compute $\gcd(153, 732)$.

△

Although the set of primes that divide two different positive integers a and b may be different, we could nevertheless write both a and b as the product of powers of all the primes involved. For example, by combining the prime factors of

$$12300 = 2^2 \cdot 3 \cdot 5^2 \cdot 41, \quad \text{and} \quad 34128 = 2^4 \cdot 3^3 \cdot 79,$$

we could write them as

$$12300 = 2^2 \cdot 3^1 \cdot 5^2 \cdot 41^1 \cdot 79^0, \quad \text{and} \quad 34128 = 2^4 \cdot 3^3 \cdot 5^0 \cdot 41^0 \cdot 79^1.$$

It follows that
$$\gcd(12300, 34128) = 2^2 \cdot 3^1 \cdot 5^0 \cdot 41^0 \cdot 79^0 = 12.$$

The generalization is immediate.

Theorem 5.6.4 *If $a = p_1^{e_1} p_2^{e_2} \cdots p_t^{e_t}$ and $b = p_1^{f_1} p_2^{f_2} \cdots p_t^{f_t}$ for some distinct primes p_i, where $e_i, f_i \geq 0$ for each i, then $\gcd(a, b) = p_1^{\min(e_1, f_1)} p_2^{\min(e_2, f_2)} \cdots p_t^{\min(e_t, f_t)}$.*

In this theorem, we allow the exponents to be zero. In the usual prime-power factorization, the exponents have to be positive.

Hands-On Exercise 5.6.2   Compute $\gcd(2^3 \cdot 5 \cdot 7 \cdot 11^2, 2^2 \cdot 3^2 \cdot 5^2 \cdot 7^2)$.

$\triangle$

Definition.   The *least common multiple* of the integers a and b, denoted $\operatorname{lcm}(a, b)$, is the smallest positive common multiple of both a and b. $\diamond$

Theorem 5.6.5 *If $a = p_1^{e_1} p_2^{e_2} \cdots p_t^{e_t}$ and $b = p_1^{f_1} p_2^{f_2} \cdots p_t^{f_t}$ for some distinct primes p_i, where $e_i, f_i \geq 0$ for each i, then $\operatorname{lcm}(a, b) = p_1^{\max(e_1, f_1)} p_2^{\max(e_2, f_2)} \cdots p_t^{\max(e_t, f_t)}$.*

Hands-On Exercise 5.6.3   Compute $\operatorname{lcm}(2^3 \cdot 5 \cdot 7 \cdot 11^2, 2^2 \cdot 3^2 \cdot 5^2 \cdot 7^2)$.

$\triangle$

Corollary 5.6.6 *For any positive integers a and b, we have $ab = \gcd(a, b) \cdot \operatorname{lcm}(a, b)$.*

Proof: For each i, one of the two numbers e_i and f_i is the minimum, and the other is the maximum. Hence,
$$e_i + f_i = \min(e_i, f_i) + \max(e_i, f_i),$$
from which we obtain
$$p_i^{e_i} p_i^{f_i} = p_i^{e_i + f_i} = p_i^{\min(e_i, f_i) + \max(f_i, f_i)} = p_i^{\min(e_i, f_i)} p_i^{\max(e_i, f_i)}.$$

Therefore, ab equals the product of $\gcd(a, b)$ and $\operatorname{lcm}(a, b)$.   ∎

Example 5.6.2   Since $12300 = 2^2 \cdot 3^1 \cdot 5^2 \cdot 41^1 \cdot 79^0$, and $34128 = 2^4 \cdot 3^3 \cdot 5^0 \cdot 41^0 \cdot 79^1$, it follows that
$$\operatorname{lcm}(12300, 34128) = 2^4 \cdot 3^3 \cdot 5^2 \cdot 41^1 \cdot 79^1 = 34981200.$$

We have seen that $\gcd(12300, 34128) = 12$, and we do have $12 \cdot 34981200 = 12300 \cdot 34128$.   ▲

Hands-On Exercise 5.6.4   Knowing that $\gcd(246, 426) = 6$, how would you compute the value of $\mathrm{lcm}(246, 426)$?

△

Example 5.6.3   When we add two fractions, we first take the common denominator, as in

$$\frac{7}{8} + \frac{5}{12} = \frac{7}{8} \cdot \frac{3}{3} + \frac{5}{12} \cdot \frac{2}{2} = \frac{21 + 10}{24} = \frac{31}{24}.$$

Clear enough, the least common denominator is precisely the least common multiple of the two denominators.   ▲

Example 5.6.4   The control panel of a machine has two signal lights, one red and one blue. The red light blinks once every 10 seconds, and the blue light blinks once every 14 seconds. When the machine is turned on, both lights blink simultaneously. After how many seconds will they blink at the same time again?

Solution: This problem illustrates a typical application of least common multiple. The red light blinks at 10, 20, 30, ... seconds, while the blue light blinks at 14, 28, 42, ... seconds. In general, the red light blinks at t seconds if t is a multiple of 10, and the blue light blinks when t is a multiple of 14. Therefore, both lights blink together when t is a multiple of both 10 and 14. The next time it happens will be $\mathrm{lcm}(10, 14) = 70$ seconds later.   ▲

Hands-On Exercise 5.6.5   Two comets travel on fixed orbits around the earth. One of them returns to Earth every 35 years, the other every 42 years. If they both appear in 2012, when is the next time they will return to Earth in the same year?

△

Hands-On Exercise 5.6.6   Given relatively prime positive integers m and n, what are the possible values of $\mathrm{lcm}(4m - 6n, 6m + 4n)$?

△

Example 5.6.5   What does $2\mathbb{Z} \cap 3\mathbb{Z}$ equal to?

Solution: Assume $x \in 2\mathbb{Z} \cap 3\mathbb{Z}$, then $x \in 2\mathbb{Z}$ and $x \in 3\mathbb{Z}$. This means x is a multiple of both 2 and 3. Consequently, x is a multiple of $\mathrm{lcm}(2, 3) = 6$, which means $x \in 6\mathbb{Z}$. Therefore, $2\mathbb{Z} \cap 3\mathbb{Z} \subseteq 6\mathbb{Z}$.

Next, assume $x \in 6\mathbb{Z}$, then x is a multiple of 6. Consequently, x is a multiple of 2, as well as a multiple of 3. This means $x \in 2\mathbb{Z}$, and $x \in 3\mathbb{Z}$. As a result, $x \in 2\mathbb{Z} \cap 3\mathbb{Z}$. Therefore, $6\mathbb{Z} \subseteq 2\mathbb{Z} \cap 3\mathbb{Z}$. Together with $2\mathbb{Z} \cap 3\mathbb{Z} \subseteq 6\mathbb{Z}$, we conclude that $2\mathbb{Z} \cap 3\mathbb{Z} = 6\mathbb{Z}$.   ▲

Hands-On Exercise 5.6.7   What does $4\mathbb{Z} \cap 6\mathbb{Z}$ equal to?

△

Summary and Review

- There are infinitely many primes.
- Any positive integer $n > 1$ can be uniquely factored into a product of prime powers.
- Primes can be considered as the building blocks (through multiplication) of all positive integers exceeding one.
- Given two positive integers a and b, their least common multiple is denoted as $\mathrm{lcm}(a, b)$.
- For any positive integers a and b, we have $ab = \gcd(a, b) \cdot \mathrm{lcm}(a, b)$.

Exercises 5.6

1. Find the prime-power factorization of these integers.

   (a) 4725   (b) 9702
   (c) 180625   (d) 1662405

2. Find the least common multiple of each of the following pairs of integers.

   (a) 27, 81   (b) 24, 84   (c) 120, 615
   (d) 412, 936   (e) 1380, 3020   (f) 1122, 3672

3. Richard follows a very rigid routine. He orders a pizza for lunch every 10 days, and has dinner with his parents every 25 days. If he orders a pizza for lunch and has dinner with his parents today, when will he do both on the same day again?

4. Compute $\gcd(15 \cdot 50, 25 \cdot 21)$, and $\mathrm{lcm}(15 \cdot 50, 25 \cdot 21)$.

5. What does $10\mathbb{Z} \cap 15\mathbb{Z}$ equal to? Prove your claim.

6. Let m and n be positive integers. What does $m\mathbb{Z} \cap n\mathbb{Z}$ equal to? Prove your claim.

7. Let p be an odd prime. Show that

   (a) p is of the form $4k + 1$ or of the form $4k + 3$ for some nonnegative integer k.

   (b) p is of the form $6k + 1$ or of the form $6k + 5$ for some nonnegative integer k.

8. Give three examples of an odd prime p of each of the following forms

   (a) $4k + 1$ (b) $4k + 3$
   (c) $6k + 1$ (d) $6k + 5$

9. Prove that any prime of the form $3n + 1$ is also of the form $6k + 1$.

10. Prove that if a positive integer n is of the form $3k + 2$, then it has a prime factor of the same form.

    Hint: Consider its contrapositive.

11. Prove that 5 is the only prime of the form $n^2 - 4$.

    Hint: Consider the factorization of $n^2 - 4$.

12. Use the result "Any odd prime p is of the form $6k + 1$ or of the form $6k + 5$ for some nonnegative integer k" to prove the following results.

    (a) If $p \geq 5$ is a prime, then $p^2 + 2$ is composite.
    (b) If $p \geq q \geq 5$ are primes, then $24 \mid (p^2 - q^2)$.

5.7   Modular Arithmetic

Modular arithmetic uses only a fixed number of possible results in all its computation. For instance, there are only 12 hours on the face of a clock. If the time now is 7 o'clock, 20 hours later will be 3 o'clock; and we do not say 27 o'clock! This example explains why modular arithmetic is referred to by some as ***clock arithmetic***.

Example 5.7.1   Assume the current time is 2:00 P.M. Write this as 14:00. Sixty five hours later, it would be 79:00. Since

$$79 = 24 \cdot 3 + 7,$$

it will be 7:00 or 7 A.M.   ▲

Hands-On Exercise 5.7.1   Designate Sunday, Monday, Tuesday, ..., Saturday as Day 0, 1, 2, ..., 6. If today is Monday, then it is Day 1. What day of the week will it be two years from now? Assume there are 365 days in a year.

△

In the clock example, we essentially regard 27 o'clock the same as 3 o'clock. They key is, we are only interested in the remainder when a value is divided by 12.

$m_1 \equiv m_2 \ (mod \ n)$
$\Leftrightarrow n \mid (m_1 - m_2).$

Definition.   Let $n \geq 2$ be a fixed integer. We say the two integers m_1 and m_2 are ***congruent modulo n***, denoted

$$m_1 \equiv m_2 \pmod{n}$$

if and only if $n \mid (m_1 - m_2)$. The integer n is called the ***modulus*** of the congruence.

What does this notion of congruence have to do with remainders? The next result describes their connection.

Theorem 5.7.1 *Let $n \geq 2$ be a fixed integer. For any two integers m_1 and m_2,*

$$m_1 \equiv m_2 \ (mod \ n) \quad \Leftrightarrow \quad m_1 \bmod n = m_2 \bmod n.$$

Remark.   Do not confuse the two notations. The notation "$(\bmod \ n)$" after $m_1 \equiv m_2$ indicates a congruence relation, in which "mod n" are enclosed by a pair of parentheses, and the notation is placed at the end of the congruence. In contrast, the "mod" between m_1 and n, without parentheses, is a binary operation that yields the remainder when m_1 is divided by n.   ◇

Proof: ($\Rightarrow$) Assume $m_1 \equiv m_2 \pmod n$. The definition of congruence implies that we have $n \mid (m_1 - m_2)$. Hence,

$$m_1 - m_2 = nq$$

for some integer q. Let $m_1 = nq_1 + r_1$ and $m_2 = nq_2 + r_2$ for some integers q_1, q_2, r_1, r_2, such that $0 \leq r_1, r_2 < n$. Then

$$nq = m_1 - m_2 = n(q_1 - q_2) + r_1 - r_2.$$

Since $r_1 - r_2 = n(q - q_1 + q_2)$, we conclude that $n \mid r_1 - r_2$. However, $0 \leq r_1, r_2 < n$ implies that $|r_1 - r_2| < n$. Therefore, we must have $r_1 - r_2 = 0$, or $r_1 = r_2$. It follows that $m_1 \bmod n = m_2 \bmod n$.

($\Leftarrow$) Assume $m_1 \bmod n = m_2 \bmod n$. According to the Division Algorithm, the remainder in an integer division is unique. Thus, $m_1 = nq_1 + r$ and $m_2 = nq_2 + r$ for some integers q_1, q_2, r such that $0 \leq r < n$. Then

$$m_1 - m_2 = (nq_1 + r) - (nq_2 + r) = n(q_1 - q_2).$$

Therefore, $n \mid (m_1 - m_2)$.   ∎

Recall the definition of congruence.

Corollary 5.7.2 *Let $n \geq 2$ be a fixed integer. Then*

$$a \equiv 0 \pmod n \quad \Leftrightarrow \quad n \mid a.$$

Theorem 5.7.1 tells us $m_1 \equiv m_2 \pmod n$ if and only if m_1 and m_2 share the same remainder when they are divided by n. Given any integer m,

$$m \bmod n \in \{0, 1, 2, \ldots, n-1\}.$$

The final answer in modular arithmetic is always between 0 and $n-1$, inclusive.

We call these values the **residues modulo n**. In modular arithmetic, when we say "**reduced modulo n**," we mean whatever result we obtain, we divide it by n, and report only the smallest possible nonnegative residue.

The next theorem is fundamental to modular arithmetic.

Theorem 5.7.3 *Let $n \geq 2$ be a fixed integer. If $a \equiv b \pmod n$ and $c \equiv d \pmod n$, then*

$$\begin{aligned} a + c &\equiv b + d &\pmod n, \\ ac &\equiv bd &\pmod n. \end{aligned}$$

Proof: Assume $a \equiv b \pmod n$ and $c \equiv d \pmod n$. Then $n \mid (a - b)$ and $n \mid (c - d)$. We can write

$$a - b = ns, \qquad \text{and} \qquad c - d = nt$$

for some integers s and t. Consequently,

$$(a + c) - (b + d) = (a - b) + (c - d) = ns + nt = n(s + t),$$

where $s + t$ is an integer. This proves that $a + c \equiv b + d \pmod n$. We also have

$$ac - bd = (b + ns)(d + nt) - bd = bnt + nsd + n^2 st = n(bt + sd + nst),$$

where $bt + sd + nst$ is an integer. Thus, $n \mid (ac - bd)$, which means $ac \equiv bd \pmod n$.   ∎

Because of Theorem 5.7.3, we can add or multiply an integer to both sides of a congruence without altering the congruences.

Example 5.7.2 We can use subtraction to reduce 2370 modulo 11. Any multiple of 11 is congruent to 0 modulo 11. So we have, for example,

$$2370 \equiv 2370 \pmod{11}, \qquad \text{and} \qquad 0 \equiv -2200 \pmod{11}.$$

Applying Theorem 5.7.3, we obtain

$$2370 \equiv 2370 - 2200 = 170 \quad (\text{mod } 11).$$

Use subtraction to reduce m modulo n.

What this means is: *we can keep subtracting appropriate multiples of n from m until the answer is between 0 and n − 1, inclusive.* It does not matter which multiple of 11 you use. The point is, pick one that you can think of quickly, and keep repeating the process. Continuing in this fashion, we find

$$170 \equiv 170 - 110 = 60 \quad (\text{mod } 11).$$

Since $60 - 55 = 5$, we determine that $2370 \equiv 5 \pmod{11}$.   ▲

Hands-On Exercise 5.7.2   Reduce 12457 to the smallest nonnegative residue modulo 17.

△

In modular arithmetic, the final answer is always between 0 and n − 1, inclusive.

Example 5.7.3   In a similar manner, if m is negative, we can keep adding multiples of n to it until the answer is positive. For example,

$$-278 \equiv -278 + 300 = 52 \quad (\text{mod } 11).$$

it is obvious that $52 \equiv 52 - 44 = 8 \pmod{11}$. Thus, $-278 \equiv 8 \pmod{11}$.   ▲

Hands-On Exercise 5.7.3   Evaluate −3275 mod 11. This is the same as reducing −3275 to the smallest nonnegative residue modulo 11.

△

In a complicated computation, reduce the result from each intermediate step before you carry on with the next step. This will simplify the computation tremendously. To further speed up the computation, we can use negative values in the intermediate step. Nonetheless, the final answer must be between 0 and $n − 1$.

Example 5.7.4   Reduce $37^2 \cdot 41 - 53 \cdot 2$ modulo 7.

We can use negative values in the intermediate steps.

Solution: Take note that

$$
\begin{aligned}
37 &\equiv 37 - 35 = 2 \quad (\text{mod } 7), \\
41 &\equiv 41 - 42 = -1 \quad (\text{mod } 7), \\
53 &\equiv 53 - 49 = 4 \quad (\text{mod } 7).
\end{aligned}
$$

Therefore,

$$37^2 \cdot 41 - 53 \cdot 2 \equiv 2^2 \cdot (-1) - 4 \cdot 2 = -12 \quad (\text{mod } 7).$$

We determine that $37^2 \cdot 41 - 53 \cdot 2 \equiv 2 \pmod{7}$.   ▲

Hands-On Exercise 5.7.4   Evaluate $56^3 \cdot 22 \cdot 17 - 35 \cdot 481 \pmod{9}$.

△

Tedious computation may become rather simple under modular arithmetic.

Example 5.7.5   Show that if an integer n is not divisible by 3, then $n^2 - 1$ is always divisible by 3. Equivalently, show that if an integer n is not divisible by 3, then $n^2 - 1 \equiv 0 \pmod{3}$.

Solution 1:   Let n be an integer not divisible by 3, then either $n \equiv 1 \pmod 3$, or $n \equiv 2 \pmod 3$.

- *Case 1.* If $n \equiv 1 \pmod 3$, then

$$n^2 - 1 \equiv 1^2 - 1 = 0 \pmod 3.$$

- *Case 2.* If $n \equiv 2 \pmod 3$, then

$$n^2 - 1 \equiv 2^2 - 1 = 3 \equiv 0 \pmod 3.$$

In both cases, we have found that $n^2 - 1$ is divisible by 3.   ▲

Solution 2:   Let n be an integer not divisible by 3, then either $n \equiv 1 \pmod 3$, or $n \equiv 2 \pmod 3$. This is equivalent to saying $n \equiv \pm 1 \pmod 3$. Then

$$n^2 - 1 \equiv (\pm 1)^2 - 1 = 1 - 1 = 0 \pmod 3,$$

which means $n^2 - 1$ is divisible by 3.   ▲

Hands-On Exercise 5.7.5   Use modular arithmetic to show that $5 \mid (n^5 - n)$ for any integer n.

△

Hands-On Exercise 5.7.6   Use modular arithmetic to show that $n(n+1)(2n+1)$ is divisible by 6 for any integer n.

See Hands-On Exercise 3.2.4 and Example 3.5.1.

△

Raising an integer to a large power poses a serious problem. We cannot just raise an integer to a large power, because the result could be so large that the calculator or computer has to convert it into a decimal value and start using scientific notation to handle it. Consequently, the answer will not be accurate.

A better solution is to reduce the intermediate results modulo n after each multiplication. This will produce an accurate result, but it will take a long time to finish if the power is huge.

Fortunately, there is a much faster way to perform exponentiation that uses a lesser number of multiplications.

Example 5.7.6   Evaluate 5^{29} (mod 11).

Solution: First, write the exponent 29 as a sum of powers of 2. We can do it by inspection. Start with the highest power of 2 that is less than or equal to 29, and then work with whatever is left in the sum:

$$29 = 16 + 13 = 16 + 8 + 5 = 16 + 8 + 4 + 1.$$

Write 29 as a sum of powers of 2.

We are essentially expressing 29 in base 2. We can now write

$$5^{29} = 5^{16+8+4+1} = 5^{16} \cdot 5^8 \cdot 5^4 \cdot 5.$$

These powers of 5 can be obtained by means of **repeated squaring**:

$$
\begin{aligned}
5^1 &= 5, \\
5^2 &= 5^2, \\
5^4 &= (5^2)^2, \\
5^8 &= (5^4)^2, \\
5^{16} &= (5^8)^2, \\
& \vdots
\end{aligned}
$$

The method of repeated squaring.

The iteration is simple: each new power is obtained by squaring the previous power. Since we are doing modular arithmetic, we want to reduce each intermediate result modulo 11:

$$
\begin{aligned}
5 &= 5 & & & &(\text{mod } 11) \\
5^2 &= 25 \equiv & 3 & & &(\text{mod } 11) \\
5^4 &\equiv 3^2 = & 9 &= -2 & &(\text{mod } 11) \\
5^8 &\equiv 9^2 \equiv (-2)^2 &= & 4 & &(\text{mod } 11) \\
5^{16} &\equiv 4^2 = & 16 &\equiv 5 & &(\text{mod } 11)
\end{aligned}
$$

It follows that

$$5^{29} = 5^{16} \cdot 5^8 \cdot 5^4 \cdot 5 \equiv 5 \cdot 4 \cdot (-2) \cdot 5 \pmod{11}.$$

After simplification, we find $5^{29} \equiv 9$ (mod 11).   ▲

Hands-On Exercise 5.7.7   Use repeated squaring to find 7^{45} (mod 11).

△

Hands-On Exercise 5.7.8 Use repeated squaring to evaluate 9^{58} (mod 23).

$\triangle$

In modular arithmetic, we are basically working with the remainders only. The set of integers $\{0, 1, 2, \ldots, n-1\}$ is called the **set of integers modulo n**, and is denoted by $\mathbb{Z}_n$ (pronounced as Z mod n). In addition, we define two new arithmetic operations on $\mathbb{Z}_n$. They are called "addition" and "multiplication" because they work like the usual addition and multiplication, except that we have to apply the mod operation to the results. To distinguish them from the usual addition and multiplication, we denote them by $\oplus$ and $\odot$, and are called "circled plus" and "circled dot," respectively. Formally,

$$a \oplus b = (a + b) \bmod n, \quad \text{and} \quad a \odot b = (a \cdot b) \bmod n.$$

$\mathbb{Z}_n$ is pronounced Z mod n.

The addition and multiplication tables for $\mathbb{Z}_6$ are listed below.

$\oplus$	0	1	2	3	4	5
0	0	1	2	3	4	5
1	1	2	3	4	5	0
2	2	3	4	5	0	1
3	3	4	5	0	1	2
4	4	5	0	1	2	3
5	5	0	1	2	3	4

$\odot$	0	1	2	3	4	5
0	0	0	0	0	0	0
1	0	1	2	3	4	5
2	0	2	4	0	2	4
3	0	3	0	3	0	3
4	0	4	2	0	4	2
5	0	5	4	3	2	1

Compare them to the tables for $\mathbb{Z}_7$.

$\oplus$	0	1	2	3	4	5	6
0	0	1	2	3	4	5	6
1	1	2	3	4	5	6	0
2	2	3	4	5	6	0	1
3	3	4	5	6	0	1	2
4	4	5	6	0	1	2	3
5	5	6	0	1	2	3	4
6	6	0	1	2	3	4	5

$\odot$	0	1	2	3	4	5	6
0	0	0	0	0	0	0	0
1	0	1	2	3	4	5	6
2	0	2	4	6	1	3	5
3	0	3	6	2	5	1	4
4	0	4	1	5	2	6	3
5	0	5	3	1	6	4	2
6	0	6	5	4	3	2	1

In both addition tables, all possible values appear in every row and every column. The same is true in the nonzero rows and nonzero columns in the multiplication table for $\mathbb{Z}_7$. However, some of the rows in the multiplication table for $\mathbb{Z}_6$ do not contain all the integers in $\mathbb{Z}_6$. This suggests that the algebraic properties of $\mathbb{Z}_n$ depend on the value of n.

In fact, whenever n is prime, the addition and multiplication tables of $\mathbb{Z}_n$ behave like the ones in $\mathbb{Z}_7$. It can be shown that when n is prime, $\mathbb{Z}_n$ has the following properties.

1. Both $\oplus$ and $\odot$ are **commutative**, meaning

$$a \oplus b = b \oplus a \qquad \text{and} \qquad a \odot b = b \odot a$$

for all $a, b \in \mathbb{Z}_n$.

2. Both $\oplus$ and $\odot$ are **associative**, meaning that

$$(a \oplus b) \oplus c = a \oplus (b \oplus c) \qquad \text{and} \qquad (a \odot b) \odot c = a \odot (b \odot c)$$

for all $a, b, c \in \mathbb{Z}_n$.

3. The operations $\oplus$ and $\odot$ satisfy the **distributive laws**

$$a \odot (b \oplus c) = (a \odot b) \oplus (a \odot c) \qquad \text{and} \qquad (b \oplus c) \odot a = (b \odot a) \oplus (c \odot a)$$

for all $a, b, c \in \mathbb{Z}_n$.

4. The integer 0 is the **additive identity**, meaning that $a \oplus 0 = 0 \oplus a = a$ for all $a \in \mathbb{Z}_n$.

5. For every $a \in \mathbb{Z}_n$, there exists a unique integer $a' \in \mathbb{Z}_n$ such that $a \oplus a' = 0$. This integer a' is called the **additive inverse** or **negative** of a, and is denoted by $-a$.

6. The integer 1 is the **multiplicative identity**, meaning that $a \odot 1 = 1 \odot a = a$ for all $a \in \mathbb{Z}_n$.

7. For every integer $a \in \mathbb{Z}_n^*$ (hence, $a \neq 0$), there exists a unique nonzero integer $a' \in \mathbb{Z}_n$ such that $a \odot a' = 1$. This integer a' is called the **multiplicative inverse** or **reciprocal** of a, and is denoted by a^{-1}.

Example 5.7.7   From the tables above, only 1 and 5 have multiplicative inverses in $\mathbb{Z}_6$. In fact,

$$1 \cdot 1 = 1 \qquad \text{and} \qquad 5 \cdot 5 = 1 \qquad \text{in } \mathbb{Z}_6$$

imply that $1^{-1} = 1$, and $5^{-1} = 5$ in $\mathbb{Z}_6$. On the other hand, every nonzero integer in $\mathbb{Z}_7$ has a multiplicative inverse:

$$1^{-1} = 1, \quad 2^{-2} = 4, \quad 3^{-1} = 5, \quad 4^{-1} = 2, \quad 5^{-1} = 3, \quad \text{and} \quad 6^{-1} = 6.$$

Be sure to verify these inverses.   ▲

In general, given any set of numbers, we can define arithmetic operations in any way we like, provided that they obey certain rules. This produces an **algebraic structure**. For example, we call a set of elements S with two binary operations denoted $\oplus$ and $\odot$ a **field**, and write $\langle S, \oplus, \odot \rangle$ or $(S, \oplus, \odot)$, if it satisfies all seven properties listed above. Both $\langle \mathbb{R}, +, \cdot \rangle$ and $\langle \mathbb{Q}, +, \cdot \rangle$ are fields, but $\langle \mathbb{Z}, +, \cdot \rangle$ is not, because multiplicative inverse of a does not exist if $a \neq \pm 1$.

Theorem 5.7.4 *The algebraic structure $\langle \mathbb{Z}_n, \oplus, \odot \rangle$ is a field if and only if n is prime.*

Proof: Verification of most of the properties is rather straightforward, with the exception of the existence of the multiplicative inverse, which we shall prove here. Since n is a prime, any $a \in \mathbb{Z}^*$ must be relatively prime to n. Hence,

$$as + nt = 1$$

for some integers s and t. Modulo n, we find $nt = 0$, hence, $as + nt = 1$ becomes

$$as = 1.$$

Therefore $a^{-1} \equiv s \pmod{n}$.   ∎

The theorem tells us that if n is prime, then $\mathbb{Z}_n$ is a field, hence, every nonzero integer has a multiplicative inverse.

Example 5.7.8 Determine 7^{-1} (mod 29).

Solution: We want to find a number a' such that $7a' \equiv 1$ (mod 29). Note that $\gcd(7, 29) = 1$. Using extended Euclidean algorithm, we find

$$7(-4) + 29 \cdot 1 = 1.$$

Since $29 \cdot 1 \equiv 0$ (mod 29), after reducing modulo 29, we find

$$7(-4) \equiv 1 \pmod{29}.$$

This implies that $7^{-1} \equiv -4 \equiv 25$ (mod 29). ▲

When n is composite, $\mathbb{Z}_n$ is not a field. Then not every nonzero integer in it has a multiplicative inverse. Of course, some special nonzero integers may still have multiplicative inverses.

Hands-On Exercise 5.7.9 Determine 8^{-1} (mod 45).

△

Example 5.7.9 Solve the equation $7x - 3 = 5$ over $\mathbb{Z}_{29}$.

Solution: From $7x - 3 = 5$, we find $7x = 8$. Recall that what this equation really means is

$$7x \equiv 8 \pmod{29}.$$

The answer is not $x = \frac{8}{7}$, because $\mathbb{Z}_{29}$ only contains integers as its elements. This is what we should do: multiply 7^{-1} to both sides of the congruence:

$$7^{-1} \cdot 7x \equiv 7^{-1} \cdot 8 \pmod{29}.$$

Since $7^{-1} \cdot 7 \equiv 1$ (mod 29), we now have

$$x \equiv 7^{-1} \cdot 8 \pmod{29}.$$

To simulate division, we have to multiply by the multiplicative inverse.

In a way, we use multiplicative inverse to simulate division. In this case, $7^{-1} \equiv 7$ (mod 29). Hence, $x \equiv 7 \cdot 8 \equiv 26$ (mod 29). ▲

Hands-On Exercise 5.7.10 Solve the equation $8x + 23 = 12$ over $\mathbb{Z}_{45}$.

△

Example 5.7.10 Explain why 3^{-1} does not exist in $\mathbb{Z}_{24}$.

Solution: Suppose 3^{-1} exists in $\mathbb{Z}_{24}$, say, $3^{-1} \equiv z \pmod{24}$. This means $3z \equiv 1 \pmod{24}$. Hence,

$$3z = 24q + 1$$

for some integer q. This in turn implies that

$$1 = 3z - 24q = 3(z - 8q),$$

which is clearly impossible because $z - 8q$ is an integer. This contradiction shows that 3^{-1} does not exist in $\mathbb{Z}_{24}$.   ▲

Both $\mathbb{R}$ and $\mathbb{Q}$ are infinite fields, while $\mathbb{Z}_n$ is a finite field when n is prime. The next result is a truly amazing one, because it proclaims that the number of elements in any finite field (one with finitely many elements) must be the power of a certain prime. Unfortunately, we are unable to prove it here, because it is beyond the scope of this course.

Theorem 5.7.5 *There exists a finite field of n elements if and only if n is the power of a prime.*

Summary and Review

- Modular arithmetic modulo n uses the mod operation to reduce the answers of all computation to within 0 through $n - 1$.
- Instead of waiting until we obtain the final answer before we reduce it modulo n, it is easier to reduce every immediate result modulo n before moving on to the next step in the computation.
- We can use negative integers in the intermediate steps.
- The set of integers $\{0, 1, 2, \ldots, n - 1\}$, together with modular arithmetic modulo n, is denoted as $\mathbb{Z}_n$.
- For $a \cdot a' \equiv 1 \pmod{n}$, we say that a' is the multiplicative inverse of a, and denote it a^{-1}.
- For some $a \in \mathbb{Z}_n$, the multiplicative inverse a^{-1} may not exist. If it exists, we can use it to simulate division.

Exercises 5.7

1. Construct the addition and multiplication tables for $\mathbb{Z}_8$. Which nonzero elements have multiplicative inverses (reciprocals)? What are their multiplicative inverses?

2. Repeat the last problem with $\mathbb{Z}_9$.

3. Find the sum and product of 1053 and 1761 in $\mathbb{Z}_{17}$.

4. Some of the results we derived earlier can be easily proven via modular arithmetic. For example, show that if an integer n is not divisible by 3, then $n \equiv \pm 1 \pmod{3}$. What can you say about $n^2 \pmod{3}$? Therefore what form must n^2 take?

5. Show that no integer of the form $m^2 + 1$ is a multiple of 7.

   Hint: What are the possible values of $m \pmod{7}$? Compare this to the last problem.

6. What are the possible values of $m \pmod{13}$ such that $m^2 + 1$ is a multiple of 13?

   Hint: Compute $m^2 + 1 \pmod{13}$ for each value of m.

7. Find the value of 4^{45} in $\mathbb{Z}_{11}$

   (a) using the fact that $45 = 3 \cdot 3 \cdot 5$

   (b) using repeated squaring

8. Use repeated squaring to evaluate $5^{23} \pmod{11}$.

9. Solve these equations

   (a) $2x + 5 = 10$ over $\mathbb{Z}_{13}$

   (b) $37x + 28 = 25$ over $\mathbb{Z}_{57}$

   (c) $12 - 24x = 15$ over $\mathbb{Z}_{35}$

10. Let p and q be odd primes.

    (a) Show that p takes the form of either $6k + 1$ or $6k + 5$.

        Hint: First, explain why being odd restricts p to the form of $6k + 1$, $6k + 3$, and $6k + 5$. Next, argue why $p \neq 6k + 3$.

    (b) What could p be congruent to, modulo 24?

    (c) Show that if $p \geq q \geq 5$, then $24 \mid (p^2 - q^2)$.

        Hint: What are the possible values of p^2 and q^2 modulo 24?

11. Use modular arithmetic to prove that, if n is an integer not divisible by 5, then $n^4 - 1$ is divisible by 5.

12. Use modular arithmetic to prove that $8 \mid (5^{2n} + 7)$ for any integer $n \geq 0$.

13. Use modular arithmetic to prove that $3 \mid (2^{2n} - 1)$ for any integer $n \geq 0$.

14. Use modular arithmetic to prove that $5 \mid (3^{3n+1} + 2^{n+1})$ for any integer $n \geq 0$.

Chapter 6

Functions

6.1 Functions: An Introduction

The functions we studied in calculus are real functions, which are defined over a set of real numbers, and the results they produce are also real. In this chapter, we shall study their generalization over other sets. The definition could be difficult to grasp at the beginning, so we would start with a brief introduction.

Most students view real functions as computational devices. However, in the generalization, functions are not restricted to computation only. A better way to look at functions is their input-output relationship. Let f denote a function. Given an element (which need not be a number), we call the result from f the ***image of x under f***, and write $f(x)$, which is read as "f of x."

Imagine f as a machine. It takes the input value x, and returns $f(x)$ as the output value. This input-output relationship is depicted in Figure 6.1 in two different ways.

Figure 6.1: Two pictorial views of a function as a machine.

The question is: how could we obtain $f(x)$? A function need not involve any computation. Consequently, we cannot speak of "computing" the value of $f(x)$. Instead, we talk about what is the rule we follow to obtain $f(x)$. This rule can be described in many forms. We can, of course, use a computational rule. But a table, an algorithm, or even a verbal description also work as well.

When we say a real function is defined over the real numbers, we mean the input values must be real numbers. The output values are also real numbers. In general, the input and output values need not be of the same type. The ***nearest integer function***, denoted $[x]$, rounds the real number x to the nearest integer. Here, the images (the output values) are integers. Consequently, we need to distinguish the set of input values from the set of possible output values. We call them the ***domain*** and the ***codomain***, respectively, of the function.

Example 6.1.1   When a professor reports the final letter grades for the students in her class, we can regard this as a function g. The domain is the set of students in her class, and the codomain could be the set of letter grades $\{A, B, C, D, F\}$.   ▲

We said the codomain is the set of *possible* output values, because not every element in the codomain needs to appear as the image of some element from the domain. If no student fails the professor's class in Example 6.1.1, no one will receive the final grade F. The collection of the images (the final letter grades) form a subset of the codomain. We call this subset the **range** of the function g. The range of a function can be a *proper* subset of the codomain. Hence, the codomain of a function is different from the set of its images. If the range of a function does equal to the codomain, we say that the function is **onto**.

Example 6.1.2   For the nearest integer function $h(x) = [x]$, the domain is $\mathbb{R}$. The codomain is $\mathbb{Z}$, and the range is also $\mathbb{Z}$. Hence, the nearest integer function is onto.   ▲

Example 6.1.3   Let x be a real number. The **greatest integer function** $\lfloor x \rfloor$ returns the greatest integer less than or equal to x. For example,

$$\lfloor \sqrt{50} \rfloor = 7, \qquad \lfloor -6.34 \rfloor = -7, \qquad \text{and} \qquad \lfloor 15 \rfloor = 15.$$

Therefore, $\lfloor x \rfloor$ returns x if it is an integer, otherwise, it rounds x *down* to the next closest integer. Hence, it is also called the **floor function** of x. It is clear that its domain is $\mathbb{R}$, and the codomain and range are both $\mathbb{Z}$.   ▲

Hands-On Exercise 6.1.1   Let x be a real number. The **least integer function** $\lceil x \rceil$ returns the least integer greater than or equal to x. For example,

$$\lceil \sqrt{50} \rceil = 8, \qquad \lceil -6.34 \rceil = -6, \qquad \text{and} \qquad \lceil 15 \rceil = 15.$$

Thus, $\lceil x \rceil$ returns x if it is an integer, otherwise, it rounds x *up* to the next closest integer. Hence, it is also called the **ceiling function** of x. What is its domain and codomain?

△

We impose two restrictions on the input-output relationships that we call functions. For any fixed input value x, the output from a function must be the same every time we use the function. As a machine, it spits out the same answer every time we feed the same value x to it. As a calculator, it displays the same answer on its screen every time we enter the same value x, and push the button for the function. We call the output value the image of x, and write $f(x)$. The first important requirement for a function f to be well-defined is: the image $f(x)$ is *unique* for any fixed x-value.

A good machine must perform properly. In terms of a function f, we must be able to obtain $f(x)$ for any value x (and, of course, produce only one result for each x). This is perhaps a little bit too demanding. A remedy is to restrict our attention to those x's over which f would work. The set of legitimate input values is precisely what we call the domain of the function. Consequently, the second requirement says: for every element x from the domain, the output value $f(x)$ should be well-defined. This is the mathematical way of saying that the value $f(x)$ can be obtained.

Example 6.1.4   Compare this to a calculator. If you enter a negative number and press the $\sqrt{}$ button, an error message will appear. To be able to compute the square root of a number, the number must be nonnegative. The domain of a function is the set of acceptable input values for which meaningful results can be found. For the square root function, the domain is $\mathbb{R}^+ \cup \{0\}$, which is the set of nonnegative real numbers.   ▲

Hands-On Exercise 6.1.2 For the square root function, we may regard its codomain as $\mathbb{R}$. What is its range? Is the function onto?

$\triangle$

Hands-On Exercise 6.1.3 For the square root function, can we say its domain is $\mathbb{R}^+ \cup 0$? Explain.

$\triangle$

The two conditions for a function to be well-defined are often combined and written as if it were only one condition:

> *A function f is well-defined if every element x from the domain has a unique image in the codomain.*

Every element in the domain has a unique image.

When you examine this definition closer, you will find the two separate requirements:

- every element in the domain has an image under f, and
- the image is unique.

In the next section, we shall present the complete formal definition.

Summary and Review

- A function is a rule that assigns to every element in the domain a unique image in the codomain.

Exercises 6.1

1. Complete the following table:

x	5.7	π	e	-7.2	-0.8	9
$\lfloor x \rfloor$						
$\lceil x \rceil$						
$[x]$						

2. What is the domain and the codomain of the cube root function? Is it onto?

3. For the square root function, how would you use the interval notation to describe the domain?

4. For the square root function, which set complement would you use to describe the domain?

6.2 Definition of Functions

Definition. Let A and B be nonempty sets. A **function** from A to B is a rule that assigns to *every element* of A a *unique* element in B. We call A the **domain**, and B the **codomain**, of the function. If the function is called f, we write $f\colon A \to B$. Given $x \in A$, its associated element in B is called its **image** under f. We denote it $f(x)$, which is pronounced as "f of x." $\Diamond$

A function is sometimes called a **map** or **mapping**. Hence, we sometimes say f **maps** x to its image $f(x)$. Functions are also called **transformations**.

Example 6.2.1   The function $f\colon \{a, b, c\} \to \{1, 3, 5, 9\}$ is defined according to the rule

$$f(a) = 1, \qquad f(b) = 5, \qquad \text{and} \qquad f(c) = 9.$$

It is a well-defined function. The rule of assignment can be summarized in a table:

x	a	b	c
$f(x)$	1	5	9

We can also describe the assignment rule pictorially with an **arrow diagram**, as shown in Figure 6.2.   ▲

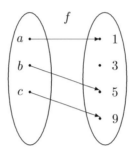

Figure 6.2: An example of a well-defined function.

The two key requirements of a function are

Every element in the domain has a unique image.

- every element in the domain has an image under f, and
- the image is unique.

You may want to remember that every element in A has exactly one "partner" in B.

Example 6.2.2   Figure 6.3 depicts two examples of non-functions. In the one on the left, one of the elements in the domain has no image associated with it. In the one on the right, one of the elements in the domain has two images assigned to it. Both are not functions.   ▲

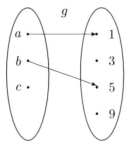 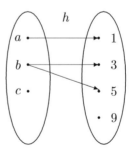

Figure 6.3: Two types of non-functions.

Hands-On Exercise 6.2.1   Do these rules

x	a	b	c
$f(x)$	5	3	3

x	b	c
$g(x)$	9	5

x	a	b	b	c
$h(x)$	1	5	3	9

produce well-defined functions from $\{a, b, c\}$ to $\{1, 3, 5, 9\}$? Explain.

$\triangle$

Hands-On Exercise 6.2.2   Does the definition

$$r(x) = \begin{cases} x & \text{if today is Monday,} \\ 2x & \text{if today is not Monday} \end{cases}$$

produce a well-defined function from $\mathbb{R}$ to $\mathbb{R}$? Explain.

$\triangle$

Hands-On Exercise 6.2.3   Does the definition

$$s(x) = \begin{cases} 5 & \text{if } x < 2, \\ 7 & \text{if } x > 3, \end{cases}$$

produce a well-defined function from $\mathbb{R}$ to $\mathbb{R}$? Explain.

$\triangle$

Example 6.2.3   The function $f\colon [0, \infty) \to \mathbb{R}$ defined by

$$f(x) = \sqrt{x}$$

is well-defined. So is the function $g\colon [2, \infty) \to \mathbb{R}$ defined as

$$g(x) = \sqrt{x - 2}.$$

Can you explain why the domain is $[2, \infty)$?   ▲

Example 6.2.4   Let A denote the set of students taking Discrete Mathematics, and $G = \{A, B, C, D, F\}$, and $\ell(x)$ is the final grade of student x in Discrete Mathematics. Every student should receive a final grade, and the instructor has to report one and only one final grade for each student. This is precisely what we call a function.   ▲

Example 6.2.5   The function $n\colon \wp(\{a, b, c, d\}) \to \mathbb{Z}$ is defined as $n(S) = |S|$. It evaluates the cardinality of a subset of $\{a, b, c, d\}$. For example,

$$n(\{a, c\}) = n(\{b, d\}) = 2.$$

Note that $n(\emptyset) = 0$.   ▲

Hands-On Exercise 6.2.4   Consider Example 6.2.5. What other subsets S of $\{a, b, c, d\}$ also yield $n(S) = 2$? What are the smallest and the largest images the function n can produce?

$\triangle$

Example 6.2.6   Consider a function $f \colon \mathbb{Z}_7 \to \mathbb{Z}_5$. The domain and the codomain are,

$$\mathbb{Z}_7 = \{0, 1, 2, 3, 4, 5, 6\}, \quad \text{and} \quad \mathbb{Z}_5 = \{0, 1, 2, 3, 4\},$$

Exercise caution when the domain and codomain involve different moduli.

respectively. Not only are their elements different, their binary operations are different too. In the domain $\mathbb{Z}_7$, the arithmetic is performed modulo 7, but the arithmetic in the codomain $\mathbb{Z}_5$ is done modulo 5. So we need to be careful in describing the rule of assignment if a computation is involved. We could say, for example,

$$f(x) = z, \quad \text{where } z \equiv 3x \pmod 5.$$

Consequently, starting with any element x in $\mathbb{Z}_7$, we consider x as an ordinary integer, multiply by 3, and reduce the answer modulo 5 to obtain the image $f(x)$. For brevity, we shall write

$$f(x) \equiv 3x \pmod 5.$$

We summarize the images in the following table:

n	0	1	2	3	4	5	6
$f(n)$	0	3	1	4	2	0	3

Take note that the images start repeating after $f(4) = 2$.   ▲

Hands-On Exercise 6.2.5   Tabulate the images of $g \colon \mathbb{Z}_{10} \to \mathbb{Z}_5$ defined by

$$g(x) \equiv 3x \pmod 5.$$

$\triangle$

Definition.   The **graph** of a function $f \colon A \to B$ is the set of ordered pairs (x, y) from $A \times B$ such that $y = f(x)$. $\diamondsuit$

The graph of a function, in this general definition, may not look like the kind of graphs we expected from real functions. A graph is, by definition, a set of *ordered pairs*.

Example 6.2.7   The graph of the function f in Example 6.2.6 is the set of ordered pairs

$$\{(0, 0), (1, 3), (2, 1), (3, 4), (4, 2), (5, 0), (6, 3)\}.$$

If one insists, we could display the graph of a function using an xy-plane that resembles the usual Cartesian plane. Keep in mind: the elements x and y come from A and B, respectively. We can "plot" the graph for f in Example 6.2.6 as shown below.

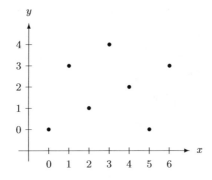

Besides using a graphical representation, we can also use a $(0, 1)$-matrix. A $(0, 1)$-matrix is a matrix whose entries are 0 and 1. For the function f, we use a 7×5 matrix, whose rows and columns correspond to the elements of A and B, respectively, and put one in the (i, j)th entry if $j = f(i)$, and zero otherwise. The resulting matrix is

$$
\begin{array}{c}
 \\ 0 \\ 1 \\ 2 \\ 3 \\ 4 \\ 5 \\ 6
\end{array}
\begin{array}{ccccc}
0 & 1 & 2 & 3 & 4 \\
\begin{pmatrix}
1 & 0 & 0 & 0 & 0 \\
0 & 0 & 0 & 1 & 0 \\
0 & 1 & 0 & 0 & 0 \\
0 & 0 & 0 & 0 & 1 \\
0 & 0 & 1 & 0 & 0 \\
1 & 0 & 0 & 0 & 0 \\
0 & 0 & 0 & 1 & 0
\end{pmatrix}
\end{array}
$$

We call it the ***incidence matrix*** for the function f.   ▲

Hands-On Exercise 6.2.6   "Plot" the graph of g in Hands-On Exercise 6.2.5. Also construct its incidence matrix.

                                                                                                        △

Summary and Review

- A function f from a set A to a set B (called the domain and the codomain, respectively) is a rule that describes how a value in the codomain B is assigned to an element from the domain A.
- But it is not just any rule; rather, the rule must assign to every element x in the domain a unique value in the codomain.
- This unique value is called the image of x under the function f, and is denoted $f(x)$.
- We use the notation $f \colon A \to B$ to indicate that the name of the function is f, the domain is A, and the codomain is B.
- The graph of a function $f \colon A \to B$ is the collection of all ordered pairs (x, y) from $A \times B$ such that $y = f(x)$.
- The graph of a function may not be a curve, as in the case of a real function. It can be just a collection of points.
- We can also display the images of a function in a table, or represent the function with an incidence matrix.

Exercises 6.2

1. What subset A of $\mathbb{R}$ would you use to make $f: A \to \mathbb{R}$ defined by $f(x) = \sqrt{3x - 7}$ a well-defined function?

2. What subset A of $\mathbb{R}$ would you use to make

   (a) $g: A \to \mathbb{R}$, where $g(x) = \sqrt{(x - 3)(x - 7)}$

   (b) $h: A \to \mathbb{R}$, where $h(x) = \dfrac{x + 2}{\sqrt{(x - 2)(5 - x)}}$

   well-defined functions?

3. Which of these data support a well-defined function from $\{1, 2, 3, 4\}$ to $\{1, 2, 3, 4\}$? Explain.

x	1	2	3
$f(x)$	3	4	2

x	1	2	3	4
$g(x)$	2	4	3	2

x	1	2	3	3	4
$h(x)$	2	4	3	2	3

4. Which of the following are the graphical representation or incidence matrix of well-defined functions from $\{1, 2, 3, 4\}$ to $\{1, 2, 3, 4\}$? Explain.

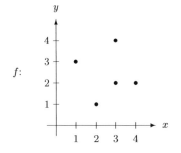

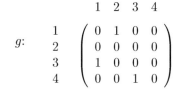

5. Determine whether these are well-defined functions. Explain.

   (a) $f: \mathbb{R} \to \mathbb{R}$, where $f(x) = \dfrac{3}{x^2 + 5}$.

   (b) $g: (5, \infty) \to \mathbb{R}$, where $g(x) = \dfrac{7}{\sqrt{x - 4}}$.

   (c) $h: \mathbb{R} \to \mathbb{R}$, where $h(x) = -\sqrt{7 - 4x + 4x^2}$.

6. Determine whether these are well-defined functions. Explain.

   (a) $s: \mathbb{R} \to \mathbb{R}$, where $x^2 + [s(x)]^2 = 9$.

   (b) $t: \mathbb{R} \to \mathbb{R}$, where $|x - t(x)| = 4$.

7. Below are the graph of the function p and the incidence matrix for the function q, respectively, from $\{1, 2, 3, 4\}$ to $\{1, 2, 3, 4\}$.

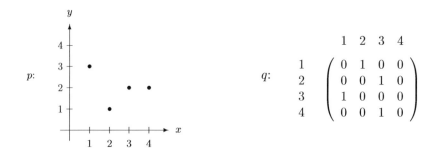

Complete the following table:

x	1	2	3	4
$p(x)$				

x	1	2	3	4
$q(x)$				

8. Let T be your family tree that includes your biological mother, your maternal grand-mother, your maternal great-grandmother, and so on, and all of their female descendants. Determine which of the following define a function from T to T.

   (a) $h_1\colon T \to T$, where $h_1(x)$ is the mother of x.

   (b) $h_2\colon T \to T$, where $h_2(x)$ is x's sister.

   (c) $h_3\colon T \to T$, where $h_3(x)$ is an aunt of x.

   (d) $h_4\colon T \to T$, where $h_4(x)$ is the eldest daughter of x's maternal grandmother.

9. For each of the following functions, determine the image of the given x.

   (a) $k_1\colon \mathbb{N} - \{1\} \to \mathbb{N}$, $k_1(x) =$ smallest prime factor of x, $x = 217$.

   (b) $k_2\colon \mathbb{Z}_{11} \to \mathbb{Z}_{11}$, $k_2(x) \equiv 3x \pmod{11}$, $x = 6$.

   (c) $k_3\colon \mathbb{Z}_{15} \to \mathbb{Z}_{15}$, $k_3(x) \equiv 3x \pmod{15}$, $x = 6$.

10. For each of the following functions, determine the images of the given x-values.

   (a) $\ell_1\colon \mathbb{Z} \to \mathbb{Z}$, $\ell_1(x) = x \bmod 7$, $x = 250$, $x = 0$, and $x = -16$.

   Remark: Recall that, without parentheses, the notation "mod" means the binary operation mod.

   (b) $\ell_2\colon \mathbb{Z} \to \mathbb{Z}$, $\ell_2(x) = \gcd(x, 24)$, $x = 100$, $x = 0$, and $x = -21$.

6.3   One-to-One Functions

We distinguish two special families of functions: the one-to-one functions and the onto functions. We shall discuss one-to-one functions in this section, and onto functions in the next.

Definition.   A function $f\colon A \to B$ is said to be ***one-to-one*** if

$$x_1 \neq x_2 \Rightarrow f(x_1) \neq f(x_2)$$

for all elements $x_1, x_2 \in A$. A one-to-one function is also called an ***injection***, and we call a function ***injective*** if it is one-to-one. A function that is not one-to-one is referred to as ***many-to-one***. $\diamond$

To be one-to-one, distinct elements must have distinct images.

Any well-defined function is either one-to-one or many-to-one. A function cannot be one-to-many because no element can have multiple images. The difference between one-to-one and many-to-one functions is whether there exist distinct elements that share the same image. There are no repeated images in a one-to-one function.

Example 6.3.1   The ***identity function*** on any nonempty set A

$$i_A\colon A \to A, \qquad i_A(x) = x,$$

maps any element back to itself. It is clear that all identity functions are one-to-one.   ▲

Example 6.3.2   The function $h\colon A \to A$ defined by $h(x) = c$ for some fixed element $c \in A$, is an example of a ***constant function***. It is a function with only one image. This is the exact opposite of an identity function. It is clearly *not* one-to-one unless $|A| = 1$.   ▲

For domains with a small number of elements, one can use inspection on the images to determine if the function is one-to-one. This becomes impossible if the domain contains a larger number of elements.

In practice, it is easier to use the contrapositive of the definition to test whether a function is one-to-one:

$$f(x_1) = f(x_2) \Rightarrow x_1 = x_2.$$

Use this definition to prove that a function is one-to-one.

Example 6.3.3   Is the function $f \colon \mathbb{R} \to \mathbb{R}$ defined by $f(x) = 3x + 2$ one-to-one?

Solution: Assume $f(x_1) = f(x_2)$, which means

$$3x_1 + 2 = 3x_2 + 2.$$

Thus $3x_1 = 3x_2$, which implies that $x_1 = x_2$. Therefore f is one-to-one.   ▲

Hands-On Exercise 6.3.1   Determine whether the function $g \colon \mathbb{R} \to \mathbb{R}$ defined by $g(x) = 5 - 7x$ is one-to-one.

△

Hands-On Exercise 6.3.2   Determine whether the function $h \colon [2, \infty) \to \mathbb{R}$ defined by $h(x) = \sqrt{x - 2}$ is one-to-one.

△

Interestingly, sometimes we can use calculus to determine if a real function is one-to-one. A real function f is ***increasing*** if

$$x_1 < x_2 \Rightarrow f(x_1) < f(x_2),$$

and ***decreasing*** if

$$x_1 < x_2 \Rightarrow f(x_1) > f(x_2).$$

Obviously, both increasing and decreasing functions are one-to-one. From calculus, we know that

- A function is increasing over an open interval (a, b) if $f'(x) > 0$ for all $x \in (a, b)$.
- A function is decreasing over an open interval (a, b) if $f'(x) < 0$ for all $x \in (a, b)$.

Therefore, if the derivative of a function is always positive, or always negative, then the function must be one-to-one.

Example 6.3.4   The function $p \colon \mathbb{R} \to \mathbb{R}$ defined by

$$p(x) = 2x^3 - 5$$

is one-to-one, because $p'(x) = 6x^2 > 0$ for any $x \in \mathbb{R}^*$. Likewise, the function $q \colon \left(-\frac{\pi}{2}, \frac{\pi}{2} \right) \to \mathbb{R}$ defined by

$$q(x) = \tan x$$

is also one-to-one, because $q'(x) = \sec^2 x > 0$ for any $x \in \left(-\frac{\pi}{2}, \frac{\pi}{2} \right)$.   ▲

Hands-On Exercise 6.3.3   Use both methods to show that the function $k\colon (0, \infty) \to \mathbb{R}$ defined by $k(x) = \ln x$ is one-to-one.

$\triangle$

Example 6.3.5   The function $h\colon \mathbb{R} \to \mathbb{R}$ given by $h(x) = x^2$ is not one-to-one because some of its images are identical. For example, $h(3) = h(-3) = 9$. It is a many-to-one function. Likewise, the absolute value function $|x|$ is not one-to-one.

The functions $p\colon [\,0, \infty) \to \mathbb{R}$ defined by $p(x) = x^2$ and $q\colon [\,0, \infty) \to \mathbb{R}$ defined by $q(x) = |x|$ are one-to-one. Whether a function is one-to-one depends not only on its formula, but also on its domain. Consequently, sometimes we may be able to convert a many-to-one function into a one-to-one function by modifying its domain. ▲

*You can use counterexamples to show that a function is **not** one-to-one.*

Example 6.3.6   Construct a one-to-one function from $[\,1,3\,]$ to $[\,2,5\,]$.

Solution: There are many possible solutions. In any event, start with a graph. We can use a straight line graph. The domain $[\,1,3\,]$ lies on the x-axis, and the codomain $[\,2,5\,]$ lies on the y-axis. Hence the graph should cover the boxed region in Figure 6.4.

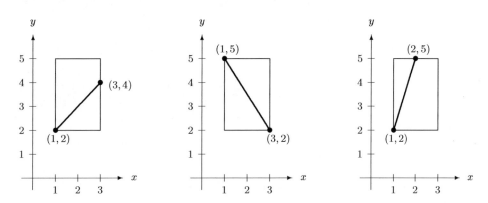

Figure 6.4: Three candidates for one-to-one functions from $[\,1,3\,]$ to $[\,2,5\,]$.

All three graphs do not produce duplicate images. We need to cover all x-values from 1 to 3 in order for the function to be well-defined. This leaves only the first two graphs as legitimate examples.

Every number in the domain must have an image.

To determine the formula for f, we need to derive the equation of the line. Take the first graph as our choice. The line joins the point $(1, 2)$ to the point $(3, 4)$. Thus, its equation is

$$\frac{y - 2}{x - 1} = \frac{4 - 2}{3 - 1} = 1.$$

The last step is to write the answer in the form of $f(x) = \dots$. We have to express y in terms of x. We find $y = x + 1$. Hence,

$$f\colon [\,1,3\,] \to [\,2,5\,], \qquad f(x) = x + 1$$

is an example of a one-to-one function. ▲

Hands-On Exercise 6.3.4   Construct a one-to-one function from $[1, 3]$ to $[2, 5]$ based on the second graph in Example 6.3.6.

$\triangle$

Hands-On Exercise 6.3.5   Construct a one-to-one function from $[3, 8]$ to $[2, 5]$.

$\triangle$

Example 6.3.7   Determine whether the function $g : \mathbb{Z}_{43} \to \mathbb{Z}_{43}$ defined by

$$g(x) \equiv 11x - 5 \pmod{43}$$

is one-to-one.

Solution: Assume $g(x_1) = g(x_2)$. This means

$$11x_1 - 5 \equiv 11x_2 - 5 \pmod{43},$$

which implies

$$11x_1 \equiv 11x_2 \pmod{43}.$$

Notice that $4 \cdot 11 = 44 \equiv 1 \pmod{43}$, hence $11^{-1} \equiv 4 \pmod{43}$. Multiplying 4 to both sides of the last congruence yields

$$44x_1 \equiv 44x_2 \pmod{43},$$

which is equivalent to, since $44 \equiv 1 \pmod{43}$,

$$x_1 \equiv x_2 \pmod{43}.$$

Therefore, $x_1 = x_2$ in $\mathbb{Z}_{43}$. This proves that g is one-to-one.   ▲

Hands-On Exercise 6.3.6   Is the function $h : \mathbb{Z}_{15} \to \mathbb{Z}_{15}$ defined by

$$h(x) \equiv 4x - 11 \pmod{15}$$

a one-to-one function?

$\triangle$

Hands-On Exercise 6.3.7 Show that the function $k: \mathbb{Z}_{15} \to \mathbb{Z}_{15}$ defined by

$$k(x) \equiv 5x - 11 \pmod{15}$$

is not one-to-one by finding $x_1 \neq x_2$ such that $k(x_1) = k(x_2)$.

You can use a counterexample to show that a function is not one-to-one.

$\triangle$

Example 6.3.8 In the last hands-on exercise, we should not rely on the non-existence of 5^{-1} in $\mathbb{Z}_{15}$ to prove that k is not one-to-one. One must consider the interaction between the domain, the codomain, and the definition of the function. For example, despite the fact that 5^{-1} does not exist in $\mathbb{Z}_{15}$, the function $p: \mathbb{Z}_3 \to \mathbb{Z}_{15}$ defined by

$$p(x) \equiv 5x - 11 \pmod{15}$$

is one-to-one, because $p(0) = 4$, $p(1) = 9$, and $p(2) = 14$ are distinct images. ▲

The last example illustrates the trickiness in a function with different moduli in its domain and codomain. Use caution when you deal with such functions! Sometimes, infinite sets also pose a challenge. Because there is an infinite supply of elements, we may obtain results that appear to be impossible for finite sets.

Example 6.3.9 The function $f: \mathbb{Z} \to \mathbb{Z}$ defined by

$$f(n) = \begin{cases} \frac{n}{2} & \text{if } n \text{ is even} \\ \frac{n+1}{2} & \text{if } n \text{ is odd} \end{cases}$$

is not one-to-one, because, for example, $f(0) = f(-1) = 0$. The function $g: \mathbb{Z} \to \mathbb{Z}$ defined by

$$g(n) = 2n$$

is one-to-one, because if $g(n_1) = g(n_2)$, then $2n_1 = 2n_2$ implies that $n_1 = n_2$. ▲

Hands-On Exercise 6.3.8 Show that the function $h: \mathbb{Z} \to \mathbb{N}$ defined by

$$h(n) = \begin{cases} 2n + 1 & \text{if } n \geq 0, \\ -2n & \text{if } n < 0, \end{cases}$$

is one-to-one.

$\triangle$

Example 6.3.10 Let A be the set of all married individuals from a monogamous community who are neither divorced nor widowed. Then the function $s: A \to A$ defined by

$$s(x) = \text{spouse of } x$$

is one-to-one. The reason is, it is impossible to have $x_1 \neq x_2$ and yet $s(x_1) = s(x_2)$. ▲

Summary and Review

- A function f is said to be one-to-one if $f(x_1) = f(x_2) \Rightarrow x_1 = x_2$.
- No two images of a one-to-one function are the same.
- To show that a function f is *not* one-to-one, all we need is to find two different x-values that produce the same image; that is, find $x_1 \neq x_2$ such that $f(x_1) = f(x_2)$.

Exercises 6.3

1. Which of the following functions are one-to-one? Explain.

    (a) $f: \mathbb{R} \to \mathbb{R}$, $f(x) = x^3 - 2x^2 + 1$.

    (b) $g: [2, \infty) \to \mathbb{R}$, $f(x) = x^3 - 2x^2 + 1$.

2. Which of the following functions are one-to-one? Explain.

    (a) $p: \mathbb{R} \to \mathbb{R}$, $h(x) = e^{1-2x}$.

    (b) $q: \mathbb{R} \to \mathbb{R}$, $p(x) = |1 - 3x|$.

3. Construct a one-to-one function $f: (1, 3) \to (2, 5)$ so that $f: [1, 3) \to [2, 5)$ is still one-to-one.

4. Construct a one-to-one function $g: [2, 5) \to (1, 4]$.

5. Determine which of the following are one-to-one functions.

    (a) $f: \mathbb{Z} \to \mathbb{Z}$; $f(n) = n^3 + 1$
    (b) $g: \mathbb{Q} \to \mathbb{Q}$; $g(x) = n^2$
    (c) $h: \mathbb{R} \to \mathbb{R}$; $h(x) = x^3 - x$
    (d) $k: \mathbb{R} \to \mathbb{R}$; $k(x) = 5^x$

6. Determine which of the following are one-to-one functions.

    (a) $p: \wp(\{1, 2, 3, \ldots, n\}) \to \{0, 1, 2, \ldots, n\}$; $p(S) = |S|$
    (b) $q: \wp(\{1, 2, 3, \ldots, n\}) \to \wp(\{1, 2, 3, \ldots, n\})$; $q(S) = \overline{S}$

7. Determine which of the following functions are one-to-one.

    (a) $f_1: \{1, 2, 3, 4, 5\} \to \{a, b, c, d\}$; $f_1(1) = b$, $f_1(2) = c$, $f_1(3) = a$, $f_1(4) = a$, $f_1(5) = c$
    (b) $f_2: \{1, 2, 3, 4\} \to \{a, b, c, d, e\}$; $f_2(1) = c$, $f_2(2) = b$, $f_2(3) = a$, $f_2(4) = d$
    (c) $f_3: \mathbb{Z} \to \mathbb{Z}$; $f_5(n) = -n$

    (d) $f_4: \mathbb{Z} \to \mathbb{Z}$; $f_4(n) = \begin{cases} 2n & \text{if } n < 0 \\ -3n & \text{if } n \geq 0 \end{cases}$

8. Determine which of the following functions are one-to-one.

    (a) $g_1: \{1, 2, 3, 4, 5\} \to \{a, b, c, d, e\}$; $g_1(1) = b$, $g_1(2) = b$, $g_1(3) = b$, $g_1(4) = a$, $g_1(5) = d$
    (b) $g_2: \{1, 2, 3, 4, 5\} \to \{a, b, c, d, e\}$; $g_2(1) = d$, $g_2(2) = b$, $g_2(3) = e$, $g_2(4) = a$, $g_2(5) = c$

    (c) $g_3: \mathbb{N} \to \mathbb{N}$; $g_3(n) = \begin{cases} (n+1)/2 & \text{if } n \text{ is odd} \\ n/2 & \text{if } n \text{ is even} \end{cases}$

    (d) $g_4: \mathbb{N} \to \mathbb{N}$; $g_4(n) = \begin{cases} n + 1 & \text{if } n \text{ is odd} \\ n - 1 & \text{if } n \text{ is even} \end{cases}$

9. List all the one-to-one functions from $\{1, 2\}$ to $\{a, b, c, d\}$.

    Hint: List the images of each function.

10. Is it possible to find a one-to-one function from $\{1, 2, 3, 4\}$ to $\{1, 2\}$? Explain.

11. Determine which of the following functions are one-to-one.

(a) $f: \mathbb{Z}_{10} \to \mathbb{Z}_{10}$; $h(n) \equiv 3n \pmod{10}$.

(b) $g: \mathbb{Z}_{10} \to \mathbb{Z}_{10}$; $g(n) \equiv 5n \pmod{10}$.

(c) $h: \mathbb{Z}_{36} \to \mathbb{Z}_{36}$; $h(n) \equiv 3n \pmod{36}$.

12. Determine which of the following functions are one-to-one.

(a) $r: \mathbb{Z}_{36} \to \mathbb{Z}_{36}$; $r(n) \equiv 5n \pmod{36}$.

(b) $s: \mathbb{Z}_{10} \to \mathbb{Z}_{10}$; $s(n) \equiv n + 5 \pmod{10}$.

(c) $t: \mathbb{Z}_{10} \to \mathbb{Z}_{10}$; $t(n) \equiv 3n + 5 \pmod{10}$.

13. Determine which of the following functions are one-to-one.

(a) $\alpha: \mathbb{Z}_{12} \to \mathbb{Z}_7$; $\alpha(n) \equiv 2n \pmod{7}$.

(b) $\beta: \mathbb{Z}_8 \to \mathbb{Z}_{12}$; $\beta(n) \equiv 3n \pmod{12}$.

(c) $\gamma: \mathbb{Z}_6 \to \mathbb{Z}_{12}$; $\gamma(n) \equiv 2n \pmod{12}$.

(d) $\delta: \mathbb{Z}_{12} \to \mathbb{Z}_{36}$; $\delta(n) \equiv 6n \pmod{36}$.

14. Give an example of a one-to-one function f from $\mathbb{N}$ to $\mathbb{N}$ that is not the identity function.

6.4   Onto Functions

One-to-one functions focus on the elements in the domain. We do not want any two of them sharing a common image. Onto functions focus on the codomain. We want to know if it contains elements not associated with any element in the domain.

Definition.   A function $f: A \to B$ is **onto** if, for every element $b \in B$, there exists an element $a \in A$ such that
$$f(a) = b.$$
An onto function is also called a **surjection**, and we say it is **surjective**.   ◇

Example 6.4.1   The graph of the piecewise-defined functions $h: [1,3] \to [2,5]$ defined by

$$h(x) = \begin{cases} 3x - 1 & \text{if } 1 \leq x \leq 2, \\ -3x + 11 & \text{if } 2 < x \leq 3, \end{cases}$$

is displayed on the left in Figure 6.5. It is clearly onto, because, given any $y \in [2,5]$, we can find at least one $x \in [1,3]$ such that $h(x) = y$. Likewise, the function $k: [1,3] \to [2,5]$ defined by

$$k(x) = \begin{cases} 3x - 1 & \text{if } 1 \leq x \leq 2, \\ 5 & \text{if } 2 < x \leq 3, \end{cases}$$

is also onto. Its graph is displayed on the right of Figure 6.5.   ▲

Hands-On Exercise 6.4.1   The two functions in Example 6.4.1 are onto but not one-to-one. Construct a one-to-one and onto function f from $[1,3]$ to $[2,5]$.

△

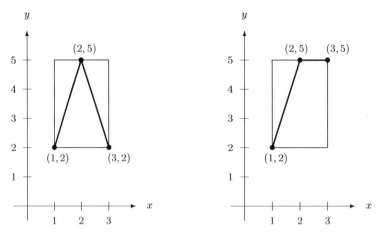

Figure 6.5: Two onto functions from $[1,3]$ to $[2,5]$.

Hands-On Exercise 6.4.2   Construct a function $g\colon [1,3] \to [2,5]$ that is one-to-one but not onto.

$\triangle$

Hands-On Exercise 6.4.3   Find a subset B of $\mathbb{R}$ that would make the function $s\colon \mathbb{R} \to B$ defined by $s(x) = x^2$ an onto function.

$\triangle$

Example 6.4.2   Construct a function $g\colon (5,8) \to \mathbb{R}$ that is both one-to-one and onto.

Remark.   This is a challenging problem. Since the domain is an open interval, a straight line graph does not work, because it will not cover every number in the codomain. $\diamondsuit$

Solution: The solution is based on the observation that the function $h\colon \left(-\frac{\pi}{2}, \frac{\pi}{2}\right) \to \mathbb{R}$ defined by $h(x) = \tan x$ is one-to-one and onto. For this to work in this problem, we need to shift and scale the interval $(5,8)$ to the same size as $\left(-\frac{\pi}{2}, \frac{\pi}{2}\right)$.

First, we have to shift the center of the interval $(5,8)$ to the center of the interval $\left(-\frac{\pi}{2}, \frac{\pi}{2}\right)$. The midpoint of the interval $(5,8)$ is $\frac{5+8}{2} = \frac{13}{2}$, and the midpoint of $\left(-\frac{\pi}{2}, \frac{\pi}{2}\right)$ is 0. Hence, we need to shift the interval $(5,8)$ to the left $\frac{13}{2}$ units. This means we need to use the transformation $x - \frac{13}{2}$. The two endpoints 5 and 8 become $-\frac{3}{2}$ and $\frac{3}{2}$, respectively:

x	5	$\frac{13}{2}$	8
$x - \frac{13}{2}$	$-\frac{3}{2}$	0	$\frac{3}{2}$

After the transformation $x - \frac{13}{2}$, the original interval $(5,8)$ becomes the interval $\left(-\frac{3}{2}, \frac{3}{2}\right)$. Next, we want to stretch the interval $\left(-\frac{3}{2}, \frac{3}{2}\right)$ into $\left(-\frac{\pi}{2}, \frac{\pi}{2}\right)$. This calls for a scaling factor of $\frac{\pi}{3}$.

x	5	$\frac{13}{2}$	8
$\frac{\pi}{3}\left(x - \frac{13}{2}\right)$	$-\frac{\pi}{2}$	0	$\frac{\pi}{2}$

Putting these transformations together, we conclude that

$$g(x) = \tan\left[\frac{\pi}{3}\left(x - \frac{13}{2}\right)\right]$$

gives a one-to-one and onto function from $(5, 8)$ to $\mathbb{R}$. ▲

Hands-On Exercise 6.4.4 Construct a function $h \colon (2, 9) \to \mathbb{R}$ that is both one-to-one and onto.

△

In general, how can we tell if a function $f \colon A \to B$ is onto? The key question is: given an element y in the codomain, is it the image of some element x in the domain? If it is, we must be able to find an element x in the domain such that $f(x) = y$. Mathematically, if the rule of assignment is in the form of a computation, then we need to solve the equation $y = f(x)$ for x. If we can *always* express x in terms of y, and if the resulting x-value is in the domain, the function is onto.

Example 6.4.3 Is the function $p \colon \mathbb{R} \to \mathbb{R}$ defined by $p(x) = 3x^2 - 4x + 5$ onto?

Solution 1: Let $y = 3x^2 - 4x + 5$, we want to know if we can always express x in terms of y. Rearranging the equation, we find

$$3x^2 - 4x + (5 - y) = 0.$$

We want this equation to be solvable over $\mathbb{R}$, that is, we want its solutions to be real. This requires its discriminant to be nonnegative. So we need

$$(-4)^2 - 4 \cdot 3 \cdot (5 - y) = 12y - 44 \geq 0.$$

We have real solutions only when $y \geq \frac{11}{3}$. This means, when $y < \frac{11}{3}$, we cannot find an x-value such that $p(x) = y$. Therefore, p is not onto. ▲

Solution 2: By completing the square, we find

$$p(x) = 3x^2 - 4x + 5 = 3\left(x - \frac{2}{3}\right)^2 + \frac{11}{3} \geq \frac{11}{3}.$$

Since $p(x) \not< \frac{11}{3}$, it is clear that p is not onto. ▲

Hands-On Exercise 6.4.5 The function $g \colon \mathbb{R} \to \mathbb{R}$ is defined as $g(x) = 3x + 11$. Prove that it is onto.

△

Example 6.4.4   Is the function $p \colon \mathbb{R} \to \mathbb{R}$ defined by

$$p(x) = \begin{cases} 4x + 1 & \text{if } x \leq 3 \\ \frac{1}{2}x & \text{if } x > 3 \end{cases}$$

an onto function?

Solution: The graphs $y = 4x + 1$ and $y = \frac{1}{2}x$ are both increasing. For $x \leq 3$, the y-values cover the range $(-\infty, 13)$, and for $x > 3$, the y-values cover the range $\left(\frac{3}{2}, \infty\right)$. Since these two y-ranges overlap, all the y-values are being covered by the images. Therefore, p is onto.   ▲

Hands-On Exercise 6.4.6   Determine whether

$$f(x) = \begin{cases} 3x + 1 & \text{if } x \leq 2 \\ 4x & \text{if } x > 2 \end{cases}$$

is an onto function.

△

Example 6.4.5   Consider the function $g \colon \mathbb{Z}_{43} \to \mathbb{Z}_{43}$ defined by

$$g(x) \equiv 11x - 5 \pmod{43}.$$

Let

$$y = g(x) \equiv 11x - 5 \pmod{43},$$

then

$$x \equiv 11^{-1}(y + 5) \equiv 4(y + 5) \pmod{43}.$$

This shows that g is onto.   ▲

Hands-On Exercise 6.4.7   Show that the function $h \colon \mathbb{Z}_{23} \to \mathbb{Z}_{23}$ defined by $h(x) \equiv 5x + 8$ (mod 23) is onto.

△

Example 6.4.6   Is the function $u \colon \mathbb{Z} \to \mathbb{Z}$ defined by

$$u(n) = \begin{cases} 2n & \text{if } n \geq 0 \\ -n & \text{if } n < 0 \end{cases}$$

one-to-one? Is it onto?

Solution: Since $u(-2) = u(1) = 2$, the function u is not one-to-one. Since $u(n) \geq 0$ for any $n \in \mathbb{Z}$, the function u is not onto.   ▲

Hands-On Exercise 6.4.8   Is the function $v \colon \mathbb{N} \to \mathbb{N}$ defined by $v(n) = n+1$ onto? Explain.

$\triangle$

Example 6.4.7   The function s in Example 6.3.10 is both one-to-one and onto. It provides a one-to-one correspondence between the elements of A by matching a married individual to his/her spouse.   ▲

Hands-On Exercise 6.4.9   Is the function h_1 in Exercises 6.2, Problem 8, an onto function? Explain.

$\triangle$

Summary and Review

- A function $f \colon A \to B$ is onto if, for every element $b \in B$, there exists an element $a \in A$ such that $f(a) = b$.
- To show that f is an onto function, set $y = f(x)$, and solve for x, or show that we can always express x in terms of y for any $y \in B$.
- To show that a function is *not* onto, all we need is to find an element $y \in B$, and show that no x-value from A would satisfy $f(x) = y$.

Exercises 6.4

1. Which of the following functions are onto? Explain!

   (a) $f \colon \mathbb{R} \to \mathbb{R}$, $f(x) = x^3 - 2x^2 + 1$.
   (b) $g \colon [2, \infty) \to \mathbb{R}$, $g(x) = x^3 - 2x^2 + 1$.

2. Which of the following functions are onto? Explain!

   (a) $p \colon \mathbb{R} \to \mathbb{R}$, $p(x) = e^{1-2x}$.
   (b) $q \colon \mathbb{R} \to \mathbb{R}$, $q(x) = |1 - 3x|$.

3. Construct a one-to-one function $f \colon [1,3] \to [2,5]$ that is not onto.

4. Construct an onto function $g \colon [2,5) \to (1,4]$ that is not one-to-one.

5. Determine which of the following are onto functions.

   (a) $f \colon \mathbb{Z} \to \mathbb{Z}$; $f(n) = n^3 + 1$
   (b) $g \colon \mathbb{Q} \to \mathbb{Q}$; $g(x) = n^2$
   (c) $h \colon \mathbb{R} \to \mathbb{R}$; $h(x) = x^3 - x$
   (d) $k \colon \mathbb{R} \to \mathbb{R}$; $k(x) = 5^x$

6. Determine which of the following are onto functions.

   (a) $p \colon \wp(\{1,2,3,\ldots,n\}) \to \{0,1,2,\ldots,n\}$; $p(S) = |S|$
   (b) $q \colon \wp(\{1,2,3,\ldots,n\}) \to \wp(\{1,2,3,\ldots,n\})$; $q(S) = \overline{S}$

7. Determine which of the following functions are onto.

   (a) $f_1 \colon \{1,2,3,4,5\} \to \{a,b,c,d\}$; $f_1(1) = b$, $f_1(2) = c$, $f_1(3) = a$, $f_1(4) = a$, $f_1(5) = c$
   (b) $f_2 \colon \{1,2,3,4\} \to \{a,b,c,d,e\}$; $f_2(1) = c$, $f_2(2) = b$, $f_2(3) = a$, $f_2(4) = d$

(c) $f_3 \colon \mathbb{Z} \to \mathbb{Z}$; $f_5(n) = -n$

(d) $f_4 \colon \mathbb{Z} \to \mathbb{Z}$; $f_4(n) = \begin{cases} 2n & \text{if } n < 0 \\ -3n & \text{if } n \geq 0 \end{cases}$

8. Determine which of the following functions are onto.

    (a) $g_1 \colon \{1,2,3,4,5\} \to \{a,b,c,d,e\}$; $g_1(1) = b$, $g_1(2) = b$, $g_1(3) = b$, $g_1(4) = a$, $g_1(5) = d$

    (b) $g_2 \colon \{1,2,3,4,5\} \to \{a,b,c,d,e\}$; $g_2(1) = d$, $g_2(2) = b$, $g_2(3) = e$, $g_2(4) = a$, $g_2(5) = c$

    (c) $g_3 \colon \mathbb{N} \to \mathbb{N}$; $g_3(n) = \begin{cases} (n+1)/2 & \text{if } n \text{ is odd} \\ n/2 & \text{if } n \text{ is even} \end{cases}$

    (d) $g_4 \colon \mathbb{N} \to \mathbb{N}$; $g_4(n) = \begin{cases} n+1 & \text{if } n \text{ is odd} \\ n-1 & \text{if } n \text{ is even} \end{cases}$

9. Is it possible for a function from $\{1,2\}$ to $\{a,b,c,d\}$ to be onto? Explain.

10. List all the onto functions from $\{1,2,3,4\}$ to $\{a,b\}$?

    Hint: List the images of each function.

11. Determine which of the following functions are onto.

    (a) $f \colon \mathbb{Z}_{10} \to \mathbb{Z}_{10}$; $h(n) \equiv 3n \pmod{10}$.

    (b) $g \colon \mathbb{Z}_{10} \to \mathbb{Z}_{10}$; $g(n) \equiv 5n \pmod{10}$.

    (c) $h \colon \mathbb{Z}_{36} \to \mathbb{Z}_{36}$; $h(n) \equiv 3n \pmod{36}$.

12. Determine which of the following functions are onto.

    (a) $r \colon \mathbb{Z}_{36} \to \mathbb{Z}_{36}$; $r(n) \equiv 5n \pmod{36}$.

    (b) $s \colon \mathbb{Z}_{10} \to \mathbb{Z}_{10}$; $s(n) \equiv n + 5 \pmod{10}$.

    (c) $t \colon \mathbb{Z}_{10} \to \mathbb{Z}_{10}$; $t(n) \equiv 3n + 5 \pmod{10}$.

13. Determine which of the following functions are onto.

    (a) $\alpha \colon \mathbb{Z}_{12} \to \mathbb{Z}_{7}$; $\alpha(n) \equiv 2n \pmod{7}$.

    (b) $\beta \colon \mathbb{Z}_{8} \to \mathbb{Z}_{12}$; $\beta(n) \equiv 3n \pmod{12}$.

    (c) $\gamma \colon \mathbb{Z}_{6} \to \mathbb{Z}_{12}$; $\gamma(n) \equiv 2n \pmod{12}$.

    (d) $\delta \colon \mathbb{Z}_{12} \to \mathbb{Z}_{36}$; $\delta(n) \equiv 6n \pmod{36}$.

14. Give an example of a function $f \colon \mathbb{N} \to \mathbb{N}$ that is

    (a) neither one-to-one nor onto   (b) one-to-one but not onto

    (c) onto but not one-to-one   (d) both one-to-one and onto

6.5   Properties of Functions

In this section, we will study some properties of functions. To facilitate our discussion, we need to introduce some notations. Some students may find them confusing and difficult to use. Besides memorizing the definitions, try to understand what they really mean.

Definition.   Given a function $f \colon A \to B$, and $C \subseteq A$, the ***image of C under f*** is defined as

$$f(C) = \{f(x) \mid x \in C\}.$$

In words, $f(C)$ is the set of all the images of the elements of C.   ◇

Remark.   A few remarks about the definition:

1. It is about the image of a *subset* C of the domain of A. Do not confuse it with the image of an *element* x from A.

2. Therefore, do not merely say "the image." Be specific: the image of an element, or the image of a subset.

3. Better yet: include the notation $f(x)$ or $f(C)$ in the discussion.

4. While $f(x)$ is an *element* in the codomain, $f(C)$ is a *subset* of the codomain.

5. Perhaps, the most important thing to remember is:

$$\boxed{\text{If } y \in f(C), \text{ then } y \in B, \text{ and there exists an } x \in C \text{ such that } f(x) = y.}$$ *Remember this!*

This key observation is often what we need to start a proof with. $\diamondsuit$

Definition.   Let $f\colon A \to B$ be a function. The ***image*** or ***range*** of f, denoted im f, is defined as the set $f(A)$. Hence, im f is the set of all possible images that f can assume. $\diamondsuit$

The definition implies that a function $f\colon A \to B$ is onto if im $f = B$. Unfortunately, this observation is of limited use, because it is not always easy to find im f.

Example 6.5.1   For the function $f\colon \mathbb{R} \to \mathbb{R}$ defined by

$$f(x) = x^2,$$

we find im $f = [0, \infty)$. We also have, for example, $f([2, \infty)) = [4, \infty)$. It is clear that f is neither one-to-one nor onto.   ▲

Example 6.5.2   For the function $g\colon \mathbb{Z} \to \mathbb{Z}$ defined by

$$g(n) = n + 3,$$

we find im $g = \mathbb{Z}$, and $g(\mathbb{N}) = \{4, 5, 6, \ldots\}$. The function g is both one-to-one and onto.   ▲

Hands-On Exercise 6.5.1   The function $p\colon \mathbb{R} \to \mathbb{R}$ is defined as $p(x) = 3x + 11$. Find $p(\mathbb{R}^+)$ and im p.

$\triangle$

Hands-On Exercise 6.5.2   The function $q\colon \mathbb{R} \to \mathbb{R}$ is defined as $q(x) = x^2 - x - 7$. Find im q.

$\triangle$

Example 6.5.3   The function $h\colon \mathbb{Z}_{15} \to \mathbb{Z}_{15}$ is defined by

$$h(x) \equiv 5x - 11 \pmod{15}.$$

From the tabulated data

x	0	1	2	3	4	5	6	$\cdots$	14
$f(x)$	4	9	14	4	9	14	4	$\cdots$	14

it becomes clear that the images repeat the pattern 4, 9, 14 five times. Therefore, we determine that $\operatorname{im} h = \{4, 9, 14\}$.   ▲

Hands-On Exercise 6.5.3   Determine $h(\{0, 3, 4\})$, where h is defined in Example 6.5.3.

△

Example 6.5.4   Determine $f(\{(0, 2), (1, 3)\})$, where the function $f \colon \{0, 1, 2\} \times \{0, 1, 2, 3\} \to \mathbb{Z}$ is defined according to
$$f(a, b) = a + b.$$

Remark: Strictly speaking, we should write $f((a, b))$ because the argument is an ordered pair of the form (a, b). However, we often write $f(a, b)$, because f can be viewed as a two-variable function. The first variable comes from $\{0, 1, 2\}$, the second comes from $\{0, 1, 2, 3\}$, and we add them to form the image.   ◇

Solution: Because
$$f(0, 2) = 0 + 2 = 2, \qquad \text{and} \qquad f(1, 3) = 1 + 3 = 4,$$
we determine that $f(\{(0, 2), (1, 3)\}) = \{2, 4\}$.   ▲

Hands-On Exercise 6.5.4   Find $\operatorname{im} f$, where f is defined in Example 6.5.4.

△

We are now ready to present the first collection of properties of functions.

Theorem 6.5.1 *Given* $f \colon A \to B$, *the following properties hold for any* $C_1, C_2 \subseteq A$.

(a) $f(C_1 \cup C_2) = f(C_1) \cup f(C_2)$

(b) $f(C_1 \cap C_2) \subseteq f(C_1) \cap f(C_2)$

(c) $f(C_1 - C_2) \supseteq f(C_1) - f(C_2)$

(d) $C_1 \subseteq C_2 \Rightarrow f(C_1) \subseteq f(C_2)$

Remark.   These results provide excellent opportunities to learn how to write mathematical proofs. We only provide the proof of (a) below, and leave the proofs of (b)–(d) as exercises. In (a), we want to establish the equality of two sets. One way to prove that $S = T$ is to show that $S \subseteq T$, and $T \subseteq S$. Now, in order to prove that $S \subseteq T$, we need to show that $z \in S$ implies $z \in T$; to show that $T \subseteq S$, we want to prove that $z \in T$ implies $z \in s$.   ◇

Proof of (a):   First, we want to show that $f(C_1 \cup C_2) \subseteq f(C_1) \cup f(C_2)$. Let $y \in f(C_1 \cup C_2)$, then there exists $x \in C_1 \cup C_2$ such that $f(x) = y$. Having $x \in C_1 \cup C_2$ means either $x \in C_1$ or $x \in C_2$, so we have to consider two cases.

- If $x \in C_1$, then $f(x) \in f(C_1)$.
- If $x \in C_2$, then $f(x) \in f(C_2)$.

Thus, $y = f(x)$ belongs to either $f(C_1)$ or $f(C_2)$, which means $y = f(x) \in f(C_1) \cup f(C_2)$. This proves that $f(C_1 \cup C_2) \subseteq f(C_1) \cup f(C_2)$.

Next, we want to show that $f(C_1) \cup f(C_2) \subseteq f(C_1 \cup C_2)$. Let $y \in f(C_1) \cup f(C_2)$, then y belongs to either $f(C_1)$ or $f(C_2)$.

- If $y \in f(C_1)$, then there exists $x_1 \in C_1$ such that $f(x_1) = y$.
- If $y \in f(C_2)$, then there exists $x_2 \in C_2$ such that $f(x_2) = y$.

These two possibilities together imply that there exists an element x belonging to either C_1 or C_2, that is, $x \in C_1 \cup C_2$, such that $f(x) = y$. This means $f(x) \in f(C_1 \cup C_2)$. This proves that $f(C_1) \cup f(C_2) \subseteq f(C_1 \cup C_2)$. This concludes the proof of $f(C_1 \cup C_2) = f(C_1) \cup f(C_2)$. ∎

Hands-On Exercise 6.5.5   Prove part (b) of Theorem 6.5.1.

△

Remark.   Part (b) of Theorem 6.5.1 only gives a subset relationship. The reason is: having $y \in f(C_1)$ and $y \in f(C_2)$ does not necessarily mean that y is the image of the same element. Since f can be many-to-one, it is possible to have $x_1 \in C_1 - C_2$ and $x_2 \in C_2 - C_1$ such that $f(x_1) = f(x_2) = y$. Consider $f \colon \{1, 2, 3\} \to \{a, b\}$ defined by

$$f(1) = f(3) = a, \qquad \text{and} \qquad f(2) = b.$$

If $C_1 = \{1, 2\}$ and $C_2 = \{2, 3\}$, then $f(C_1) = f(C_2) = \{a, b\}$, and

$$f(C_1 \cap C_2) = f(\{2\}) = \{b\} \subset \{a, b\} = f(C_1) \cap f(C_2).$$

Therefore, we can only conclude that $y \in f(C_1 \cap C_2) \Rightarrow y \in f(C_1) \cap f(C_2)$. ◇

Definition.   Given a function $f \colon A \to B$, and $D \subseteq B$, the **preimage of D under f** is defined as

$$f^{-1}(D) = \{x \in A \mid f(x) \in D\}.$$

Hence, $f^{-1}(D)$ is the set of elements in the domain whose images are in C. The symbol $f^{-1}(D)$ is also pronounced as "f inverse of D." ◇

Remark.   Some remarks about the definition:

1. The preimage of D is a subset of the domain A.

2. In particular, the preimage of B is always A.

3. The key thing to remember is:

$$\boxed{\text{If } x \in f^{-1}(D), \text{ then } x \in A, \text{ and } f(x) \in D.}$$

4. It is possible that $f^{-1}(D) = \emptyset$ for some subset D. If this happens, f is not onto.

5. Therefore, f is onto if and only if $f^{-1}(\{b\}) \neq \emptyset$ for every $b \in B$. ◇

Example 6.5.5   If $t\colon \mathbb{R} \to \mathbb{R}$ is defined by $t(x) = x^2 - 5x + 5$, find $t^{-1}(\{-1\})$.

Solution: We want to find x such that $t(x) = x^2 - 5x + 5 = -1$. Hence, we have to solve the equation

$$0 = x^2 - 5x + 6 = (x - 2)(x - 3).$$

The solutions are $x = 2$ and $x = 3$. Therefore, $t^{-1}(\{-1\}) = \{2, 3\}$.   ▲

Hands-On Exercise 6.5.6   If $k\colon \mathbb{Q} \to \mathbb{R}$ is defined by $k(x) = x^2 - x - 7$, find $k^{-1}(\{3\})$.

                                                                                                                                △

Example 6.5.6   For the function $f\colon \{0, 1, 2\} \times \{0, 1, 2, 3\} \to \mathbb{Z}$ defined by

$$f(a, b) = a + b,$$

we find

$$\begin{aligned}
f^{-1}(\{3\}) &= \{(0, 3), (1, 2), (2, 1)\}, \\
f^{-1}(\{4\}) &= \{(1, 3), (2, 2)\}.
\end{aligned}$$

Since preimages are sets, we need to write the answers in set notation.   ▲

Hands-On Exercise 6.5.7   Find $h^{-1}(\{4\})$ and $h^{-1}(\{2\})$, where the function h is defined in Example 6.5.3.

                                                                                                                                △

Theorem 6.5.2 .   *Given $f\colon A \to B$, and $D_1, D_2 \subseteq B$, the following properties hold.*

    (a) $f^{-1}(D_1 \cup D_2) = f^{-1}(D_1) \cup f^{-1}(D_2)$

    (b) $f^{-1}(D_1 \cap D_2) = f^{-1}(D_1) \cap f^{-1}(D_2)$

    (c) $f^{-1}(D_1 - D_2) = f^{-1}(D_1) - f^{-1}(D_2)$

    (d) $D_1 \subseteq D_2 \Rightarrow f^{-1}(D_1) \subseteq f^{-1}(D_2)$

Proof of (a):   First, we want to prove that $f^{-1}(D_1 \cup D_2) \subseteq f^{-1}(D_1) \cup f^{-1}(D_2)$. Let $x \in f^{-1}(D_1 \cup D_2)$, then $f(x) \in D_1 \cup D_2$. This means either $f(x) \in D_1$ or $f(x) \in D_2$.

- If $f(x) \in D_1$, then $x \in f^{-1}(D_1)$.
- If $f(x) \in D_2$, then $x \in f^{-1}(D_2)$.

Since x belongs to either $f^{-1}(D_1)$ or $f^{-1}(D_2)$, we determine that $x \in f^{-1}(D_1) \cup f^{-1}(D_2)$. Therefore, $f^{-1}(D_1 \cup D_2) \subseteq f^{-1}(D_1) \cup f^{-1}(D_2)$.

    Next, we want to prove that $f^{-1}(D_1) \cup f^{-1}(D_2) \subseteq f^{-1}(D_1 \cup D_2)$. Let $x \in f^{-1}(D_1) \cup f^{-1}(D_2)$. Then x belongs to either $f^{-1}(D_1)$ or $x \in f^{-1}(D_2)$.

- If $x \in f^{-1}(D_1)$, then $f(x) \in D_1$.
- If $x \in f^{-1}(D_2)$, then $f(x) \in D_2$.

Hence, $f(x)$ belongs to either D_1 or D_2, which means $f(x) \in D_1 \cup D_2$. Thus, $x \in f^{-1}(D_1 \cup D_2)$. We have proved that $f^{-1}(D_1) \cup f^{-1}(D_2) \subseteq f^{-1}(D_1 \cup D_2)$. Together with $f^{-1}(D_1 \cup D_2) \subseteq f^{-1}(D_1) \cup f^{-1}(D_2)$, we conclude that $f^{-1}(D_1 \cup D_2) = f^{-1}(D_1) \cup f^{-1}(D_2)$. ■

Hands-On Exercise 6.5.8   Prove part (b) of Theorem 6.5.2.

$\triangle$

Whether a function $f: A \to B$ is one-to-one or onto can be determined by the cardinality of the preimages.

- f is one-to-one if and only if $|f^{-1}(\{b\})| \leq 1$ for every $b \in B$.
- f is onto if and only if $|f^{-1}(\{b\})| \geq 1$ for every $b \in B$.

If A and B are *finite* sets, then

- $|A| \leq |B|$ if f is one-to-one, and
- $|A| \geq |B|$ if f is onto.

In particular, if f is one-to-one and onto, we have $|A| = |B|$.

Example 6.5.7   A function $f: \mathbb{Z}_{14} \to \mathbb{Z}_{10}$ cannot be one-to-one because in order for it to be one-to-one, we need 14 distinct images. Since the codomain has only 10 elements, it is impossible for it to come up with 14 different images.

Likewise, a function $g: \mathbb{Z}_{23} \to \mathbb{Z}_{57}$ cannot be onto because the domain has 23 elements, hence, we can have at most 23 different images. But the codomain has 57 elements, therefore, some of its elements must be left unused. ▲

Example 6.5.8   Consider the function $h: \mathbb{Z}_{23} \to \mathbb{Z}_{57}$ defined by

$$h(x) \equiv 43x \pmod{57}.$$

If $y \equiv 43x \pmod{57}$, then, since $43^{-1} \equiv 4 \pmod{57}$, we find, in $\mathbb{Z}_{23}$,

$$x = 43^{-1}y = 4y.$$

Since we can also express x in terms of y, we declare that f is onto. Yet, we have learned from the previous example that f cannot be onto. Is there any contradiction?

Be sure you know which modulus you are using.

Solution: There is an error in the argument. We should have said

$$x \equiv 43^{-1}y \equiv 4y \pmod{57}.$$

Since x is reduced modulo 57, its value may exceed 23. If this happens, $x \notin \mathbb{Z}_{23}$. For example, if $y = 11$, we would have $x = 44 \notin \mathbb{Z}_{23}$. Even if we reduce 44 modulo 23, we obtain $x \equiv 21 \pmod{23}$, we would have

$$43 \cdot 21 \equiv 48 \not\equiv 11 \pmod{57}.$$

So it is still not the correct preimage. This example again illustrates the importance of taking caution when a function involves different moduli in its domain and codomain.   ▲

Summary and Review

- Given a function $f\colon A \to B$, the image of $C \subseteq A$ is defined as $f(C) = \{f(x) \mid x \in C\}$.
- If $y \in f(C)$, then $y \in B$, and there exists an $x \in C$ such that $f(x) = y$.
- See Theorem 6.5.1 for a list of properties of the image of a set.
- The preimage of $D \subseteq B$ is defined as $f^{-1}(D) = \{x \in A \mid f(x) \in D\}$.
- If $x \in f^{-1}(D)$, then $x \in A$, and $f(x) \in D$.
- See Theorem 6.5.2 for a list of properties of the preimage of a set.

Exercises 6.5

1. For each of the following functions, find the image of C, and the preimage of D.

    (a) $f_1\colon \{1,2,3,4,5\} \to \{a,b,c,d\}$; $f_1(1) = b$, $f_1(2) = c$, $f_1(3) = a$, $f_1(4) = a$, $f_1(5) = c$;
    $C = \{1,3\}$, $D = \{a.c\}$.

    (b) $f_2\colon \{1,2,3,4\} \to \{a,b,c,d,e\}$; $f_2(1) = c$, $f_2(2) = b$, $f_2(3) = a$, $f_2(4) = d$;
    $C = \{1,3\}$, $D = \{b,d\}$.

    (c) $f_3\colon \{1,2,3,4,5\} \to \{a,b,c,d,e\}$; $f_3(1) = b$, $f_3(2) = b$, $f_3(3) = b$, $f_3(4) = a$, $f_3(5) = d$;
    $C = \{1,3,5\}$, $D = \{c\}$.

    (d) $f_4\colon \{1,2,3,4,5\} \to \{a,b,c,d,e\}$; $f_4(1) = d$, $f_4(2) = b$, $f_4(3) = e$, $f_4(4) = a$, $f_4(5) = c$;
    $C = \{3\}$, $D = \{c\}$.

2. For each of the following functions, find the image of C, and the preimage of D.

    (a) $f_5\colon \mathbb{Z} \to \mathbb{Z}$; $f_5(n) = -n$; $C = 2\mathbb{Z}$, $D = \mathbb{N}$.

    (b) $f_6\colon \mathbb{Z} \to \mathbb{Z}$; $f_6(n) = \begin{cases} 2n & \text{if } n < 0, \\ -3n & \text{if } n \geq 0; \end{cases}$ $C = \mathbb{N}$, $D = 2\mathbb{Z}$.

    (c) $f_7\colon \mathbb{N} \to \mathbb{N}$; $f_7(n) = \begin{cases} (n+1)/2 & \text{if } n \text{ is odd}, \\ n/2 & \text{if } n \text{ is even}; \end{cases}$ $C = D = 2\mathbb{N}$.

    (d) $f_8\colon \mathbb{N} \to \mathbb{N}$; $f_8(n) = \begin{cases} n+1 & \text{if } n \text{ is odd}, \\ n-1 & \text{if } n \text{ is even}; \end{cases}$ $C = D = 2\mathbb{N}$.

3. The function $s\colon \mathbb{Z}_{12} \to \mathbb{Z}_{12}$ is defined as

$$s(x) \equiv 4x + 7 \pmod{12}.$$

    (a) Find $s(\{2,5,7\})$.
    (b) Find $s^{-1}(\{2,5,7\})$.
    (c) Find $\operatorname{im} s$.

4. The function $t: \mathbb{Z}_{15} \to \mathbb{Z}_{15}$ is defined as

$$t(x) \equiv 3x^2 - 5 \quad (\mathrm{mod}\ 15).$$

   (a) Find $t(\{2, 3, 5, 13\})$.

   (b) Find $t^{-1}(\{1, 5, 7\})$.

   (c) Find $\mathrm{im}\, t$.

5. The function $u: \mathbb{R} \to \mathbb{R}$ is defined as $u(x) = 3x + 11$, and the function $v: \mathbb{Z} \to \mathbb{R}$ is defined as $v(x) = 3x + 11$.

   (a) Find $u([3, 5))$ and $v(\{3, 4, 5\})$.

   (b) Find $u^{-1}((2, 7])$ and $v^{-1}((2, 7])$.

6. Is the function $h: \mathbb{Z} \to \mathbb{Z}$ defined by

$$h(n) = \begin{cases} 2n & \text{if } n \geq 0 \\ -n & \text{if } n < 0 \end{cases}$$

   one-to-one? Is it onto?

7. Define the $r: \mathbb{Z} \times \mathbb{Z} \to \mathbb{Q}$ according to $r(m, n) = 3^m 5^n$.

   (a) Find $r(\{1, 2, 3\} \times \{-1, 0, 1\})$.

   (b) Find $r^{-1}\left(\left\{\frac{25}{27}\right\}\right)$.

   (c) Find $r^{-1}(D)$, where $D = \{3, 9, 27, 81, \dots\}$.

8. Define the function $p: \mathbb{Z} \times \mathbb{Z} \to \mathbb{Z}$ according to $p(x, y) = 12x + 15y$.

   (a) Find $p^{-1}(\{18\})$. You may use the set-builder notation to describe your answer.

   (b) Find $\mathrm{im}\, p$.

9. The sum of the entries in a particular row in a matrix is called a row sum, and the sum of the entries in a particular column is called a column sum. Discuss how can we use the row sums and column sums of the incidence matrix of a function to determine if the function is well-defined, one-to-one, and onto.

10. Below is the incidence matrix of the function $f: \{a, b, c, d, e\} \to \{\alpha, \beta, \gamma, \delta, \epsilon\}$:

$$\begin{array}{c} \\ a \\ b \\ c \\ d \\ e \end{array} \begin{array}{ccccc} \alpha & \beta & \gamma & \delta & \epsilon \\ \left(\begin{array}{ccccc} 0 & 0 & 0 & 0 & 1 \\ 0 & 0 & 0 & 1 & 0 \\ 1 & 0 & 0 & 0 & 0 \\ 0 & 0 & 1 & 0 & 0 \\ 1 & 0 & 0 & 0 & 0 \end{array} \right) \end{array}$$

   (a) Find $f(\{a, d, e\})$.
   (b) Find $f^{-1}(\{\alpha, \beta, \epsilon\})$.
   (c) Find $\mathrm{im}\, f$.

11. Consider the function h_1 defined in Problem 8a in Exercises 6.2. What is $h_1^{-1}(\{m\})$, if m represents your mother?

12. Let S denote the maternal family tree, that includes you, your mother, your maternal grandmother, your maternal great-grandmother, and so on. Define a function $M: S \to S$ by letting $M(x)$ be the mother of x. Determine $\mathrm{im}\, M$.

13. Prove part (c) of Theorem 6.5.1.

14. Prove part (c) of Theorem 6.5.2.

15. (a) Prove part (d) of Theorem 6.5.1.

    (b) Prove part (d) of Theorem 6.5.2.

16. Construct an example of a function $f: A \to B$, and $C_1, C_2 \subseteq A$ such that $f(C_1 - C_2) \supsetneq f(C_1) - f(C_2)$. See part (c) of Theorem 6.5.1.

17. Given a function $f: A \to B$, and $C \subset A$, since $f(C)$ is a subset of B, the preimage of this subset is indicated by the notation $f^{-1}(f(C))$. Consider the function $f: \mathbb{Z} \to \mathbb{Z}$ defined by $f(x) = x^2$, and $C = \{0, 1, 2, 3\}$.

    (a) Find $f(C)$.

    (b) Find $f^{-1}(f(C))$.

18. Prove that $C \subseteq f^{-1}(f(C))$ for any function $f: A \to B$, and $C \subseteq A$.

6.6   Inverse Functions

A **bijection** is a function that is both one-to-one and onto. Naturally, if a function is a bijection, we say that it is **bijective**. If a function $f: A \to B$ is a bijection, we can define another function g that essentially reverses the assignment rule associated with f. Then, applying the function g to any element y from the codomain B, we are able to obtain an element x from the domain A such that $f(x) = y$. Let us refine this idea into a more concrete definition.

Definition. Let $f: A \to B$ be a bijective function. Its **inverse function** is the function $f^{-1}: B \to A$ with the property that

$$f^{-1}(b) = a \Leftrightarrow b = f(a).$$

Pronounce f^{-1} as "f inverse."

The notation f^{-1} is pronounced as "f inverse." See Figure 6.6 for a pictorial view of an inverse function.

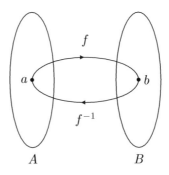

Figure 6.6: The pictorial view of an inverse function.

Why is $f^{-1}: B \to A$ a well-defined function? For it to be well-defined, every element $b \in B$ must have a unique image. This means given any element $b \in B$, we must be able to find one and only one element $a \in A$ such that $f(a) = b$. Such an a exists, because f is onto, and there is only one such element a because f is one-to-one. Therefore, f^{-1} is a well-defined function.

If a function f is defined by a computational rule, then the input value x and the output value y are related by the equation $y = f(x)$. In an inverse function, the role of the input and output are switched. Therefore, we can find the inverse function f^{-1} by following these steps:

(i) Interchange the role of x and y in the equation $y = f(x)$. That is, write $x = f(y)$.

(ii) Solve for y. That is, express y in terms of x. The resulting expression is $f^{-1}(x)$.

Be sure to write the final answer in the form $f^{-1}(x) = \ldots$ Do not forget to include the domain and the codomain, and describe them properly.

Example 6.6.1 To find the inverse function of $f \colon \mathbb{R} \to \mathbb{R}$ defined by $f(x) = 2x + 1$, we start with the equation $y = 2x + 1$. Next, interchange x with y to obtain the new equation

$$x = 2y + 1.$$

Solving for y, we find $y = \frac{1}{2}(x - 1)$. Therefore, the inverse function is

$$f^{-1} \colon \mathbb{R} \to \mathbb{R}, \qquad f^{-1}(x) = \frac{1}{2}(x - 1).$$

It is important to describe the domain and the codomain, because they may not be the same as the original function. ▲

Example 6.6.2 The function $s \colon \left[-\frac{\pi}{2}, \frac{\pi}{2} \right] \to [-1, 1]$ defined by $s(x) = \sin x$ is a bijection. Its inverse function is

$$s^{-1} \colon [-1, 1] \to \left[-\frac{\pi}{2}, \frac{\pi}{2} \right], \qquad s^{-1}(x) = \arcsin x.$$

The function $\arcsin x$ is also written as $\sin^{-1} x$, which follows the same notation we use for inverse functions. ▲

Hands-On Exercise 6.6.1 The function $f \colon [-3, \infty) \to [0, \infty)$ is defined as $f(x) = \sqrt{x + 3}$. Show that it is a bijection, and find its inverse function.

△

Hands-On Exercise 6.6.2 Find the inverse function of $g \colon \mathbb{R} \to (0, \infty)$ defined by $g(x) = e^x$.

△

Remark. Exercise caution with the notation. Assume the function $f \colon \mathbb{Z} \to \mathbb{Z}$ is a bijection. The notation $f^{-1}(3)$ means the image of 3 under the inverse function f^{-1}. If $f^{-1}(3) = 5$, we know that $f(5) = 3$. The notation $f^{-1}(\{3\})$ means the preimage of the set $\{3\}$. In this case, we find $f^{-1}(\{3\}) = \{5\}$. The results are essentially the same *if the function is bijective.*

If a function $g \colon \mathbb{Z} \to \mathbb{Z}$ is many-to-one, then it does not have an inverse function. This makes the notation $g^{-1}(3)$ meaningless. Nonetheless, $g^{-1}(\{3\})$ is well-defined, because it means the preimage of $\{3\}$. If $g^{-1}(\{3\}) = \{1, 2, 5\}$, we know $g(1) = g(2) = g(5) = 3$.

In general, $f^{-1}(D)$ means the preimage of the subset D under the function f. Here, the function f can be any function. If f is a bijection, then $f^{-1}(D)$ can also mean the image of the subset D under the inverse function f^{-1}. There is no confusion here, because the results are the same. ◇

Example 6.6.3 The function $f \colon \mathbb{R} \to \mathbb{R}$ is defined as

$$f(x) = \begin{cases} 3x & \text{if } x \leq 1, \\ 2x + 1 & \text{if } x > 1. \end{cases}$$

Find its inverse function.

Solution: Since f is a piecewise-defined function, we expect its inverse function to be piecewise-defined as well. First, we need to find the two ranges of input values in f^{-1}. The images for $x \leq 1$ are $y \leq 3$, and the images for $x > 1$ are $y > 3$. Hence, the codomain of f, which becomes the domain of f^{-1}, is split into two halves at 3. The inverse function should look like

$$f^{-1}(x) = \begin{cases} ??? & \text{if } x \leq 3, \\ ??? & \text{if } x > 3. \end{cases}$$

Next, we determine the formulas in the two ranges. We find

$$f^{-1}(x) = \begin{cases} \frac{1}{3}x & \text{if } x \leq 3, \\ \frac{1}{2}(x-1) & \text{if } x > 3. \end{cases}$$

The details are left to you as an exercise.   ▲

Hands-On Exercise 6.6.3   Find the inverse function of $g \colon \mathbb{R} \to \mathbb{R}$ defined by

$$g(x) = \begin{cases} 3x + 5 & \text{if } x \leq 6, \\ 5x - 7 & \text{if } x > 6. \end{cases}$$

Be sure you describe g^{-1} properly.

△

Example 6.6.4   The function $g \colon \mathbb{Z}_{10} \to \mathbb{Z}_{10}$ is defined by $g(x) \equiv 7x + 2 \pmod{10}$. Find its inverse function.

Solution: From $x = g(y) \equiv 7y + 2 \pmod{10}$, we obtain

$$y \equiv 7^{-1}(x-2) \equiv 3(x-2) \pmod{10}.$$

Hence, the inverse function $g^{-1} \colon \mathbb{Z}_{10} \to \mathbb{Z}_{10}$ is defined by $g^{-1}(x) \equiv 3(x-2) \pmod{10}$.   ▲

Hands-On Exercise 6.6.4   The function $h \colon \mathbb{Z}_{57} \to \mathbb{Z}_{57}$ defined by $h(x) \equiv 49x - 3 \pmod{57}$. Find its inverse function.

△

Example 6.6.5   Define $h \colon \mathbb{Z}_{10} \to \mathbb{Z}_{10}$ according to $h(x) = 2(x+3) \bmod 10$. Does h^{-1} exist?

Solution: Since 2^{-1} does not exist, we suspect the answer is no. In fact, $h(x)$ is always even, and it is easy to verify that $\operatorname{im} h = \{0, 2, 4, 6, 8\}$. Since h is not onto, h^{-1} does not exist.   ▲

Example 6.6.6 Find the inverse function of $f: \mathbb{Z} \to \mathbb{N} \cup \{0\}$ defined by

$$f(n) = \begin{cases} 2n & \text{if } n \geq 0, \\ -2n - 1 & \text{if } n < 0. \end{cases}$$

Solution: In an inverse function, the domain and the codomain are switched, so we have to start with $f^{-1}: \mathbb{N} \cup \{0\} \to \mathbb{Z}$ before we describe the formula that defines f^{-1}. Writing $n = f(m)$, we find

$$n = \begin{cases} 2m & \text{if } m \geq 0, \\ -2m - 1 & \text{if } m < 0. \end{cases}$$

We need to consider two cases.

(i) If $n = 2m$, then n is even, and $m = \frac{n}{2}$.

(ii) If $n = -2m - 1$, then n is odd, and $m = -\frac{n+1}{2}$.

Therefore, the inverse function is defined by

$$f^{-1}: \mathbb{N} \cup \{0\} \to \mathbb{Z}, \qquad f^{-1}(n) = \begin{cases} \frac{n}{2} & \text{if } n \text{ is even,} \\ -\frac{n+1}{2} & \text{if } n \text{ is odd.} \end{cases}$$

Verify this with some numeric examples. ▲

Hands-On Exercise 6.6.5 The function $f: \mathbb{Z} \to \mathbb{N}$ is defined as

$$f(n) = \begin{cases} -2n & \text{if } n < 0, \\ 2n + 1 & \text{if } n \geq 0. \end{cases}$$

Find its inverse.

△

Let A and B be finite sets. If there exists a bijection $f: A \to B$, then the elements of A and B are in one-to-one correspondence via f. Hence, $|A| = |B|$. This idea provides the basis for some interesting proofs.

Example 6.6.7 Let $A = \{a_1, a_2, \ldots, a_n\}$ be an n-element sets. Recall that the power set $\wp(A)$ contains all the subsets of A, and

$$\{0, 1\}^n = \{(b_1, b_2, \ldots, b_n) \mid b_i \in \{0, 1\} \text{ for each } i, \text{ where } 1 \leq i \leq n\}.$$

Define $F: \wp(A) \to \{0, 1\}^n$ according to $F(S) = (x_1, x_2, \ldots, x_n)$, where

$$x_i = \begin{cases} 1 & \text{if } a_i \in S, \\ 0 & \text{if } a_i \notin S. \end{cases}$$

Simply put, $F(S)$ is an ordered n-tuple whose ith entry is either 1 or 0, indicating whether S contains the ith element of A (1 for yes, and 0 for no).

It is clear that F is a bijection. For $n = 8$, we have, for example,

$$F(\{a_2, a_5, a_8\}) = (0, 1, 0, 0, 1, 0, 0, 1),$$

and

$$F^{-1}\big((1,1,0,0,0,1,1,0)\big) = \{a_1, a_2, a_6, a_7\}.$$

The function F defines a one-to-one correspondence between the subsets of A and the ordered n-tuples in $\{0,1\}^n$. Since there are two choices for each entry in these ordered n-tuples, we have 2^n such ordered n-tuples. This proves that $|\wp(A)| = 2^n$, that is, A has 2^n subsets.   ▲

Hands-On Exercise 6.6.6   Consider the function F defined in Example 6.6.7. Assume $n = 8$. Find $F(\emptyset)$ and $F^{-1}\big((1,0,1,1,1,0,0,0)\big)$.

△

Summary and Review

- A bijection is a function that is both one-to-one and onto.
- The inverse of a bijection $f: A \to B$ is the function $f^{-1}: B \to A$ with the property that

$$f(x) = y \Leftrightarrow x = f^{-1}(y).$$

- In brief, an inverse function reverses the assignment rule of f. It starts with an element y in the codomain of f, and recovers the element x in the domain of f such that $f(x) = y$.

Exercises 6.6

1. Which of the following functions are bijections? Explain!

   (a) $f: \mathbb{R} \to \mathbb{R}$, $f(x) = x^3 - 2x^2 + 1$.

   (b) $g: [2, \infty) \to \mathbb{R}$, $g(x) = x^3 - 2x^2 + 1$.

   (c) $h: \mathbb{R} \to \mathbb{R}$, $h(x) = e^{1-2x}$.

   (d) $p: \mathbb{R} \to \mathbb{R}$, $p(x) = |1 - 3x|$.

   (e) $q: [2, \infty) \to [0, \infty)$, $q(x) = \sqrt{x - 2}$.

2. For those functions that are not bijections in the last problem, can we modify their codomains to change them into bijections?

3. Let f and g be the functions from $(1, 3)$ to $(4, 7)$ defined by

$$f(x) = \frac{3}{2}x + \frac{5}{2}, \qquad \text{and} \qquad g(x) = -\frac{3}{2}x + \frac{17}{2}.$$

   Find their inverse functions. Be sure to describe their domains and codomains.

4. Find the inverse function $f: \mathbb{R} \to \mathbb{R}$ defined by

$$f(x) = \begin{cases} 3x + 5 & \text{if } x \le 6, \\ 5x - 7 & \text{if } x > 6. \end{cases}$$

   Be sure you describe f^{-1} correctly and properly.

5. The function $g: [1, 3] \to [4, 7]$ is defined according to

$$g(x) = \begin{cases} x + 3 & \text{if } 1 \le x < 2, \\ 11 - 2x & \text{if } 2 \le x \le 3. \end{cases}$$

   Find its inverse function. Be sure you describe it correctly and properly.

6. Find the inverse of the function $r: (0, \infty) \to \mathbb{R}$ defined by $r(x) = 4 + 3 \ln x$.

7. Find the inverse of the function $s: \mathbb{R} \to (-\infty, -3)$ defined by $s(x) = 4 - 7e^{2x}$.

8. Find the inverse of each of the following bijections.

   (a) $h: \{1, 2, 3, 4, 5\} \to \{a, b, c, d, e\}$, $h(1) = e$, $h(2) = c$, $h(3) = b$, $h(4) = a$, $h(5) = d$.

   (b) $k: \{1, 2, 3, 4, 5\} \to \{1, 2, 3, 4, 5\}$, $k(1) = 3$, $k(2) = 1$, $k(3) = 5$, $k(4) = 4$, $k(5) = 2$.

9. Find the inverse of each of the following bijections.

   (a) $u: \mathbb{Q} \to \mathbb{Q}$, $u(x) = 3x - 2$.

   (b) $v: \mathbb{Q} - \{1\} \to \mathbb{Q} - \{2\}$, $v(x) = \frac{2x}{x-1}$.

   (c) $w: \mathbb{Z} \to \mathbb{Z}$, $w(n) = n + 3$.

10. Find the inverse of each of the following bijections.

    (a) $r: \mathbb{Z}_{12} \to \mathbb{Z}_{12}$, $r(n) \equiv 7n \pmod{12}$.

    (b) $s: \mathbb{Z}_{33} \to \mathbb{Z}_{33}$, $s(n) \equiv 7n + 5 \pmod{33}$.

    (c) $t: \mathbb{Z} \to \mathbb{N} \cup \{0\}$, $t(n) = \begin{cases} 2n - 1 & \text{if } n > 0 \\ -2n & \text{if } n \leq 0 \end{cases}$

11. The images of the bijection $\alpha: \{1, 2, 3, 4, 5, 6, 7, 8\} \to \{a, b, c, d, e, f, g, h\}$ are given below.

x	1	2	3	4	5	6	7	8
$\alpha(x)$	g	a	d	h	b	e	f	c

   Find its inverse function.

12. Below is the incidence matrix for the bijection $\beta: \{a, b, c, d, e, f\} \to \{x, y, z, u, v, w\}$.

$$
\begin{array}{c}
\begin{array}{cccccc} u & v & w & x & y & z \end{array} \\
\begin{array}{c} a \\ b \\ c \\ d \\ e \\ f \end{array}
\left(\begin{array}{cccccc}
0 & 1 & 0 & 0 & 0 & 0 \\
1 & 0 & 0 & 0 & 0 & 0 \\
0 & 0 & 0 & 0 & 1 & 0 \\
0 & 0 & 1 & 0 & 0 & 0 \\
0 & 0 & 0 & 0 & 0 & 1 \\
0 & 0 & 0 & 1 & 0 & 0
\end{array} \right)
\end{array}
$$

   Find its inverse function.

6.7   Composite Functions

Given functions $f: A \to B$ and $g: B \to C$, the **composite function**, $g \circ f$, which is pronounced as "g circle f", is defined as

> Write $(g \circ f)(x)$
> instead of $g \circ f(x)$.

$$ g \circ f: A \to C, \qquad (g \circ f)(x) = g(f(x)). $$

The image is obtained in two steps. First, $f(x)$ is obtained. Next, it is passed to g to obtain the final result. It works like connecting two machines to form a bigger one, see Figure 6.7. We can also use an arrow diagram to provide another pictorial view, see Figure 6.8.

Numeric value of $(g \circ f)(x)$ can be computed in two steps. For example, to compute $(g \circ f)(5)$, we first compute the value of $f(5)$, and then the value of $g(f(5))$. To find the algebraic description of $(g \circ f)(x)$, we need to compute and simplify the formula for $g(f(x))$. In this case, it is often easier to start from the "outside" function. More precisely, start with g, and write the

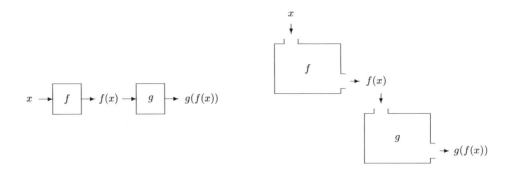

Figure 6.7: A composite function, viewed as input-output machines.

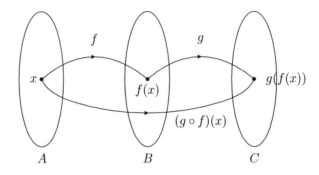

Figure 6.8: Another pictorial view of a composite function.

intermediate answer in terms of $f(x)$, then substitute in the definition of $f(x)$ and simplify the result.

Example 6.7.1   Assume $f, g \colon \mathbb{R} \to \mathbb{R}$ are defined as $f(x) = x^2$, and $g(x) = 3x + 1$. We find

$$(g \circ f)(x) = g(f(x)) = 3[f(x)] + 1 = 3x^2 + 1,$$
$$(f \circ g)(x) = f(g(x)) = [g(x)]^2 = (3x + 1)^2.$$

Therefore,

$$g \circ f \colon \mathbb{R} \to \mathbb{R}, \qquad (g \circ f)(x) = 3x^2 + 1,$$
$$f \circ g \colon \mathbb{R} \to \mathbb{R}, \qquad (f \circ g)(x) = (3x + 1)^2.$$

We note that, in general, $f \circ g \neq g \circ f$.   ▲

Hands-On Exercise 6.7.1   If $p, q \colon \mathbb{R} \to \mathbb{R}$ are defined as $p(x) = 2x + 5$, and $q(x) = x^2 + 1$, determine $p \circ q$ and $q \circ p$. Do not forget to describe the domain and the codomain.

△

Hands-On Exercise 6.7.2   The functions $f, g \colon \mathbb{Z}_{12} \to \mathbb{Z}_{12}$ are defined by

$$f(x) \equiv 7x + 2 \quad (\mathrm{mod}\ 12), \qquad \text{and} \qquad g(x) \equiv 5x - 3 \quad (\mathrm{mod}\ 12).$$

Compute the composite function $f \circ g$.

$\triangle$

Example 6.7.2   Define $f, g \colon \mathbb{R} \to \mathbb{R}$ as

$$f(x) = \begin{cases} 3x + 1 & \text{if } x < 0, \\ 2x + 5 & \text{if } x \geq 0, \end{cases}$$

and $g(x) = 5x - 7$. Find $g \circ f$.

Solution: Since f is a piecewise-defined function, we expect the composite function $g \circ f$ is also a piecewise-defined function. It is defined by

$$(g \circ f)(x) = g(f(x)) = 5f(x) - 7 = \begin{cases} 5(3x + 1) - 7 & \text{if } x < 0, \\ 5(2x + 5) - 7 & \text{if } x \geq 0. \end{cases}$$

After simplification, we find

$$g \circ f \colon \mathbb{R} \to \mathbb{R}, \qquad (g \circ f)(x) = \begin{cases} 15x - 2 & \text{if } x < 0, \\ 10x + 18 & \text{if } x \geq 0. \end{cases}$$

In this example, it is rather obvious what the domain and codomain are. Nevertheless, it is always a good practice to include them when we describe a function.   ▲

Hands-On Exercise 6.7.3   The functions $f \colon \mathbb{R} \to \mathbb{R}$ and $g \colon \mathbb{R} \to \mathbb{R}$ are defined by

$$f(x) = 3x + 2, \qquad \text{and} \qquad g(x) = \begin{cases} x^2 & \text{if } x \leq 5, \\ 2x - 1 & \text{if } x > 5. \end{cases}$$

Determine $f \circ g$.

$\triangle$

The next example further illustrates why it is often easier to start with the outside function g in the derivation of the formula for $g(f(x))$.

Example 6.7.3   The function $p \colon [1, 5] \to \mathbb{R}$ is defined by

$$p(x) = \begin{cases} 2x + 3 & \text{if } 1 \leq x < 3, \\ 5x - 2 & \text{if } 3 \leq x \leq 5; \end{cases}$$

and the function $q \colon \mathbb{R} \to \mathbb{R}$ by

$$q(x) = \begin{cases} 4x & \text{if } x < 7, \\ 3x & \text{if } x \geq 7. \end{cases}$$

Describe the function $q \circ p$.

Solution: Since

$$(q \circ p)(x) = q(p(x)) = \begin{cases} 4p(x) & \text{if } p(x) < 7, \\ 3p(x) & \text{if } p(x) \geq 7, \end{cases}$$

we have to find out when will $p(x) < 7$, and when will $p(x) \geq 7$, because these conditions determine what we need to do next to continue the computation. Since $p(x)$ is computed in two different ways, we have to analyze two cases.

- **Case 1**: $1 \leq x < 3$. In this case, $p(x)$ is defined as $2x + 3$. This is an increasing function, hence,

$$p(x) \geq p(1) = 2 \cdot 1 + 3 = 5, \qquad \text{and} \qquad p(x) < p(3) = 2 \cdot 3 + 3 = 9.$$

  For some xs in this range, we have $p(x) < 7$, but for other x-values, we have $p(x) \geq 7$. We need to know the cut-off point. This happens when $p(x) = 2x + 3 = 7$, that is, when $x = 2$. This leads to two subcases.

  - **Case 1a**: When $1 \leq x < 2$, we have $p(x) = 2x + 3 < 7$. Thus,

$$q(p(x)) = 4p(x) = 4(2x + 3) = 8x + 12.$$

  - **Case 1b**: When $2 \leq x < 3$, we have $p(x) = 2x + 3 \geq 7$. Thus,

$$q(p(x)) = 3p(x) = 3(2x + 3) = 6x + 9.$$

- **Case 2**: $3 \leq x \leq 5$. In this case, $p(x)$ is computed as $5x - 2$. This is an increasing function, hence $p(x) \geq p(3) = 5 \cdot 3 - 2 = 13$. Since $p(x)$ is always greater than 7, we find

$$q(p(x)) = 3p(x) = 3(5x - 2) = 15x - 6.$$

Combining these cases, we determine that the composite function $q \circ p : [1, 5] \to \mathbb{R}$ is defined by

$$(q \circ p)(x) = \begin{cases} 8x + 12 & \text{if } 1 \leq x < 2, \\ 6x + 9 & \text{if } 2 \leq x < 3, \\ 15x - 6 & \text{if } 3 \leq x \leq 5. \end{cases}$$

Study this example again to make sure that you understand it thoroughly.   ▲

Hands-On Exercise 6.7.4   The functions $f, g : \mathbb{Z} \to \mathbb{Z}$ are defined by

$$f(n) = \begin{cases} n + 1 & \text{if } n \text{ is even} \\ n - 1 & \text{if } n \text{ is odd} \end{cases} \qquad g(n) = \begin{cases} n + 3 & \text{if } n \text{ is even} \\ n - 7 & \text{if } n \text{ is odd} \end{cases}$$

Determine $f \circ g$.

△

Strictly speaking, $g \circ f$ is well-defined if the codomain of f equals to the domain of g. It is clear that $g \circ f$ is still well-defined if im f is a subset of the domain of g. Hence, if

$$f : A \to B, \quad g : C \to D,$$

then $g \circ f$ is well-defined if $B \subseteq C$, or more generally, im $f \subseteq C$.

Example 6.7.4   Let $\mathbb{R}^*$ denote the set of nonzero real numbers. Suppose

$$f\colon \mathbb{R}^* \to \mathbb{R}, \qquad f(x) = 1/x,$$
$$g\colon \mathbb{R} \to (0, \infty), \qquad g(x) = 3x^2 + 11.$$

Determine $f \circ g$ and $g \circ f$. Be sure to specify their domains and codomains.

Solution: To compute $f \circ g$, we start with g, whose domain is $\mathbb{R}$. Hence, $\mathbb{R}$ is the domain of $f \circ g$. The result from g is a number in $(0, \infty)$. The interval $(0, \infty)$ contains positive numbers only, so it is a subset of $\mathbb{R}^*$. Therefore, we can continue our computation with f, and the final result is a number in $\mathbb{R}$. Hence, the codomain of $f \circ g$ is $\mathbb{R}$. The image is computed according to $f(g(x)) = 1/g(x) = 1/(3x^2 + 11)$. We are now ready to present our answer:

$$f \circ g\colon \mathbb{R} \to \mathbb{R}, \qquad (f \circ g)(x) = \frac{1}{3x^2 + 11}.$$

In a similar manner, the composite function $g \circ f\colon \mathbb{R}^* \to (0, \infty)$ is defined as

$$(g \circ f)(x) = \frac{3}{x^2} + 11.$$

Be sure you understand how we determine the domain and codomain of $g \circ f$.   ▲

Hands-On Exercise 6.7.5   Let $\mathbb{Z}$ denote the set of integers. Determine $h \circ g$, where

$$g\colon \mathbb{Z} \to \mathbb{R}, \qquad g(x) = \sqrt{|x|},$$
$$h\colon \mathbb{R} \to \mathbb{R}, \qquad h(x) = (x - 5)^2.$$

Is $g \circ h$ well-defined? Explain!

△

As usual, take extra caution with modular arithmetic.

Example 6.7.5   Define $f\colon \mathbb{Z}_{15} \to \mathbb{Z}_{23}$ and $g\colon \mathbb{Z}_{23} \to \mathbb{Z}_{32}$ according to

$$f(x) \equiv 3x + 5 \pmod{23},$$
$$g(x) \equiv 2x + 1 \pmod{32}.$$

We may expect $g \circ f\colon \mathbb{Z}_{15} \to \mathbb{Z}_{23}$ to be defined as

$$(g \circ f)(x) \equiv 2(3x + 5) + 1 \equiv 6x + 11) \pmod{32}.$$

In particular, $(g \circ f)(8) \equiv 59 \equiv 27 \pmod{32}$.

If we perform the computation one step at a time, we find $f(8) \equiv 29 \equiv 6 \pmod{23}$, from which we obtain

$$(g \circ f)(8) = g(f(8)) = g(6) \equiv 13 \pmod{32}.$$

which is not what we have just found. Can you explain why?

Solution: The source of the problem is the different moduli used in f and g. The composite function should be defined as

$$(g \circ f)(x) \equiv 2r + 1 \pmod{32}, \qquad \text{where } r \equiv 3x + 5 \pmod{23}.$$

In a way, this definition forces us to carry out the computation in two steps. Consequently, we will obtain the correct answer $(g \circ f)(8) = 13$.   ▲

There is a closed connection between a bijection and its inverse function, from the perspective of composition.

Theorem 6.7.1 *For a bijective function* $f: A \to B$,

$$f^{-1} \circ f = i_A, \qquad \text{and} \qquad f \circ f^{-1} = i_B,$$

where i_A *and* i_B *denote the identity function on* A *and* B, *respectively.*

Proof: To prove that $f^{-1} \circ f = i_A$, we need to show that $(f^{-1} \circ f)(a) = a$ for all $a \in A$. Assume $f(a) = b$. Then, because f^{-1} is the inverse function of f, we know that $f^{-1}(b) = a$. Therefore,

$$(f^{-1} \circ f)(a) = f^{-1}(f(a)) = f^{-1}(b) = a,$$

which is what we want to show. The proof of $f \circ f^{-1} = i_B$ procceds in the exact same manner, and is omitted here.   ■

Example 6.7.6   Show that the functions $f, g: \mathbb{R} \to \mathbb{R}$ defined by $f(x) = 2x + 1$ and $g(x) = \frac{1}{2}(x - 1)$ are inverse functions of each other.

Remark.   The problem does not ask you to *find* the inverse function of f or the inverse function of g. Instead, the answers are given to you already. You job is to *verify* that the answers are indeed correct, that the functions are inverse functions of each other.   ◇

Solution: Form the two composite functions $f \circ g$ and $g \circ f$, and check whether they *both* equal to the identity function:

$$(f \circ g)(x) = f(g(x)) = 2g(x) + 1 = 2\left[\tfrac{1}{2}(x - 1)\right] + 1 = x,$$
$$(g \circ f)(x) = g(f(x)) = \tfrac{1}{2}\left[f(x) - 1\right] = \tfrac{1}{2}\left[(2x + 1) - 1\right] = x.$$

To **verify** *that g is the inverse function of f, you just have to check whether* **both** *$f \circ g$ and $g \circ f$ are identity functions.*

We conclude that f and g are inverse functions of each other.   ▲

Hands-On Exercise 6.7.6   Verify that $f: \mathbb{R} \to \mathbb{R}^+$ defined by $f(x) = e^x$, and $g: \mathbb{R}^+ \to \mathbb{R}$ defined by $g(x) = \ln x$, are inverse functions of each other.

△

Theorem 6.7.2 *Suppose* $f: A \to B$ *and* $g: B \to C$. *Let* i_A *and* i_B *denote the identity function on* A *and* B, *respectively. We have the following results.*

    (a) $f \circ i_A = f$ *and* $i_B \circ f = f$.
    (b) *If both* f *and* g *are one-to-one, then* $g \circ f$ *is also one-to-one.*
    (c) *If both* f *and* g *are onto, then* $g \circ f$ *is also onto.*
    (d) *If both* f *and* g *are bijective, then* $g \circ f$ *is also bijective. In fact,* $(g \circ f)^{-1} = f^{-1} \circ g^{-1}$.

Proof: (a) To show that $f \circ i_A = f$, we need to show that $(f \circ i_A)(a) = f(a)$ for all $a \in A$. This follows from direct computation:

$$(f \circ i_A)(a) = f(i_A(a)) = f(a).$$

The proofs of $i_B \circ f = f$ and (b)–(d) are left as exercises.   ■

Example 6.7.7   The converses of (b) and (c) in Theorem 6.7.2 are false, as demonstrated in the functions

$$f:\mathbb{Z} \to \mathbb{Z}, \qquad f(x) = 2x,$$
$$g:\mathbb{Z} \to \mathbb{Z}, \qquad g(x) = \lfloor x/2 \rfloor.$$

Here, $g \circ f = i_{\mathbb{Z}}$, so $g \circ f$ is one-to-one, and it is obvious that f is also one-to-one, but g is not one-to-one. It is easy to see that both g and $g \circ f$ are onto, but f is not.   ▲

Summary and Review

- The composition of two functions $f: A \to B$ and $g: B \to C$ is the function $g \circ f: A \to C$ defined by $(g \circ f)(x) = g(f(x))$.
- If $f: A \to B$ is bijective, then $f^{-1} \circ f = i_A$ and $f \circ f^{-1} = i_B$.
- To check whether $f: A \to B$ and $g: B \to A$ are inverse of each other, we need to show that

  - $(g \circ f)(x) = g(f(x)) = x$ for all $x \in A$, *and*
  - $(f \circ g)(y) = f(g(y)) = y$ for all $y \in B$.

Exercises 6.7

1. The functions $g, f:\mathbb{R} \to \mathbb{R}$ are defined by $f(x) = 5x - 1$ and $g(x) = 3x^2 + 4$. Determine $f \circ g$ and $g \circ f$.

2. The function $h: (0, \infty) \to (0, \infty)$ is defined by $h(x) = x + \frac{1}{x}$. Determine $h \circ h$. Simplify your answer as much as possible.

3. The functions $g, f:\mathbb{R} \to \mathbb{R}$ are defined by $f(x) = 1 - 3x$ and $g(x) = x^2 + 1$. Evaluate $f(g(f(0)))$.

4. The functions $p: (2, 8] \to \mathbb{R}$ and $q:\mathbb{R} \to \mathbb{R}$ are defined by

$$p(x) \;=\; \begin{cases} 3x - 1 & \text{if } 2 < x \le 4, \\ 17 - 2x & \text{if } 4 < x \le 8, \end{cases}$$

$$q(x) \;=\; \begin{cases} 4x - 1 & \text{if } x < 3, \\ 3x + 1 & \text{if } x \ge 3. \end{cases}$$

   Evaluate $q \circ p$.

5. Describe $g \circ f$.

   (a) $f:\mathbb{Z} \to \mathbb{N}, \quad f(n) = n^2 + 1; \qquad g:\mathbb{N} \to \mathbb{Q}, \quad g(n) = \frac{1}{n}$.
   (b) $f:\mathbb{R} \to (0, 1), \quad f(x) = 1/(x^2 + 1); \qquad g: (0, 1) \to (0, 1), \quad g(x) = 1 - x$.
   (c) $f:\mathbb{Q} - \{2\} \to \mathbb{Q}^*, \quad f(x) = 1/(x - 2); \qquad g:\mathbb{Q}^* \to \mathbb{Q}^*, \quad g(x) = 1/x$.
   (d) $f:\mathbb{R} \to [1, \infty), \quad f(x) = x^2 + 1; \qquad g: [1, \infty) \to [0, \infty) \quad g(x) = \sqrt{x - 1}$.
   (e) $f:\mathbb{Q} - \{10/3\} \to \mathbb{Q} - \{3\}, \quad f(x) = 3x - 7; \qquad g:\mathbb{Q} - \{3\} \to \mathbb{Q} - \{2\}, \quad g(x) = 2x/(x - 3)$.

6. Describe $g \circ f$.

   (a) $f:\mathbb{Z} \to \mathbb{Z}_5, \quad f(n) \equiv n \pmod 5; \qquad g:\mathbb{Z}_5 \to \mathbb{Z}_5, \quad g(n) \equiv n + 1 \pmod 5$.
   (b) $f:\mathbb{Z}_8 \to \mathbb{Z}_{12}, \quad f(n) \equiv 3n \pmod{12}; \qquad g:\mathbb{Z}_{12} \to \mathbb{Z}_6, \quad g(n) \equiv 2n \pmod 6$.

7. Describe $g \circ f$.

   (a) $f:\{1, 2, 3, 4, 5\} \to \{1, 2, 3, 4, 5\}, \quad f(1) = 5, f(2) = 3, f(3) = 2, f(4) = 1, f(5) = 4;$
   $g:\{1, 2, 3, 4, 5\} \to \{1, 2, 3, 4, 5\}; \quad g(1) = 3, g(2) = 1, g(3) = 5, g(4) = 4, g(5) = 2$

(b) $f: \{a, b, c, d, e\} \to \{1, 2, 3, 4, 5\}$; $f(a) = 5$, $f(b) = 1$, $f(c) = 2$, $f(d) = 4$, $f(e) = 3$;
$\quad g: \{1, 2, 3, 4, 5\} \to \{a, b, c, d, e\}$; $g(1) = e$, $g(2) = d$, $g(3) = a$, $g(4) = c$, $g(5) = b$

8. Verify that $f, g: \mathbb{R} \to \mathbb{R}$ defined by

$$f(x) = \begin{cases} 11 - 2x & \text{if } x < 4 \\ 15 - 3x & \text{if } x \geq 4 \end{cases} \quad \text{and} \quad g(x) = \begin{cases} \frac{1}{3}(15 - x) & \text{if } x \leq 3 \\ \frac{1}{2}(11 - x) & \text{if } x > 3 \end{cases}$$

   are inverse to each other.

9. The functions $f, g: \mathbb{Z} \to \mathbb{Z}$ are defined by

$$f(n) = \begin{cases} 2n - 1 & \text{if } n \geq 0 \\ 2n & \text{if } n < 0 \end{cases} \quad \text{and} \quad g(n) = \begin{cases} n + 1 & \text{if } n \text{ is even} \\ 3n & \text{if } n \text{ is odd} \end{cases}$$

   Determine $g \circ f$.

10. Define the functions f and g on your maternal family tree (see Problem 8 in Exercises 6.2) according to

$$\begin{aligned} f(x) &= \text{the mother of } x, \\ g(x) &= \text{the eldest daughter of the mother of } x. \end{aligned}$$

   Describe these functions.

   (a) $f \circ g$ (b) $g \circ f$
   (c) $f \circ f$ (d) $g \circ g$

11. Given the bijections f and g, find $f \circ g$, $(f \circ g)^{-1}$ and $g^{-1} \circ f^{-1}$.

   (a) $f: \mathbb{Z} \to \mathbb{Z}$, $f(n) = n + 1$; $g: \mathbb{Z} \to \mathbb{Z}$, $g(n) = 2 - n$.
   (b) $f: \mathbb{Q} \to \mathbb{Q}$, $f(x) = 5x$; $g: \mathbb{Q} \to \mathbb{Q}$, $g(x) = \frac{x-2}{5}$.
   (c) $f: \mathbb{Q} - \{2\} \to \mathbb{Q} - \{2\}$, $f(x) = 3x - 4$; $g: \mathbb{Q} - \{2\} \to \mathbb{Q} - \{2\}$, $g(x) = \frac{x}{x-2}$.
   (d) $f: \mathbb{Z}_7 \to \mathbb{Z}_7$, $f(n) \equiv 2n + 5 \pmod 7$; $g: \mathbb{Z}_7 \to \mathbb{Z}_7$, $g(n) \equiv 3n - 2 \pmod 7$.

12. Give an example of sets A, B, and C, and of functions $f: A \to B$ and $g: B \to C$, such that $g \circ f$ and f are both one-to-one, but g is not one-to-one.

13. Prove part (b) of Theorem 6.7.2.

14. Prove part (c) of Theorem 6.7.2.

15. Prove part (d) of Theorem 6.7.2.

16. The incidence matrices for the functions $f: \{a, b, c, d, e\} \to \{x, y, z, w\}$ and $g: \{x, y, z, w\} \to \{1, 2, 3, 4, 5, 6\}$ are

$$\begin{array}{c} \\ a \\ b \\ c \\ d \\ e \end{array} \begin{pmatrix} x & y & z & w \\ 0 & 0 & 1 & 0 \\ 0 & 1 & 0 & 0 \\ 0 & 0 & 1 & 0 \\ 1 & 0 & 0 & 0 \\ 1 & 0 & 0 & 0 \end{pmatrix}, \quad \text{and} \quad \begin{array}{c} \\ x \\ y \\ z \\ w \end{array} \begin{pmatrix} 1 & 2 & 3 & 4 & 5 & 6 \\ 0 & 0 & 1 & 0 & 0 & 0 \\ 0 & 0 & 0 & 0 & 0 & 1 \\ 0 & 1 & 0 & 0 & 0 & 0 \\ 1 & 0 & 0 & 0 & 0 & 0 \end{pmatrix},$$

   respectively. Construct the incidence matrix for the composition $g \circ f$.

Chapter 7

Relations

7.1 Definition of Relations

Given two nonempty sets A and B, a function tells us how to obtain a unique element $b \in B$ from any element $a \in A$. Very often, we are only interested in some sort of relationship between the elements from these two sets. A familiar example is the equality of two numbers. By saying $a = b$, we are proclaiming that the two numbers a and b are related by being equal in value. Likewise, $a \geq b$ is another example of a relation.

Example 7.1.1 Given $a, b \in \mathbb{R}^*$, declare a and b to be related if they have the same sign. For instance, 7.14 and e are related, so are $-\pi$ and $-\sqrt{2}$. However, 5 and -2 are not. Note that a is related to b implies that b is also related to a. ▲

Example 7.1.2 For $a, b \in \mathbb{R}$, define "a is related to b" if and only if $a < b$. Take note that $3 < 5$, but $5 \not< 3$. This demonstrates that a is related to b does not necessarily imply that b is also related to a. ▲

A relationship can be one-way only.

Example 7.1.3 Let A be a set of students, and let B be a set of courses. Given $a \in A$ and $b \in B$, define "a is related to b" if and only if student a is taking course b. While it could be possible that "John Smith is related to MATH 210" because John is taking MATH 210, it is certainly absurd to say that "MATH 210 is related to John Smith," because it does not make much sense to say that MATH 210 is taking John Smith. This again illustrates that a is related to b does not necessarily imply that b is also related to a. ▲

The two sets need not be the same.

In these examples, we see that when we say "a is related to b," the order in which a and b appear may make a difference. This suggests the following definition.

Definition. A **relation** from a set A to a set B is a subset of $A \times B$. Hence, a relation R consists of ordered pairs (a, b), where $a \in A$ and $b \in B$. If $(a, b) \in R$, we say that **a is related to b**, and we also write $a\,R\,b$. ◇

A relation is a set of ordered pairs, we also write $a\,R\,b$ if a is related to b.

Remark. We can also replace R by a symbol, especially when one is readily available. This is exactly what we do in, for example, $a < b$. To say it is not true that $a < b$, we can write $a \not< b$. Likewise, if $(a, b) \notin R$, then a is not related to b, and we could write $a\,\not{R}\,b$. But the slash may not be easy to recognize when it is written over an uppercase letter. In this regard, it may be a good practice to avoid using the slash notation over a letter. Alternatively, one may use the "bar" notation $\overline{a\,R\,b}$ to indicate that a and b are not related. ◇

Example 7.1.4 Define $R = \{(a, b) \in \mathbb{R}^2 \mid a < b\}$, hence $(a, b) \in R$ if and only if $a < b$. Obviously, saying "$a < b$" is much clearer than "$a\,R\,b$." If a and b are not related, we could say $(a, b) \notin R$, or $a \not< b$. ▲

Example 7.1.5   Define

$$F = \left\{ (x, y) \in \mathbb{R}^2 \;\middle|\; y = \frac{1}{x^2 + 1} \right\}.$$

Therefore x is related to y if and only if $y = \frac{1}{x^2+1}$. We can also write

$$F = \left\{ \left(x, \frac{1}{x^2 + 1} \right) \;\middle|\; x \in \mathbb{R} \right\},$$

which may look a bit simpler.

For instance, $(1, 0.5) \in F$, but $(1, 0) \notin F$. In this case, $(2, 0.2) \in F$ is probably easier to understand than $2\,F\,0.2$. Likewise, $(1, 2) \notin F$ may be easier to read than $1 \not\mathrel{F} 2$.   ▲

Hands-On Exercise 7.1.1   Define the relation H as $\{(x, x^2 + 1) \mid x \in \mathbb{R}\}$. Determine whether the following statements

$$2\,H\,3, \quad (-4, 17) \notin H, \quad \left(\tfrac{1}{2}, \tfrac{3}{2}\right) \notin H, \quad (\sqrt{2}, 3) \in H, \quad (1, 2) \in H,$$

are true or false.

△

Hands-On Exercise 7.1.2   Let $G = \{(x, y) \in \mathbb{R}^2 \mid xy = 1\}$. Is 2 related to 0.5? How would you write it? Repeat with 4 and 0.5, and with 10 and 3.

△

Hands-On Exercise 7.1.3   In the last example, is 0 related to 3? How would you write it? Repeat with 1 and -1. Again with $\frac{1}{\sqrt{2}}$ and $\sqrt{2}$.

△

Since a relation is a set, we can describe a relation by listing its elements (that is, using the roster method).

Example 7.1.6   Let $A = \{1, 2, 3, 4, 5, 6\}$ and $B = \{1, 2, 3, 4\}$. Define $(a, b) \in R$ if and only if $(a - b) \bmod 2 = 0$. Then

$$R = \{(1, 1), (1, 3), (2, 2), (2, 4), (3, 1), (3, 3), (4, 2), (4, 4), (5, 1), (5, 3), (6, 2), (6, 4)\}.$$

We note that R consists of ordered pairs (a, b) where a and b have the same parity. Be cautious, that $1 \leq a \leq 6$ and $1 \leq b \leq 4$. Hence, it is meaningless to talk about whether $(1, 5) \in R$ or $(1, 5) \notin R$.   ▲

Hands-On Exercise 7.1.4   Let $A = \{2, 3, 4, 7\}$ and $B = \{1, 2, 3, \ldots, 12\}$. Define $a\,S\,b$ if and only if $a \mid b$. Use the roster method to describe S.

△

In the last example, 7 never appears as the first element (in the first coordinate) of any ordered pair. Likewise, 1, 5, 7, and 11 never appear as the second element (in the second coordinate) of any ordered pair.

Definition.   The **domain** of a relation $R \subseteq A \times B$ is defined as

$$\operatorname{dom} R = \{a \in A \mid (a,b) \in R \text{ for some } b \in B\},$$

and the **image** or **range** is defined as

$$\operatorname{im} R = \{b \in B \mid (a,b) \in R \text{ for some } a \in A\}.$$

Hands-On Exercise 7.1.5   Find $\operatorname{dom} S$ and $\operatorname{im} S$, where S in Hands-On Exercise 7.1.4.

$\triangle$

A relation $R \subseteq A \times B$ can be displayed graphically on a **digraph** which is also called a **directed graph**. Represent the elements from A and B by **vertices** or **dots**, and use **directed lines** (also called **directed edges** or **arcs**) to connect two vertices if the corresponding elements are related. Figure 7.1 displays a graphical representation of the relation in Example 7.1.6.

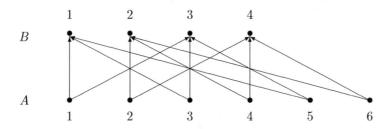

Figure 7.1: The graphical representation of the a relation.

Although a digraph gives us a clear and precise visual representation of a relation, it could become very confusing and hard to read when the relation contains many ordered pairs. As we will see in Section 7.4, we can sometimes simplify the digraphs in some special situations. Otherwise, the graphical representation is only effective for relations with a small number of ordered pairs.

We can use a **matrix representation** to describe a relation. A matrix consists of values arranged in rows and columns. A relation R from $A = \{a_1, \ldots, a_m\}$ to $B = \{b_1, \ldots, b_n\}$ can be described by an m-by-n matrix $M = (m_{ij})$ whose entry at row i and column j is defined by

$$m_{ij} = \begin{cases} 1 & \text{if } a_i \, R \, b_j, \\ 0 & \text{otherwise.} \end{cases}$$

The matrix M is called the **incidence matrix** for R.

Example 7.1.7   The incidence matrix for the relation R in Example 7.1.6 is

$$
\begin{array}{c}
\\
1\\
2\\
3\\
4\\
5\\
6
\end{array}
\begin{array}{cccc}
1 & 2 & 3 & 4 \\
\left(\begin{array}{cccc}
1 & 0 & 1 & 0 \\
0 & 1 & 0 & 1 \\
1 & 0 & 1 & 0 \\
0 & 1 & 0 & 1 \\
1 & 0 & 1 & 0 \\
0 & 1 & 0 & 1
\end{array}\right)
\end{array}
$$

in which we label the rows and columns with the elements involved in the relation.   ▲

Hands-On Exercise 7.1.6   Determine the incidence matrix for the relation S in Hands-On Exercise 7.1.4.

$\triangle$

Hands-On Exercise 7.1.7   The courses taken by John, Mary, Paul, and Sally are listed below.

> John: MATH 210, CSIT 121, MATH 223
> Mary: MATH 231, CSIT 121, MATH 210
> Paul: CSIT 120, MATH 231, MATH 223
> Sally: MATH 210, CSIT 120

Represent, using a graph and a matrix, the relation R defined as $a\,R\,b$ if student a is taking course b.

$\triangle$

Summary and Review

- Relations are generalizations of functions. A relation merely states that the elements from two sets A and B are related in a certain way.
- More formally, a relation is defined as a subset of $A \times B$.
- The domain of a relation is the set of elements in A that appear in the first coordinates of some ordered pairs, and the image or range is the set of elements in B that appear in the second coordinates of some ordered pairs.
- For brevity and for clarity, we often write $x\,R\,y$ if $(x, y) \in R$.
- Under this convention, the mathematical notations $\leq$, $\geq$, $=$, $\subseteq$, and their like, can be regarded as relational operators.

Exercises 7.1

1. Represent each of the following relations from $\{1, 2, 3, 6\}$ to $\{1, 2, 3, 6\}$ using a digraph and an incidence matrix.

    (a) $\{(x, y) \mid x = y\}$ (b) $\{(x, y) \mid x \neq y\}$ (c) $\{(x, y) \mid x < y\}$

2. Find the domain and image of each relation in Problem 1.

3. Represent each of the following relations from $\{1, 2, 3, 6\}$ to $\{1, 2, 3, 6\}$ using a digraph and an incidence matrix.

    (a) $\{(x, y) \mid x^2 \leq y\}$ (d) $\{(x, y) \mid x \text{ divides } y\}$ (c) $\{(x, y) \mid x + y \text{ is even}\}$

4. Find the domain and image of each relation in Problem 3.

5. Find the incidence matrix for each of the following relations from $\{1, 2, 3, 4\}$ to $\{1, 2, 3, 4, 5\}$.

   (a) $R = \{(1, 1), (2, 2), (2, 3), (3, 3), (3, 4), (4, 5)\}$

   (b) $S = \{(1, 1), (1, 2), (2, 2), (2, 3), (3, 3), (3, 4), (4, 4)\}$

   (c) $T = \{(1, 5), (2, 4), (3, 3), (4, 1), (4, 4)\}$

6. Determine the incidence matrix and the digraph that represent the relation R defined on $\{x \in \mathbb{Z} \mid -3 \leq x \leq 3\}$ by
   $$x \, R \, y \Leftrightarrow 3 \mid (x - y).$$

7. Determine the incidence matrix and the digraph that represent the relation S defined on $\{1, 2, 4, 5, 10, 20\}$ by
   $$x \, S \, y \Leftrightarrow (x < y \text{ and } x \text{ divides } y).$$

8. Let $D = \{1, 2, 3, \ldots, 30\}$ be the set of dates in November, and let $W = \{$Sunday, Monday, Tuesday, Wednesday, Thursday, Friday, Saturday$\}$ be the set of days of the week. For November of this year, define the relation T from D to W by
   $$(x, y) \in T \Leftrightarrow x \text{ falls on } y.$$

   List the ordered pairs in T. Is T a function from T to W?

9. Find the incidence matrix for the relation $I \subseteq \wp(\{1, 2\}) \times \wp(\{1, 2\})$, where
   $$(S, T) \in I \Leftrightarrow S \cap T \neq \emptyset.$$

10. For a relation $R \subseteq A \times A$, instead of using two rows of vertices in a digraph, we can use a digraph on the vertices that represent the elements of A. Hence, it is possible to have two directed arcs between a pair of vertices, and a loop may appear around a vertex x if $(x, x) \in R$. Find the incidence matrix for the relation represented by the following digraph:

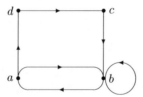

7.2 Properties of Relations

If R is a relation from A to A, then $R \subseteq A \times A$; we say that R is a ***relation on A***.

Definition. A relation R on A is said to be

- ***reflexive*** if $(a, a) \in R$ a for all $a \in A$,

- ***irreflexive*** if $(a, a) \notin R$ for all $a \in A$,

- ***symmetric*** if $(a, b) \in R \Rightarrow (b, a) \in R$ for all $a, b \in A$,

- ***antisymmetric*** if $[(a, b) \in R \wedge (b, a) \in R] \Rightarrow a = b$ for all $a, b \in A$,

- ***transitive*** if $[(a, b) \in R \wedge (b, c) \in R] \Rightarrow (a, c) \in R$ for all $a, b, c \in A$.

These are important definitions, so let us repeat them using the relational notation $a \, R \, b$:

- **reflexive** if $a\,R\,a$ for all $a \in A$,

- **irreflexive** if $a\,\not R\,a$ (that is, $\overline{a\,R\,a}$) for all $a \in A$,

- **symmetric** if $a\,R\,b \Rightarrow b\,R\,a$ for all $a, b \in A$,

- **antisymmetric** if $[(a\,R\,b) \wedge (b\,R\,a)] \Rightarrow a = b$ for all $a, b \in A$,

- **transitive** if $[(a\,R\,b) \wedge (b\,R\,c)] \Rightarrow a\,R\,c$ for all $a, b, c \in A$. $\Diamond$

Remark. A relation cannot be both reflexive and irreflexive. Hence, these two properties are mutually exclusive. If it is reflexive, then it is not irreflexive. If it is irreflexive, then it cannot be reflexive. Nonetheless, it is possible for a relation to be neither reflexive nor irreflexive. $\Diamond$

Remark. Many students find the concept of symmetry and antisymmetry confusing. Even though the name may suggest so, antisymmetry is *not* the opposite of symmetry. It is possible for a relation to be both symmetric and antisymmetric, and it is also possible for a relation to be both non-symmetric and non-antisymmetric. A good way to understand antisymmetry is to look at its contrapositive:

$$a \neq b \Rightarrow \overline{(a, b) \in R \wedge (b, a) \in R}.$$

Thus, if two distinct elements a and b are related (not every pair of elements need to be related), then either a is related to b, or b is related to a, *but not both*. Consequently, if we find *distinct* elements a and b such that $(a, b) \in R$ and $(b, a) \in R$, then R is not antisymmetric. $\Diamond$

Example 7.2.1 The **empty relation** is the subset $\emptyset$. It is clearly irreflexive, hence not reflexive. To check symmetry, we want to know whether $a\,R\,b \Rightarrow b\,R\,a$ for all $a, b \in A$. More specifically, we want to know whether $(a, b) \in \emptyset \Rightarrow (b, a) \in \emptyset$. Since $(a, b) \in \emptyset$ is always false, the implication is always true. Thus the relation is symmetric. Likewise, it is antisymmetric and transitive.

The **complete relation** is the entire set $A \times A$. It is clearly reflexive, hence not irreflexive. It is also trivial that it is symmetric and transitive. It is not antisymmetric unless $|A| = 1$.

The **identity relation** consists of ordered pairs of the form (a, a), where $a \in A$. In other words, $a\,R\,b$ if and only if $a = b$. It is reflexive (hence not irreflexive), symmetric, antisymmetric, and transitive.   ▲

Example 7.2.2 Consider the relation R on the set $A = \{1, 2, 3, 4\}$ defined by

$$R = \{(1, 1), (2, 3), (2, 4), (3, 3), (3, 4)\}.$$

- Since $(2, 2) \notin R$, and $(1, 1) \in R$, the relation is neither reflexive nor irreflexive.
- We have $(2, 3) \in R$ but $(3, 2) \notin R$, thus R is not symmetric.
- For any $a \neq b$, only one of the four possibilities $(a, b) \notin R$, $(b, a) \notin R$, $(a, b) \in R$, or $(b, a) \in R$ can occur, so R is antisymmetric.
- By going through all the ordered pairs in R, we verify that whether $(a, b) \in R$ and $(b, c) \in R$, we always have $(a, c) \in R$ as well. This shows that R is transitive.

Therefore, R is antisymmetric and transitive.   ▲

Example 7.2.3 Define the relation S on the set $A = \{1, 2, 3, 4\}$ according to

$$S = \{(2, 3), (3, 2)\}.$$

- Since $(1, 1), (2, 2), (3, 3), (4, 4) \notin S$, the relation S is irreflexive, hence, it is not reflexive.
- Since we have only two ordered pairs, and it is clear that whenever $(a, b) \in S$, we also have $(b, a) \in S$. Hence, S is symmetric.
- We have both $(2, 3) \in S$ and $(3, 2) \in S$, but $2 \neq 3$. Hence, S is not antisymmetric.
- Since $(2, 3) \in S$ and $(3, 2) \in S$, but $(2, 2) \notin S$, the relation S is not transitive.

We conclude that S is irreflexive and symmetric.   ▲

Hands-On Exercise 7.2.1 Define the relation R on the set $\mathbb{R}$ as

$$a\,R\,b \Leftrightarrow a \leq b.$$

Determine whether R is reflexive, irreflexive, symmetric, antisymmetric, or transitive.

$\triangle$

Hands-On Exercise 7.2.2 The relation S on the set $\mathbb{R}^*$ is defined as

$$a\,S\,b \Leftrightarrow ab > 0.$$

Determine whether S is reflexive, irreflexive, symmetric, antisymmetric, or transitive.

$\triangle$

Example 7.2.4 Here are two examples from geometry. Let $\mathcal{T}$ be the set of triangles that can be drawn on a plane. Define a relation S on $\mathcal{T}$ such that $(T_1, T_2) \in S$ if and only if the two triangles are similar. It is easy to check that S is reflexive, symmetric, and transitive.

Let $\mathcal{L}$ be the set of all the (straight) lines on a plane. Define a relation P on $\mathcal{L}$ according to $(L_1, L_2) \in P$ if and only if L_1 and L_2 are parallel lines. Again, it is obvious that P is reflexive, symmetric, and transitive. ▲

Example 7.2.5 The relation T on $\mathbb{R}^*$ is defined as

$$a\,T\,b \Leftrightarrow \frac{a}{b} \in \mathbb{Q}.$$

- Since $\frac{a}{a} = 1 \in \mathbb{Q}$, the relation T is reflexive; it follows that T is not irreflexive.
- The relation T is symmetric, because if $\frac{a}{b}$ can be written as $\frac{m}{n}$ for some integers m and n, then so is its reciprocal $\frac{b}{a}$, because $\frac{b}{a} = \frac{n}{m}$.
- Since $\sqrt{2}\,T\sqrt{18}$ and $\sqrt{18}\,T\sqrt{2}$, yet $\sqrt{2} \neq \sqrt{18}$, we conclude that T is not antisymmetric.
- If $\frac{a}{b}, \frac{b}{c} \in \mathbb{Q}$, then $\frac{a}{b} = \frac{m}{n}$ and $\frac{b}{c} = \frac{p}{q}$ for some nonzero integers m, n, p, and q. Then $\frac{a}{c} = \frac{a}{b} \cdot \frac{b}{c} = \frac{mp}{nq} \in \mathbb{Q}$. Hence, T is transitive.

Therefore, the relation T is reflexive, symmetric, and transitive. ▲

Hands-On Exercise 7.2.3 Consider the relation T on $\mathbb{N}$ defined by

$$a\,T\,b \Leftrightarrow a \mid b.$$

Determine whether T is reflexive, irreflexive, symmetric, antisymmetric, or transitive.

$\triangle$

Hands-On Exercise 7.2.4   The relation U on the set $\mathbb{Z}^*$ is defined as

$$a\,U\,b \Leftrightarrow a \mid b.$$

Determine whether U is reflexive, irreflexive, symmetric, antisymmetric, or transitive.

$\triangle$

Example 7.2.6   The relation U on $\mathbb{Z}$ is defined as

$$a\,U\,b \Leftrightarrow 5 \mid (a+b).$$

- The relation U is not reflexive, because $5 \nmid (1+1)$.
- It is not irreflexive either, because $5 \mid (10+10)$.
- If $5 \mid (a+b)$, it is obvious that $5 \mid (b+a)$ because $a+b = b+a$. Thus, U is symmetric.
- We claim that U is not antisymmetric. For example, $5 \mid (2+3)$ and $5 \mid (3+2)$, yet $2 \neq 3$.
- It is not transitive either. For instance, $5 \mid (1+4)$ and $5 \mid (4+6)$, but $5 \nmid (1+6)$.

The relation U is symmetric.   ▲

Hands-On Exercise 7.2.5   Determine whether the following relation V on some universal set $\mathcal{U}$ is reflexive, irreflexive, symmetric, antisymmetric, or transitive:

$$(S,T) \in V \Leftrightarrow S \subseteq T.$$

$\triangle$

Example 7.2.7   Consider the relation V on the set $A = \{0, 1\}$ is defined according to

$$V = \{(0,0), (1,1)\}.$$

- The relation V is reflexive, because $(0,0) \in V$ and $(1,1) \in V$. Hence, it is not irreflexive.
- It is clearly symmetric, because $(a, b) \in V$ always implies $(b, a) \in V$.
- Indeed, whenever $(a, b) \in V$, we must also have $a = b$, because V consists of only two ordered pairs, both of them are in the form of (a, a). It follows that V is also antisymmetric.
- A similar argument shows that V is transitive.

The relation is reflexive, symmetric, antisymmetric, and transitive.   ▲

Hands-On Exercise 7.2.6   Determine whether the following relation W on a nonempty set of individuals in a community is reflexive, irreflexive, symmetric, antisymmetric, or transitive:

$$a \, W \, b \Leftrightarrow a \text{ and } b \text{ have the same last name.}$$

$\triangle$

Example 7.2.8   Define the relation W on a nonempty set of individuals in a community as

$$a \, W \, b \Leftrightarrow a \text{ is a child of } b.$$

- Nobody can be a child of himself or herself, hence, W cannot be reflexive. Instead, it is irreflexive.
- It is obvious that W cannot be symmetric.
- It may sound weird from the definition that W is antisymmetric:

$$(a \text{ is a child of } b) \wedge (b \text{ is a child of } a) \Rightarrow a = b, \tag{7.1}$$

but it is true! The reason is, if a is a child of b, then b cannot be a child of a. This makes conjunction

$$(a \text{ is a child of } b) \wedge (b \text{ is a child of } a)$$

false, which makes the implication (7.1) true.
- A similar argument holds if b is a child of a, and if neither a is a child of b nor b is a child of a. No matter what happens, the implication (7.1) is always true. Therefore W is antisymmetric.
- It may help if we look at antisymmetry from a different angle. The contrapositive of the original definition asserts that when $a \neq b$, three things could happen:

  (i) a and b are incomparable $(\overline{a \, W \, b} \text{ and } \overline{b \, W \, a})$, that is, a and b are unrelated;

and if a and b are related, then either

  (ii) $a \, W \, b$ but $\overline{b \, W \, a}$, or
  (iii) $b \, W \, a$ but $\overline{a \, W \, b}$.

Using this observation, it is easy to see why W is antisymmetric.

- It is clear that W is not transitive.

The relation is irreflexive and antisymmetric.   ▲

Instead of using two rows of vertices in the digraph that represents a relation on a set A, we can use just one set of vertices to represent the elements of A. A directed line connects vertex a to vertex b if and only if the element a is related to the element b. If b is also related to a, the two vertices will be joined by two directed lines, one in each direction. If a is related to itself, there is a loop around the vertex representing a. See Problem 10 in Exercises 7.1.

From the graphical representation, we determine that the relation R is

- Reflexive if there is a loop at every vertex of G.

- Irreflexive if G is loopless.

- Symmetric if every pair of vertices is connected by none or exactly two directed lines in opposite directions.

- Antisymmetric if every pair of vertices is connected by none or exactly one directed line.

- Transitive if for every unidirectional path joining three vertices a, b, c, in that order, there is also a directed line joining a to c.

The incidence matrix $M = (m_{ij})$ for a relation on A is a square matrix. We find that R is

- Reflexive if every entry on the main diagonal of M is 1.

- Irreflexive if every entry on the main diagonal of M is 0.

- Symmetric if M is symmetric, that is, $m_{ij} = m_{ji}$ whenever $i \neq j$.

- Antisymmetric if $i \neq j$ implies that at least one of m_{ij} and m_{ji} is zero, that is, $m_{ij}m_{ji} = 0$.

- Transitive if $(M^2)_{ij} > 0$ implies $m_{ij} > 0$ whenever $i \neq j$.

For instance, the incidence matrix for the identity relation consists of 1s on the main diagonal, and 0s everywhere else. This is called the identity matrix. If a relation R on A is both symmetric and antisymmetric, its off-diagonal entries are all zeros, so it is a subset of the identity relation.

It is an interesting exercise to prove the test for transitivity. Apply it to Example 7.2.2 to see how it works.

Summary and Review

- A relation from a set A to itself is called a relation on A.
- Given any relation R on a set A, we are interested in five properties that R may or may not have.
- The relation R is said to be reflexive if every element is related to itself, that is, if $x \, R \, x$ for every $x \in A$.
- The relation R is said to be irreflexive if no element is related to itself, that is, if $x \, \not{R} \, x$ for every $x \in A$.
- The reflexive property and the irreflexive property are mutually exclusive, and it is possible for a relation to be neither reflexive nor irreflexive.
- The relation R is said to be symmetric if the relation can go in both directions, that is, if $x \, R \, y$ implies $y \, R \, x$ for any $x, y \in A$.
- The relation R is said to be antisymmetric if given any two *distinct* elements x and y, either (i) x and y are not related in any way, or (ii) if x and y are related, they can only be related in one direction.
- A compact way to define antisymmetry is: if $x \, R \, y$ and $y \, R \, x$, then we must have $x = y$.
- Finally, a relation is said to be transitive if we can pass along the relation and relate two elements if they are related via a third element.
- More precisely, R is transitive if $x \, R \, y$ and $y \, R \, z$ implies that $x \, R \, z$.

Exercises 7.2

1. For each relation in Problem 1 in Exercises 7.1, determine which of the five properties are satisfied.

2. For each relation in Problem 3 in Exercises 7.1, determine which of the five properties are satisfied.

3. For the relation in Problem 6 in Exercises 7.1, determine which of the five properties are satisfied.

4. For the relation in Problem 7 in Exercises 7.1, determine which of the five properties are satisfied.

5. For the relation in Problem 8 in Exercises 7.1, determine which of the five properties are satisfied.

6. For the relation in Problem 9 in Exercises 7.1, determine which of the five properties are satisfied.

7. Let S be a nonempty set and define the relation A on $\wp(S)$ by

$$(X, Y) \in A \Leftrightarrow X \cap Y = \emptyset.$$

It is clear that A is symmetric.

   (a) Explain why A is not reflexive.
   (b) Explain why A is not irreflexive.
   (c) Is A transitive?
   (d) Let $S = \{a, b, c\}$. Draw the directed graph for A, and find the incidence matrix that represents A.

8. For each of these relations on $\mathbb{N} - \{1\}$, determine which of the five properties are satisfied.

   (a) $A_1 = \{(x, y) \mid x \text{ and } y \text{ are relatively prime}\}$
   (b) $A_2 = \{(x, y) \mid x \text{ and } y \text{ are not relatively prime}\}$

9. For each of the following relations on $\mathbb{N}$, determine which of the five properties are satisfied.

   (a) $R_1 = \{(x, y) \mid x \text{ divides } y\}$
   (b) $R_2 = \{(x, y) \mid x + y \text{ is even}\}$
   (c) $R_3 = \{(x, y) \mid xy \text{ is even}\}$

10. For each of the following relations on $\mathbb{N}$, determine which of the five properties are satisfied.

   (a) $S_1 = \{(x, y) \mid y \text{ divides } x\}$
   (b) $S_2 = \{(x, y) \mid x + y \text{ is odd}\}$
   (c) $S_3 = \{(x, y) \mid xy \text{ is odd}\}$

11. For each of the following relations on $\mathbb{Z}$, determine which of the five properties are satisfied.

   (a) $U_1 = \{(x, y) \mid x \leq y\}$
   (b) $U_2 = \{(x, y) \mid x - y \text{ is odd}\}$
   (c) $U_3 = \{(x, y) \mid 3 \text{ divides } x + 2y\}$

12. For each of the following relations on $\mathbb{Z}$, determine which of the five properties are satisfied.

   (a) $V_1 = \{(x, y) \mid xy > 0\}$
   (b) $V_2 = \{(x, y) \mid x - y \text{ is even}\}$
   (c) $V_3 = \{(x, y) \mid x \text{ is a multiple of } y\}$

7.3   Equivalence Relations

Definition.   A relation on a set A is an *equivalence relation* if it is reflexive, symmetric, and transitive. We often use the tilde notation $a \sim b$ to denote an equivalence relation. $\Diamond$

Example 7.3.1   The relations in Examples 7.2.4, 7.2.5, and 7.2.7, are equivalence relations, so are those in Hands-On Exercises 7.2.2 and 7.2.6.   ▲

Example 7.3.2   Define a relation $\sim$ on $\mathbb{Z}$ by

$$a \sim b \Leftrightarrow a \equiv b \;(\text{mod } 4).$$

Verify that $\sim$ is an equivalence relation.

Solution: We need to check three properties:

- It is obvious $a \equiv a \;(\text{mod } 4)$, hence $a \sim a$. The relation $\sim$ is reflexive.
- If $a \sim b$, then $a \equiv b \;(\text{mod } 4)$. It is clear that we also have $b \equiv a \;(\text{mod } 4)$. Hence, $\sim$ is symmetric.
- If $a \sim b$ and $b \sim c$, then

$$a \equiv b \quad (\text{mod } 4), \qquad \text{and} \qquad b \equiv c \quad (\text{mod } 4).$$

It follows that $a \equiv c \;(\text{mod } 4)$. Thus $a \sim c$. This shows that $\sim$ is transitive.

Therefore, $\sim$ is an equivalence relation.   ▲

Hands-On Exercise 7.3.1   Define a relation $\sim$ on $\mathbb{Z}$ by

$$a \sim b \Leftrightarrow a \equiv b \;(\text{mod } 6).$$

Verify that $\sim$ is an equivalence relation.

$\triangle$

Hands-On Exercise 7.3.2   Let $n \geq 2$ be a positive integer. Define a relation $\sim$ on $\mathbb{Z}$ by

$$a \sim b \Leftrightarrow a \equiv b \;(\text{mod } n).$$

Verify that $\sim$ is an equivalence relation.

$\triangle$

Take a closer look at Example 7.3.2. All the integers having the same remainder when divided by 4 are related to each other. Define the sets

$$
\begin{aligned}
[0] &= \{n \in \mathbb{Z} \mid n \bmod 4 = 0\} &=& \quad 4\mathbb{Z}, \\
[1] &= \{n \in \mathbb{Z} \mid n \bmod 4 = 1\} &=& \quad 1 + 4\mathbb{Z}, \\
[2] &= \{n \in \mathbb{Z} \mid n \bmod 4 = 2\} &=& \quad 2 + 4\mathbb{Z}, \\
[3] &= \{n \in \mathbb{Z} \mid n \bmod 4 = 3\} &=& \quad 3 + 4\mathbb{Z}.
\end{aligned}
$$

It is clear that every integer belongs to exactly one of these four sets. Hence,

$$
\mathbb{Z} = [0] \cup [1] \cup [2] \cup [3].
$$

These four sets are pairwise disjoint, so $\mathbb{Z}$ is a *disjoint union* of these four sets. We say that $\{[0], [1], [2], [3]\}$ is a partition of $\mathbb{Z}$.

Definition.   A collection $\{S_1, S_2, \ldots, S_n\}$ of nonempty subsets of S is said to be a ***partition*** of S if the subsets $S_1, S_2, \ldots, S_n$ are pairwise disjoint ($S_i \cap S_j = \emptyset$ whenever $i \neq j$), and

$$
S_1 \cup S_2 \cup \cdots \cup S_n = S.
$$

The subsets $S_1, S_2, \ldots, S_n$ are called the ***parts*** or ***components*** of the partition. $\diamond$

Because of transitivity and symmetry, all the elements related to a fixed element must be related to each other. Thus, if we know one element in the group, we essentially know all its "relatives."

If you know one member in the gang, you know them all!

Definition.   Let $\sim$ be an equivalence relation on A. The set

$$
[a] = \{x \in A \mid x \sim a\}.
$$

is called the ***equivalence class*** of a. $\diamond$

Example 7.3.3   In Example 7.2.4, each equivalence class of the relation S consists of all the triangles that are similar. Note that no triangle can belong to two different equivalence classes. This means that the equivalence classes are pairwise disjoint.

In the same example, each equivalence class of the relation P consists of all the lines that are parallel. Again, take note that no line can belong to two different equivalence classes. Thus, the equivalence classes are pairwise disjoint.   ▲

Example 7.3.4   For the relation $\sim$ on $\mathbb{Z}$ defined by $a \sim b \Leftrightarrow a \equiv b \pmod 4$, there are four equivalence classes $[0], [1], [2]$ and $[3]$, and the set $\{[0], [1], [2], [3]\}$ forms a partition of $\mathbb{Z}$. Therefore,

$$
\mathbb{Z} = [0] \cup [1] \cup [2] \cup [3],
$$

and the four components $[0], [1], [2]$ and $[3]$ are pairwise disjoint.   ▲

Hands-On Exercise 7.3.3   What are the equivalence classes of the relation $\sim$ in Hands-On Exercise 7.3.1?

$\triangle$

Hands-On Exercise 7.3.4   What are the equivalence classes of the relation $\sim$ in in Hands-On Exercise 7.3.2?

$\triangle$

Hands-On Exercise 7.3.5   For each of the equivalence relations mentioned in Example 7.3.1, determine its equivalence classes.

$\triangle$

All the elements in the same equivalence class are related to each other. Therefore, the elements in $[a]$ all share the same property that a enjoys, from the viewpoint of the relation $\sim$. In Example 7.3.4, the equivalence class $[0]$ consists of elements that are multiples of 4. The equivalence class $[1]$ consists of elements that, when divided by 4, leave 1 as the remainder, and similarly for the equivalence classes $[2]$ and $[3]$. Because of the common bond between the elements in an equivalence class $[a]$, all these elements can be represented by *any* member within the equivalence class. This is the spirit behind the next theorem.

Theorem 7.3.1 *If $\sim$ is an equivalence relation on A, then $a \sim b \Leftrightarrow [a] = [b]$.*

Proof: We leave the proof as an exercise.   ■

Every element in an equivalence class can be its representative.

One may regard equivalence classes as objects with many aliases. Every element in an equivalence class can serve as its representative. So we have to take extra care when we deal with equivalence classes. Do not be fooled by the representatives, and consider two apparently different equivalence classes to be distinct when in reality they may be identical.

Example 7.3.5   Define $\sim$ on a set of individuals in a community according to

$$a \sim b \Leftrightarrow a \text{ and } b \text{ have the same last name.}$$

We have seen that $\sim$ is an equivalence relation. Each equivalence class consists of all the individuals with the same last name in the community. Hence, for example, James Smith, Lucy Smith, and Peter Smith all belong to the same equivalence class. Any Smith can serve as its representative, so we can denote it as, for example, [Peter Smith].   ▲

Example 7.3.6   Define $\sim$ on $\mathbb{R}^+$ according to

$$x \sim y \Leftrightarrow x - y \in \mathbb{Z}.$$

Hence, two real numbers are related if and only if they have the same decimal parts. It is easy to verify that $\sim$ is an equivalence relation, and each equivalence class $[x]$ consists of all the positive real numbers having the same decimal parts as x has. Notice that

$$\mathbb{R}^+ = \bigcup_{x \in (0,1]} [x],$$

which means that the equivalence classes $[x]$, where $x \in (0, 1]$, form a partition of $\mathbb{R}$.   ▲

Hands-On Exercise 7.3.6   Prove that the relation $\sim$ in Example 7.3.6 is indeed an equivalence relation.

$\triangle$

Hands-On Exercise 7.3.7 Define $\sim$ on $\mathbb{R}$ according to

$$x \sim y \Leftrightarrow x - y \in \mathbb{Z}.$$

Show that $\sim$ is an equivalence class. True or false: $-2.14 \in [5, 14]$? Explain.

$\triangle$

What makes equivalence relations so important is the following **Fundamental Theorem on Equivalence Relations**.

Theorem 7.3.2 *Given any equivalence relation on a nonempty set A, the set of equivalence classes forms a partition of A. Conversely, any partition $\{A_1, A_2, \ldots, A_n\}$ of a nonempty set A into a finite number of nonempty subsets induces an equivalence relation $\sim$ on A, where $a \sim b$ if and only if $a, b \in A_i$ for some i (thus a and b belong to the same component).*

Proof: It is clear that A is the union of the equivalence classes induced by $\sim$, so it remains to show that these equivalence classes are pairwise disjoint. Assume $[a] \cap [b] \neq \emptyset$. Let $x \in [a] \cap [b]$. Then $x \in [a]$ and $x \in [b]$. Having $x \in [a]$ means $x \sim a$, and $x \in [b]$ implies that $x \sim b$. Symmetry and transitivity imply that $a \sim b$. Theorem 7.3.1 assures that $[a] = [b]$. Therefore, if $[a] \neq [b]$, then $[a] \cap [b] = \emptyset$. This proves that the equivalence classes form a partition of A.

Let $A = A_1 \cup A_2 \cup \cdots \cup A_n$ be a partition of A, define the relation $\sim$ on A according to

$$x \sim y \Leftrightarrow x, y \in A_i \text{ for some } i.$$

It follows immediately from the definition that $x \sim x$, so the relation is reflexive. It is also clear that $x \sim y$ implies $y \sim x$, hence, the relation is symmetric. Finally, if $x \sim y$ and $y \sim z$, then $x, y \in A_i$ for some i, and $y, z \in A_j$ for some j. Since the A_is form a partition of A, the element y cannot belong to two components. This means $i = j$, hence, $x, z \in A_i$. This proves that $\sim$ is transitive. Consequently, $\sim$ is an equivalence relation. ∎

The idea behind the theorem is rather simple. Each equivalence class consists of all the "relatives" from the same family, so obviously the set A can be divided into families (equivalence classes). These families do not share any common elements (hence pairwise disjoint), because Theorem 7.3.1 states that any two equivalence classes sharing some common elements must be identical. Therefore, the families form a partition of A. Conversely, given a partition $\mathcal{P}$, we could define a relation that relates all members in the same component. This relation turns out to be an equivalence relation, with each component forming an equivalence class. This equivalence relation is referred to as the **equivalence relation induced by** $\mathcal{P}$.

Example 7.3.7 In Example 7.2.4, the relation S is an equivalence relation, and the equivalence classes are the sets of similar triangles, which form a partition of the set $\mathcal{T}$. This means any triangle belongs to one and only one equivalence class. In other words, we can classify the triangles on a plane according to their three interior angles.

The relation P in the same example is also an equivalence relation. Its equivalence classes are the sets of lines that are parallel. Every line on the plane belongs to exactly one equivalence class. Consequently, we can classify the lines on a plane by their slopes. ▲

Example 7.3.8 Over $\mathbb{Z}^*$, define

$$R_3 = \{(m, n) \mid m, n \in \mathbb{Z}^* \text{ and } mn > 0\}.$$

It is not difficult to verify that R_3 is an equivalence relation. There are only two equivalence classes: $[1]$ and $[-1]$, where $[1]$ contains all the positive integers, and $[-1]$ all the negative integers. It is obvious that $\mathbb{Z}^* = [1] \cup [-1]$.   ▲

As a line is the union of infinitely many points, a plane is the union of infinitely many parallel lines.

Example 7.3.9   For each $b \in \mathbb{R}$, define L_b to be the line in $\mathbb{R}^2$ (which is also called the xy-plane) with equation $y = 2x + b$. Then $\mathcal{L} = \{L_b \mid b \in \mathbb{R}\}$ is a partition of $\mathbb{R}^2$ because given any point on $\mathbb{R}^2$, there is only one straight line with slope 2 that can pass through it. Such a partition induces an equivalence relation $\sim$ defined by

$$(p, q) \sim (s, t) \Leftrightarrow \text{both } (p, q) \text{ and } (s, t) \text{ lie on } L_b \text{ for some } b.$$

Thus, $(p, q) \sim (s, t)$ if and only if the two points (p, q) and (s, t) lie on the same straight line of slope 2. This means $\frac{q-t}{p-s} = 2$. Therefore, we can restate the definition as

$$(p, q) \sim (s, t) \Leftrightarrow q - t = 2(p - s).$$

For example, $(1, 5) \sim (0, 3)$. In fact, $[(1, 5)]$ corresponds to the line $y = 2x + 3$ or L_3. Similarly, $[(1, 1.25)]$ corresponds to the line $y = 2x - 0.75$ or $L_{-0.75}$. In general, $L_b = [(0, b)]$.   ▲

Hands-On Exercise 7.3.8   Consider the partition of $\mathbb{R}^2$ (the xy-plane)

$$\mathbb{R}^2 = \bigcup_{b \in \mathbb{R}} L_b,$$

where L_b is the line satisfying the equation $y = 5x + b$. Determine the equivalence relation induced by this partition.

△

We have studied modular arithmetic extensively. In Hands-On Exercise 7.3.2, you have already proved the following result.

Theorem 7.3.3 *For any positive integer $n \geq 2$, the relation congruence modulo n is an equivalence relation on $\mathbb{Z}$.*

We can now provide a more rigorous definition of $\mathbb{Z}_n$.

Definition.   Let $n \geq 2$ be an integer. The equivalence classes $[0], [1], \ldots, [n-1]$ of the relation congruence modulo n are called the **residue classes modulo** n. The set

$$\mathbb{Z}_n = \big\{ [0], [1], \ldots, [n-1] \big\}$$

is called the set of residue classes modulo n.   ◇

Remark.   We define two operations $\oplus$ and $\odot$ on the elements of $\mathbb{Z}_n$ according to

$$[a] \oplus [b] = [a + b], \qquad \text{and} \qquad [a] \odot [b] = [ab].$$

We will not go into the details, but we would like to remark that $\langle \mathbb{Z}_n, \oplus, \odot \rangle$ forms an algebraic structure called ring. In practice, we seldom write $\mathbb{Z}_n = \big\{ [0], [1], \ldots, [n-1] \big\}$ because it is too cumbersome. Instead, we just write $\mathbb{Z}_n = \{0, 1, 2, \ldots, n-1\}$. However, what we really work with in $\mathbb{Z}_n$ are the residue classes represented by the integers 0 through $n-1$. $\diamond$

The incidence matrix of an equivalence relation exhibits a beautiful pattern. Conversely, by examining the incidence matrix of a relation, we can tell whether the relation is an equivalence relation.

If we can rearrange the rows and columns of an incidence matrix so that the modified incidence matrix can be divided into blocks of submatrices containing entirely 1s or entirely 0s, such that the 1-submatrices lie on the diagonal, then the underlying relation R is an equivalence relation. Here is the reason. Since the entries in each 1-submatrix are all 1s, this means the corresponding elements are all related to each other. This is the notion of transitivity. Obviously, every element is related to itself. Since the 1-submatrices lie on the diagonal, the matrix, hence the relation, is symmetric. This proves that the underlying relation is an equivalence relation. Each equivalence class consists of all the elements that correspond to the row and columns in the same 1-matrix.

Example 7.3.10 Let $A = \{1, 2, 3, 4, 5\}$ and define the relation R_1 on A by

$$R_1 = \{(1,1), (1,2), (1,3), (2,1), (2,2), (2,3), (3,1), (3,2), (3,3), (4,4), (4,4), (5,4), (5,5)\}.$$

It is clear from the incidence matrix (we add lines to make the 0- and 1-submatrices more outstanding)

$$
\begin{array}{c c}
 & \begin{array}{c c c c c} 1 & 2 & 3 & 4 & 5 \end{array} \\
\begin{array}{c} 1 \\ 2 \\ 3 \\ 4 \\ 5 \end{array} &
\left(\begin{array}{c c c | c c}
1 & 1 & 1 & 0 & 0 \\
1 & 1 & 1 & 0 & 0 \\
1 & 1 & 1 & 0 & 0 \\ \hline
0 & 0 & 0 & 1 & 1 \\
0 & 0 & 0 & 1 & 1
\end{array}\right)
\end{array}
$$

that R_1 is an equivalence relation and that it has two equivalence classes: $[1] = [2] = [3] = \{1,2,3\}$, and $[4] = [5] = \{4,5\}$, such that $A = [1] \cup [4]$. $\blacktriangle$

Example 7.3.11 Let $A = \{a, b, c, d\}$. Define the relation R_2 on A by

$$R_2 = \{(a,a), (a,c), (b,b), (b,d), (c,a), (c,c), (d,b), (d,d)\}.$$

After rewriting the incidence matrix

$$
\begin{array}{c c}
 & \begin{array}{c c c c} a & b & c & d \end{array} \\
\begin{array}{c} a \\ b \\ c \\ d \end{array} &
\left(\begin{array}{c c c c}
1 & 0 & 1 & 0 \\
0 & 1 & 0 & 1 \\
1 & 0 & 1 & 0 \\
0 & 1 & 0 & 1
\end{array}\right)
\end{array}
\quad \rightsquigarrow \quad
\begin{array}{c c}
 & \begin{array}{c c c c} a & c & b & d \end{array} \\
\begin{array}{c} a \\ c \\ b \\ d \end{array} &
\left(\begin{array}{c c | c c}
1 & 1 & 0 & 0 \\
1 & 1 & 0 & 0 \\ \hline
0 & 0 & 1 & 1 \\
0 & 0 & 1 & 1
\end{array}\right)
\end{array}
$$

it becomes clear that R_2 is an equivalence relation, with $[a] = [c] = \{a, c\}$, and $[b] = [d] = \{b, d\}$, such that $A = [a] \cup [b]$. $\blacktriangle$

Hands-On Exercise 7.3.9 The relation S defined on the set $\{1, 2, 3, 4, 5, 6\}$ is known to be

$$S = \{(1,1), (1,4), (2,2), (2,5), (2,6), (3,3),$$
$$(4,1), (4,4), (5,2), (5,5), (5,6), (6,2), (6,5), (6,6)\}.$$

Show that S is an equivalence relation by studying its incidence matrix, and rewriting it if necessary. Determine the contents of its equivalence classes.

$\triangle$

Example 7.3.12   Find the equivalence relation R induced by the partition

$$\mathcal{P} = \big\{\{1\}, \{3\}, \{2,4,5,6\}\big\}$$

of $A = \{1,2,3,4,5,6\}$.

Solution: From the two 1-element equivalence classes $\{1\}$ and $\{3\}$, we find two ordered pairs $(1,1)$ and $(3,3)$ that belong to R. From the equivalence class $\{2,4,5,6\}$, any pair of elements produce an ordered pair that belongs to R. Therefore,

$$
\begin{aligned}
R \;=\; & \{(1,1),(3,3),(2,2),(2,4),(2,5),(2,6),(4,2),(4,4),(4,5),(4,6),\\
& (5,2),(5,4),(5,5),(5,6),(6,2),(6,4),(6,5),(6,6)\}.
\end{aligned}
$$

Alternatively, we can construct the incidence matrix

$$
\begin{array}{c}
\\
1\\3\\2\\4\\5\\6
\end{array}
\begin{array}{cccccc}
1 & 3 & 2 & 4 & 5 & 6
\end{array}
$$

	1	3	2	4	5	6
1	1	0	0	0	0	0
3	0	1	0	0	0	0
2	0	0	1	1	1	1
4	0	0	1	1	1	1
5	0	0	1	1	1	1
6	0	0	1	1	1	1

from which the ordered pairs in R can be easily obtained.   ▲

Hands-On Exercise 7.3.10   Find the equivalence relation R induced by the partition

$$\mathcal{P} = \big\{\{a,d\}, \{b,c,g\}, \{e,f\}\big\}$$

of $A = \{a,b,c,d,e,f,g\}$ by listing all its ordered pairs (the roster method).

$\triangle$

Summary and Review

- A relation R on a set A is an equivalence relation if it is reflexive, symmetric, and transitive.
- If R is an equivalence relation on the set A, its equivalence classes form a partition of A.
- In each equivalence class, all the elements are related and every element in A belongs to one and only one equivalence class.
- The relation R determines the membership in each equivalence class, and every element in the equivalence class can be used to represent that equivalence class.
- In a sense, if you know one member within an equivalence class, you also know all the other elements in the equivalence class because they are all related according to R.
- Conversely, given a partition of A, we can use it to define an equivalence relation by declaring two elements to be related if they belong to the same component in the partition.

Exercises 7.3

1. Show that each of the following relations $\sim$ on $\mathbb{Z}$ is an equivalence relation, and find its equivalence classes.

   (a) $m \sim n \Leftrightarrow |m - 3| = |n - 3|$
   (b) $m \sim n \Leftrightarrow m + n$ is even

2. Show that each of the following relations $\sim$ on $\mathbb{Z}$ is an equivalence relation, and find its equivalence classes.

   (a) $m \sim n \Leftrightarrow 3 \mid (m + 2n)$
   (b) $m \sim n \Leftrightarrow 5 \mid (2m + 3n)$

3. Let T be a fixed subset of a nonempty set S. Define the relation $\sim$ on $\wp(S)$ by

   $$X \sim Y \Leftrightarrow X \cap T = Y \cap T,$$

   Show that $\sim$ is an equivalence relation. In particular, let $S = \{1, 2, 3, 4\}$ and $T = \{1, 3\}$.

   (a) True or false: $\{1, 2, 4\} \sim \{1, 4, 5\}$?
   (b) How about $\{1, 2, 4\} \sim \{1, 3, 4\}$?
   (c) Find $[\{1, 5\}]$
   (d) Describe $[X]$ for any $X \in \wp(S)$.

4. For each of the following relations $\sim$ on $\mathbb{R} \times \mathbb{R}$, determine whether it is an equivalence relation. For those that are, describe geometrically the equivalence class $[(a, b)]$.

   (a) $(x_1, y_1) \sim (x_2, y_2) \Leftrightarrow y_1 - x_1^2 = y_2 - x_2^2$.
   (b) $(x_1, y_1) \sim (x_2, y_2) \Leftrightarrow (x_1 - 1)^2 + y_1^2 = (x_2 - 1)^2 + y_2^2$

5. For each of the following relations $\sim$ on $\mathbb{R} \times \mathbb{R}$, determine whether it is an equivalence relation. For those that are, describe geometrically the equivalence class $[(a, b)]$.

   (a) $(x_1, y_1) \sim (x_2, y_2) \Leftrightarrow x_1 + y_2 = x_2 + y_1$
   (b) $(x_1, y_1) \sim (x_2, y_2) \Leftrightarrow (x_1 - x_2)(y_1 - y_2) = 0$

6. For each of the following relations $\sim$ on $\mathbb{R} \times \mathbb{R}$, determine whether it is an equivalence relation. For those that are, describe geometrically the equivalence class $[(a, b)]$.

   (a) $(x_1, y_1) \sim (x_2, y_2) \Leftrightarrow |x_1| + |y_1| = |x_2| + |y_2|$
   (b) $(x_1, y_1) \sim (x_2, y_2) \Leftrightarrow x_1 y_1 = x_2 y_2$

7. Define the relation $\sim$ on $\mathbb{Q}$ by

   $$x \sim y \Leftrightarrow 2(x - y) \in \mathbb{Z}.$$

   Show that $\sim$ is an equivalence relation. Describe the equivalence classes $[0]$ and $\left[\frac{1}{4}\right]$.

8. Define the relation $\sim$ on $\mathbb{Q}$ by

   $$x \sim y \Leftrightarrow \frac{x - y}{2} \in \mathbb{Z}.$$

   Show that $\sim$ is an equivalence relation. Describe the equivalence classes $[0]$, $[1]$ and $\left[\frac{1}{2}\right]$.

9. Consider the following relation on $\{a, b, c, d, e\}$:

   $$R = \{(a, a), (a, c), (a, e), (b, b), (b, d), (c, a), (c, c), (c, e),$$
   $$(d, b), (d, d), (e, a), (e, c), (e, e)\}.$$

   Show that it is an equivalence relation, and describe its equivalence classes.

   Hint: Use the matrix representation of the relation.

10. Each part below gives a partition of $A = \{a, b, c, d, e, f, g\}$. Find the equivalence relation on A induced by the partition.

   (a) $\mathcal{P}_1 = \big\{\{a, b\}, \{c, d\}, \{e, f\}, \{g\}\big\}$ (b) $\mathcal{P}_2 = \big\{\{a, c, e, g\}, \{b, d, f\}\big\}$
   (c) $\mathcal{P}_3 = \big\{\{a, b, d, e, f\}, \{c, g\}\big\}$ (d) $\mathcal{P}_4 = \big\{\{a, b, c, d, e, f, g\}\big\}$

11. Let $\sim$ be an equivalence relation on A. Prove that if $a \sim b$, then $[a] = [b]$.

12. Let $\sim$ be an equivalence relation on A. Prove that if $[a] = [b]$, then $a \sim b$.

7.4 Partial and Total Ordering

Two special relations occur frequently in mathematics. Both have to do with some sort of ordering of the elements in a set. A branch of mathematics is devoted to their study. As you can tell from the brief discussion in this section, they cover many familiar concepts.

Definition. A relation on a nonempty set A is called a ***partial ordering*** or a ***partial-order relation*** if it is reflexive, antisymmetric, and transitive. We often use $\preceq$ to denote a partial ordering, and called $(A, \preceq)$ a ***partially ordered set*** or a ***poset***.

Example 7.4.1 The usual "less than or equal to" relation on R, denoted $\leq$, is a perfect example of partial ordering. In fact, this is the reason why we adopt the notation $\preceq$, as it reflects the similarities between the two symbols. ▲

Example 7.4.2 Another classic example of partial ordering is the subset relation, denoted $\subseteq$, on $\wp(S)$, where S is any set of elements. Observe that S can be empty, in which case $\wp(\emptyset) = \{\emptyset\}$, and $(\wp(\emptyset), \subseteq)$ is obviously a partially ordered set. ▲

Example 7.4.3 Another standard example of poset is $(\mathbb{N}, |)$. It is easy to verify that the "divides" relation over the natural numbers is a partial ordering. Can you explain why $(\mathbb{Z}^*, |)$ is not a poset? ▲

Hands-On Exercise 7.4.1 Find a counterexample to illustrate why the "divides" relation, denoted $|$, over $\mathbb{Z}^*$ is not antisymmetric. Is the "divides" relation reflexive over $\mathbb{Z}$? How about transitivity?

△

Hands-On Exercise 7.4.2 Define the relation $\sqsubseteq$ on $\wp(\{a, b, c, d\})$ according to

$$S \sqsubseteq T \Leftrightarrow S \subseteq T \cup \{a\}.$$

Is $(\wp(\{a, b, c, d\}, \sqsubseteq)$ a poset? Which properties it does not possess? Explain.

△

Obviously, if $a \preceq b$ but $a \neq b$, then we can write $a \prec b$. We sometimes say a **precedes** b, or b **succeeds** a. We also say a is the **predecessor** of b, or b is the **successor** of a.

The digraph for a poset can be simplified. Since a is always related to a itself, it is redundant to draw a loop around every vertex. Since $a \preceq b$ and $b \preceq c$ always imply that $a \preceq c$, there is no need to include the arc (directed edge) from a to c. So we follow the convention that we only draw an arc from a to b if $a \prec b$ *and* there does not exist another element t such that $a \prec t$ and $t \prec b$. Lastly, if $a \prec b$, we can place b above a so that all the arcs are pointing upward. This suggests that we can use undirected lines to make the graph easier to read. All these modifications lead to a much simpler graphical representation called a **Hasse diagram**.

Example 7.4.4   It is clear that $(\{1, 2, 3, 4, 6, 12\}, |)$ is a poset. Its Hasse diagram is displayed below.

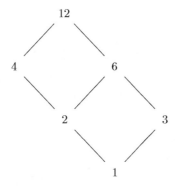

In this convention of using undirected line, the $\preceq$ relation (hence, the ordering of the elements) is read from the bottom up.   ▲

Hands-On Exercise 7.4.3   Draw the Hasse diagram for the poset $(\{1, 2, 3, 4, 6, 9, 12, 18, 36\}, |)$.

△

The definition of a poset does not require every pair of distinct elements to be comparable. This means there may exist $a \neq b$ such that $a \not\preceq b$ and $b \not\preceq a$. An example can be found in the numbers 2 and 3 in Example 7.4.4. If a partial ordering has the additional property that for any two distinct elements a and b, either $a \prec b$ or $b \prec a$ (hence, any pair of distinct elements are comparable), we call the relation a **total ordering**.

Example 7.4.5   The poset $(\mathbb{N}, \leq)$ is a totally ordered set. The poset $(\{1, 5, 25, 125\}, |)$ is also a totally ordered set. Its Hasse diagram is shown below.

It is clear that the Hasse diagram of any totally ordered set will look like the one displayed above. Consequently, a total ordering is also called a *linear ordering*. A totally ordered set is also called a *chain*.   ▲

Hands-On Exercise 7.4.4   Construct the Hasse diagram for the poset $(\{1, 2, 4, 18, 16\}, |)$. Is it a totally ordered set?

                                                                                                         △

Hands-On Exercise 7.4.5   Construct the Hasse diagram for the poset $(\wp(\{a, b, c\}), \subseteq)$.

                                                                                                         △

Summary and Review

- A relation that is reflexive, antisymmetric, and transitive is called a partial ordering.
- A set with a partial ordering is called a partially ordered set or a poset.
- A poset with every pair of distinct elements comparable is called a totally ordered set.
- A total ordering is also called a linear ordering, and a totally ordered set is also called a chain.

Exercises 7.4

1. Let A be the set of natural numbers that are divisors of 30. Construct the Hasse diagram of $(A, |)$.

2. Let $S = \{\{a\}, \{b\}, \{c\}, \{a, b\}, \{a, c\}, \{b, c\}\}$. Construct the Hasse diagram for $(S, \subseteq)$.

3. Let $(A, \preceq)$ be a poset, and B a nonempty subset of A. Show that $(B, \preceq)$ is also a poset. Naturally, we call $(B, \preceq)$ a **subposet** of $(A, \preceq)$.

4. Define the relation $\preceq$ on $\mathbb{Z}$ according to

$$a \preceq b \Leftrightarrow a = b \text{ or } a \bmod 3 < b \bmod 3.$$

   (a) Show that $(\mathbb{Z}, \preceq)$ is a poset.

   (b) Let $B = \{-3, -2, -1, 0, 1, 2, -3\}$. Construct the Hasse diagram for the subposet $(B, \preceq)$.

5. Define the relation $\preceq$ on $\mathbb{Z}$ according to

$$a \preceq b \Leftrightarrow a = b \text{ or } |a| < |b|.$$

   (a) Show that $(\mathbb{Z}, \preceq)$ is a poset.

   (b) Construct the Hasse diagram for the subposet $(B, \preceq)$, where $B = \{-2, -1, 0, 1, 2\}$.

6. Define the relation $\preceq$ on $\mathbb{Z} \times \mathbb{Z}$ according to

$$(a, b) \preceq (c, d) \Leftrightarrow (a, b) = (c, d) \text{ or } a^2 + b^2 < c^2 + d^2.$$

   (a) Show that $(\mathbb{Z} \times \mathbb{Z}, \preceq)$ is a poset.

   (b) Construct the Hasse diagram for the subposet $(B, \preceq)$, where $B = \{0, 1, 2\} \times \{0, 1, 2\}$.

7. Construct an example of a subset B of $\wp(\{a, b, c, d\})$ such that $(B, \subseteq)$ is a totally ordered set.

8. Let
$$A = \{(m, n) \mid m, n \in \mathbb{N} \text{ and } \gcd(m, n) = 1\},$$

and define the relation $\preceq$ on A according to

$$(a, b) \preceq (c, d) \Leftrightarrow ad \leq bc.$$

Prove that $(A, \preceq)$ is a totally ordered set.

Chapter 8

Combinatorics

8.1 What is Combinatorics?

Combinatorics studies the arrangements of objects according to some rules. The questions that can be asked include

- *Existence.* Do the arrangements exist?
- *Classification.* If the arrangements exist, how can we characterize and classify them?
- *Enumeration.* How many arrangements are there?
- *Construction.* Is there an algorithm for constructing all the arrangements?

Example 8.1.1 In how many ways can five people be seated at a round table? What if a certain pair of them refuses to sit next to one another? What if there are n people? ▲

Example 8.1.2 Given integers $n_1 \geq n_2 \geq \cdots \geq n_t \geq 1$, a **Young tableau** of the shape $(n_1, n_2, \ldots, n_t)$ consists of t rows of left-justified cells, with n_i cells in the ith row (counting from the top row). These cells are occupied by the integers 1 through n, where $n = n_1 + n_2 + \cdots + n_t$, such that the entries are in descending order across each row from left to right, and down each column from top to bottom. For instance, the three Young tableaux of the shape $(3, 1)$ are depicted in Figure 8.1.

4	3	2
1		

4	3	1
2		

4	2	1
3		

Figure 8.1: The three Young tableaux of the shape $(3, 1)$.

It is known that there are 35 Young tableaux of the shape $(4, 2, 1)$. Can you list all of them? In general, one may ask, how many Young tableaux are there of shape $(n_1, n_2, \ldots, n_t)$, and how can we generate all of them? ▲

Example 8.1.3 A **binary string** is a sequence of digits, each of which being 0 or 1. Let a_n be the number of binary strings of length n that do not contain consecutive 1s. It is easy to check that $a_1 = 2$, $a_2 = 3$, and $a_3 = 5$. What is the general formula for a_n? ▲

Example 8.1.4 The complexity of an algorithm tells us how many operations it requires. By comparing the complexity of several algorithms for solving the same problem, we can determine which one is most efficient. Let b_n be the number of operations required to solve a problem of size n. If it is known that

$$b_n = 2b_{n-1} + 3b_{n-2}, \qquad n \geq 3,$$

where $b_1 = 1$ and $b_2 = 3$, what is the general formula for b_n? ▲

8.2   Addition and Multiplication Principles

Recall that the cardinality of a finite set A, denoted $|A|$, is the number of elements it contains.

Example 8.2.1   If $A = \{-1, 0, 2\}$, then $|A| = 3$. Also,

$$\begin{aligned}
|\{2\}| &= 1, \\
|\{2, 5, -1, -3\}| &= 4, \\
|\{x \in \mathbb{R} \mid x^2 = 1\}| &= 2.
\end{aligned}$$

Notice that $|\emptyset| = 0$, because an empty set does not contain any element.   ▲

It becomes more interesting when we consider the cardinality of a union or an intersection of two or more sets.

Example 8.2.2   Determine $|A \cup B|$ and $|A \cap B|$ if $A = \{2, 5\}$ and $B = \{7, 9, 10\}$.

Solution: Since $A \cup B = \{2, 5, 7, 9, 10\}$, and $A \cap B = \emptyset$, it is clear that $|A \cup B| = 5$, and $|A \cap B| = 0$.   ▲

Example 8.2.3   Determine $|A \cup B|$ and $|A \cap B|$ if $A = \{2, 5\}$ and $B = \{5, 9, 10\}$.

Solution: Since $A \cup B = \{2, 5, 9, 10\}$, and $A \cap B = \{5\}$, it is clear that $|A \cup B| = 4$, and $|A \cap B| = 1$.   ▲

Hands-On Exercise 8.2.1   Let $A = \{n \in \mathbb{Z} \mid -5 \leq n \leq 3\}$, and $B = \{n \in \mathbb{Z} \mid -3 \leq n \leq 5\}$. Evaluate $|A \cap B|$ and $|A \cup B|$.

△

The difference between the last two examples is whether the two sets A and B have a nonempty intersection. Two sets A and B are **disjoint** if $A \cap B = \emptyset$. A collection of sets $A_1, A_2, \ldots, A_n$ is said to be **pairwise disjoint** if $A_i \cap A_j = \emptyset$ whenever $i \neq j$. When $A_1, A_2, \ldots, A_n$ are pairwise disjoint, their union is called a **disjoint union**.

Example 8.2.4   Let $A = \{1, 0, -1\}$, $B = \{-2, 0, 2\}$, $C = \{-2, 2\}$ and $D = \{3, 4, 5\}$. Then A, C, and D are pairwise disjoint, so are B and D, but A, B, and C are not.   ▲

Theorem 8.2.1 (Addition Principle) *If the finite sets $A_1, A_2, \ldots, A_n$ are pairwise disjoint, then*

$$|A_1 \cup A_2 \cup \cdots \cup A_n| = |A_1| + |A_2| + \cdots + |A_n|.$$

Use the addition principle only when the sets do not overlap.

Use the addition principle if we can break down the problems into *cases*, and count how many items or choices we have in each case. The total number is the sum of these individual counts. The idea is, instead of counting a large set, we divide it up into several smaller subsets, and count the size of each of them. The cardinality of the original set is the sum of the cardinalities of the smaller subsets. This divide-and-conquer approach works perfectly only when the sets are pairwise disjoint.

Example 8.2.5   To find the number of students present at a lecture, the teacher counts how many students there are in each row, then adds up the numbers to obtain the total count.   ▲

Watch for double counting!

When the sets are not disjoint, the addition principle does not give us the right answer because the elements belonging to the intersection are counted more than once. We have to compensate the over-counting by subtracting the number of times these elements are over-counted. The simplest case covers two sets.

Theorem 8.2.2 (Principle of Inclusion-Exclusion (PIE)) *For any finite sets A and B, we have*

$$|A \cup B| = |A| + |B| - |A \cap B|.$$

In general, use PIE to find the cardinality of a union of sets.

Proof: Observe that $A \cup B$ is the *disjoint union* of three sets

$$A \cup B = (A - B) \cup (A \cap B) \cup (B - A).$$

It is clear that $|A - B| = |A| - |A \cap B|$, and $|B - A| = |B| - |A \cap B|$. Therefore,

$$
\begin{aligned}
|A \cup B| &= |A - B| + |A \cap B| + |B - A| \\
&= (|A| - |A \cap B|) + |A \cap B| + (|B| - |A \cap B|) \\
&= |A| + |B| - |A \cap B|,
\end{aligned}
$$

which is what we have to prove. ∎

The principle of inclusion-exclusion also works if A and B are disjoint, because in such an event, $|A \cap B| = 0$, reducing PIE to the addition principle.

Example 8.2.6 Assume the current enrollment at a college is 4689, with 60 students taking MATH 210, 42 taking CSIT 260, and 24 taking both. Together, how many different students are taking these two courses? In other words, determine the number of students who are taking either MATH 210 or CSIT 260.

Solution: Let A be the set of students taking MATH 210, and B the set of students taking CSIT 260, Then, $|A| = 60$, $|B| = 42$, and $|A \cap B| = 24$. We want to find $|A \cup B|$. According to PIE,

$$|A \cup B| = |A| + |B| - |A \cap B| = 60 + 42 - 24 = 78.$$

Therefore, 78 students are taking either MATH 210 or CSIT 260. ▲

Example 8.2.7 Among 4689 students, 2112 of them have earned at least 60 credit hours and 2678 of them have earned at most 60 credit hours. How many students are there who have accumulated exactly 60 hours?

Solution: Let A be the set of students who have earned at least 60 credit hours, and B be the set of students who have earned at most 60 credit hours. We want to find $|A \cap B|$. According to PIE,

$$4689 = |A \cup B| = |A| + |B| - |A \cap B| = 2112 + 2678 - |A \cap B|.$$

Hence,

$$|A \cap B| = (2112 + 2678) - 4689 = 101.$$

There are 101 students who have accumulated exactly 60 credit hours. ▲

Hands-On Exercise 8.2.2 The attendance at two consecutive college football games was 72397 and 69211 respectively. If 45713 people attended both games, how many different people have watched the games?

△

Hands-On Exercise 8.2.3   The attendance at two consecutive college football games was 72397 and 69211 respectively. If 93478 different individuals attended these two games, how many have gone to both?

$\triangle$

Sometimes, it is easy to work with the complement of a set.

Lemma 8.2.3 *For any finite set S, we have*

Using complement may simplify a counting problem.

$$|\overline{S}| = |\mathcal{U}| - |S|,$$

where $\mathcal{U}$ is the universal set containing S.

Example 8.2.8   In Example 8.2.6, since there are 78 students taking either MATH 210 or CSIT 260, the number of students taking neither is $4689 - 78 = 4611$.   ▲

The principle of inclusion-exclusion can be extended to any number of sets. The situation is more complicated, because some elements may be double-counted, some triple-counted, etc. To give you a taste of the general result, here is the principle of inclusion-exclusion for three sets.

Theorem 8.2.4 *For any three finite sets A, B and C,*

$$|A \cup B \cup B| = |A| + |B| + |C| - |A \cap B| - |A \cap C| - |B \cap C| + |A \cap B \cap C|.$$

Proof: The union $A \cup B \cup C$ is the disjoint union of seven subsets:

$$A - (B \cup C), \quad B - (C \cup A), \quad C - (A \cup B), \quad (A \cap B) - (A \cap B \cap C),$$
$$(B \cap C) - (A \cap B \cap C), \quad (C \cap A) - (A \cap B \cap C), \quad \text{and} \quad A \cap B \cap C.$$

We can apply an argument similar to the one used in the union of two sets to complete the proof. We leave the details as an exercise.   ■

Hands-On Exercise 8.2.4   A group of students claims that each of them had seen at least one part of the *Back to the Future* trilogy. A quick show of hands reveals that

- 47 had watched Part I;
- 43 had watched Part II;
- 32 had watched Part III;
- 33 had watched both Parts I and II;
- 27 had watched both Parts I and III;
- 25 had watched both Parts II and III;
- 22 had watched all three parts.

How many students are there in the group?

$\triangle$

Another useful counting technique is the multiplication principle.

Theorem 8.2.5 (Multiplication Principle) *For any finite sets A and B, we have*

$$|A \times B| = |A| \cdot |B|.$$

Clearly, this can be extended to an n-fold Cartesian product.

Corollary 8.2.6 *For any finite sets $A_1, A_2, \ldots, A_n$, we have*

$$|A_1 \times A_2 \times \cdots \times A_n| = |A_1| \cdot |A_2| \cdot \cdots \cdot |A_n|.$$

In many applications, it may be helpful to use an equivalent form.

Theorem 8.2.7 (Multiplication Principle: Alternate Form) *If a task consists of k steps, and if there are n_i ways to finish step i, then the entire job can be completed in $n_1 n_2 \ldots n_k$ different ways.*

Now that we have two counting techniques, the addition principle and the multiplication principle, which one should we use? The major difference between them is whether

Which one should we use: the addition or multiplication principle? Look for keywords such as cases or groups versus steps or positions.

- the jobs can be divided into *cases*, *groups*, or *categories*; or
- each job can be broken up into *steps*.

In practice, it helps to draw a picture of the configurations that we are counting.

Example 8.2.9 How many different license plates are there if a standard license plate consists of three letters followed by three digits?

Solution: We need to decide how many choices we have in each position. Draw a picture to show the configuration. Draw six lines to represent the six positions. Above each line, describe briefly the possible candidates for that position, and under each line, write the the number of choices.

	any letter	any letter	any letter	any digit	any digit	any digit
choices:						
# of choices:	26	26	26	10	10	10

This left-to-right configuration suggests that the multiplication principle should be used. The answer is $26 \cdot 26 \cdot 26 \cdot 10 \cdot 10 \cdot 10 = 260^3$.

As you become more experienced, you can argue directly, as follows. There are 26 choices for each of the three letters, and 10 choices for each digit. So there are $26 \cdot 26 \cdot 26 \cdot 10 \cdot 10 \cdot 10 = 260^3$ different license plates. ▲

Example 8.2.10 Find the number of positive integers not exceeding 999 that end with 7.

Solution 1: The integers can have one, two, or three digits, so we have to analyze three cases.

- *Case 1.* There is only one integer with one digit, namely, the integer 7.

- *Case 2.* If there are two digits, the first could be any digit between 1 and 9, and the last digit must be 7.

	1–9	7
choices:		
# of choices:	9	1

This gives us nine choices.

- *Case 3.* If there are three digits, the first digit could be any digit between 1 and 9, the second any digit between 0 and 9, and the last digit must be 7.

	any	
choices:	1–9	digit	7
# of choices:	9	10	1

Hence, there are 90 integers in this case.

Combining the three cases, we have a total of $1+9+90 = 100$ integers that meet the requirements.

Solution 2:   The integers could be written as three-digit integers if we allow 0 as the leading digits. For instance, 7 can be written as 007, and 34 as 034. Under this agreement, we have to fill three positions where the last one is always occupied by the digit 7. The first two digits are $0, 1, 2, \ldots, 8$, or 9, so there are 10 choices for each position.

	any	any	
choices:	digit	digit	7
# of choices:	10	10	1

Together, there are $10 \cdot 10 = 100$ such integers.   ▲

Hands-On Exercise 8.2.5   How many natural numbers less than 1000000 are there that end with the digit 3?

△

Hands-On Exercise 8.2.6   How many natural numbers less than 10000 are there that end with the digit 0?

△

Example 8.2.11   Determine the number of four-digit positive integers without repeated digits.

Solution: We want to determine how many choices there are for each place value. The first digit has nine choices because it cannot be 0. Once the first digit is chosen, there are nine choices left for the second digit; and then eight choices for the next digit, and seven choices for the last digit. Together, we have $9 \cdot 9 \cdot 8 \cdot 7 = 4536$ four-digit positive integers that do not contain any repeated digits. Question: Can we start counting from the last digit?   ▲

Hands-On Exercise 8.2.7   How many six-digit natural numbers are there that do not have any repeated digit?

△

Example 8.2.12   Determine $|\wp(S)|$, where S is an n-element set.

Solution: We want to determine the number of ways to form a subset. Let the n elements be $s_1, s_2, \ldots, s_n$. To form a subset, we go through each element s_i and decide whether it should be included in the subset, thus there are two choices for each element.

element:	s_1	s_2		s_n
choices:	Y/N	Y/N	$\ldots$	Y/N
	———	———		———
# of choices:	2	2		2

We have $\underbrace{2 \cdot 2 \cdot \cdots \cdot 2}_{n \text{ factors}} = 2^n$ ways to form the subsets. Thus, $|\wp(S)| = 2^n$. ▲

Example 8.2.13 How many two-digit positive integers do not have consecutive 5s?

Solution 1: There are three *disjoint* cases:

(i) both digits are not 5,
(ii) only the first digit is 5, and
(iii) only the last digit is 5.

There are $8 \cdot 9 + 9 + 8 = 89$ integers that meet the requirement.

Solution 2: An easier solution is to consider the complement of the problem. There is only one integer with consecutive 5s, namely, the integer 55. There are 90 two-digit integers, hence $90 - 1 = 89$ of them do not have consecutive 5s. ▲

It's easier to use complement!

Hands-On Exercise 8.2.8 How many three-digit natural numbers are there that do not have consecutive 4s?

△

Example 8.2.14 In how many ways can we draw a sequence of three cards from a standard deck of 52 cards?

With or without replacements (or repetitions) makes a big difference.

Solution: This is a trick question! The answer depends on whether we can return a drawn card to the deck. With replacement, the answer is 52^3; without replacement, it is $52 \cdot 51 \cdot 50$. ▲

Example 8.2.15 A standard New York State license plate consists of three letters followed by four digits. Determine the number of standard New York State license plates with K as the first letter *or* 8 as the first digit.

Solution: The keyword "or" suggests that we are looking at a union, hence, we have to apply PIE. We need to analyze three possibilities:

- There are $26^2 \cdot 10^4$ license plates with K as the first letter.
- There are $26^3 \cdot 10^3$ license plates with 8 as the first digit.
- There are $26^2 \cdot 10^3$ license plates with K as the first letter *and* 8 as the first digit.

The answer is $26^2 \cdot 10^4 + 26^3 \cdot 10^3 - 26^2 \cdot 10^3$. ▲

Hands-On Exercise 8.2.9 To access personal account information, a customer could log in to the bank's web site with a PIN consisting of two letters followed by

(a) exactly four digits,

(b) at most six digits,

(c) at least two but at most 6 digits.

How many different PINs are there in each case?

$\triangle$

Summary and Review

- Use the addition principle if the problem can be divided into cases. Make sure the cases do not overlap.
- If the cases overlap, the number of objects belonging to the overlapping cases must be subtracted from the total to obtain the correct count.
- In particular, the principle of inclusion-exclusion states that $|A \cup B| = |A| + |B| - |A \cap B|$.
- Use the multiplication principle if the problem can be solved in several steps.
- How can we get started? Imagine you want to list all the possibilities, what is a systematic way of doing so? Follow the steps, and count how many objects you would end up with.
- It may be helpful to use a schematic diagram. Draw one line for each step. Above the lines, write the choices. Below the lines, write the number of choices. Apply the multiplication principle to finish the problem.
- If there are other cases involved, repeat, and add the results from all the possible cases.

Exercises 8.2

1. A professor surveyed the 98 students in her class to count how many of them had watched at least one of the three films in *The Lord of the Rings* trilogy. This is what she found:

   - 74 had watched Part I;
   - 57 had watched Part II;
   - 66 had watched Part III;
   - 52 had watched both Parts I and II;
   - 51 had watched both Parts I and III;
   - 45 had watched both Parts II and III;
   - 43 had watched all three parts.

   How many students did not watch any one of these three movies?

2. Forty-six students in a film class told the professor that they had watched at least one of the three films in *The Godfather* trilogy. Further inquiry led to the following data:

   - 41 had watched Part I;
   - 37 had watched Part II;
   - 33 had watched Part III;
   - 33 had watched both Parts I and II;
   - 30 had watched both Parts I and III;
   - 29 had watched both Parts II and III.

   (a) How many students had watched all three films?

   (b) How many students had watched only Part I?

(c) How many students had watched only Part II?

(d) How many students had watched only Part III?

3. Joe has 10 dress shirts and seven bow ties. In how many ways can he match the shirts with bow ties?

4. A social security number is a sequence of nine digits. Determine the number of social security numbers that satisfy the following conditions:

   (a) There are no restrictions.
   (b) The digit 8 is never used.
   (c) The sequence does not begin or end with 8.
   (d) No digit is used more than once.

5. A professor has seven books on discrete mathematics, five on number theory, and four on abstract algebra. In how many ways can a student borrow two books not both on the same subject?

   Hint: Which two subjects would the student choose?

6. How many different collections of cans can be formed from five identical Cola-Cola cans, four identical Seven-Up cans, and seven identical Mountain Dew cans?

   Hint: How many cans of Cola-Cola, Seven-Up, and Mountain Dew would you pick?

7. How many five-letter words (technically, we should call them strings, because we do not care if they make sense) can be formed using the letters A, B, C, and D, with repetitions allowed. How many of them do not contain the substring BAD?

   Hint: For the second question, consider using a complement.

8. How many different five-digit integers can be formed using the digits 1, 3, 3, 3, 5?

   Hint: The three digits 3 are identical, so we cannot tell the difference between them. Consequently, what really matters is where we put the digits 1 and 5. Once we place the digits 1 and 5, the remaining three positions must be occupied by the digits 3.

9. Four cards are chosen at random from a standard deck of 52 playing cards, with replacement allowed. This means after choosing a card, the card is return to the deck, and the deck is reshuffled before another card is selected at random. Determine the number of such four-card sequences if

   (a) There are no restrictions.
   (b) None of the cards can be spades.
   (c) All four cards are from the same suit.
   (d) The first card is an ace and the second card is not a king.
   (e) At least one of the four cards is an ace.

10. Three different mathematics final examinations and two different computer science final examinations are to be scheduled during a five-day period. Determine the number of ways to schedule these final examinations from 11 AM to 1 PM if

    (a) There are no restrictions.
    (b) No two examinations can be scheduled on the same day.
    (c) No two examinations from the same department can be scheduled on the same day.
    (d) Each mathematics examination must be the only examination for the day on which it is scheduled.

11. Determine the number of four-digit positive integers that satisfy the following conditions:

(a) There are no restrictions.
(b) No integer contains the digit 8.
(c) Every integer contains the digit 8 at least once.
(d) Every integer is a palindrome (A positive integer is a palindrome if it remains the same when read backward, for example, 3773 and 47874).

12. A box contains 12 distinct colored balls (for instance, we could label them as 1, 2, ..., 12 to distinguish them). Three of them are red, four are yellow, and five are green. Three balls are selected at random from the box, with replacement. Determine the number of sequences that satisfy the following conditions:

(a) There are no restrictions.
(b) The first ball is red, the second is yellow, and the third is green.
(c) The first ball is red, and the second and third balls are green.
(d) Exactly two balls are yellow.
(e) All three balls are green.
(f) All three balls are the same color.
(g) At least one of the three balls is red.

13. Let $A = \{a, b, c, d, e, f\}$ and $B = \{1, 2, 3, 4, 5, 6, 7, 8\}$. Determine the number of functions $f : A \to B$ that satisfy the following conditions:

(a) There are no restrictions.
(b) f is one-to-one.
(c) f is onto.
(d) $f(x)$ is odd for at least one x in A.
(e) $f(a) = 3$ or $f(b)$ is odd.
(f) $f^{-1}(4) = \{a\}$.

14. How many onto functions are there from an n-element set A to $\{a, b\}$?

8.3   Permutations

Let A be a finite set with n elements. For $1 \leq r \leq n$, an r-**permutation** of A is an *ordered* selection of r distinct elements from A. In other words, it is the *linear* arrangement of r distinct objects $a_1 a_2 \ldots a_r$, where $a_i \in A$ for each i. The number of r-permutations of an n-element set is denoted by $P(n, r)$. It also appears in many other forms and names.

- The number of permutations of n objects, taken r at a time without replacement.
- The number of ways to arrange n objects (in a sequence), taken r at a time without replacement.

All of them refer to the same number $P(n, r)$. The keywords are:

The keyword is arrangement; be sure no repetition is allowed.

(i) "*Permutation*" or "*arrangement*," both of which suggest that order does matter.
(ii) "*Without replacement*" means the entries in the permutation/arrangement are distinct.

In some textbooks, the notation $P(n, r)$ is also written as P_r^n or $_nP_r$.

Example 8.3.1   The 1-permutations of $\{a, b, c, d\}$ are

$$a, \quad b, \quad c, \quad d.$$

Consequently, $P(4, 1) = 4$. The 2-permutations of $\{a, b, c, d\}$ are

$$\begin{array}{lll} ab, & ac, & ad, \\ ba, & bc, & bd, \\ ca, & cb, & cd, \\ da, & db, & dc. \end{array}$$

Hence, $P(4,2) = 12$. What are the 3-permutations and 4-permutations of $\{a, b, c, d\}$? Can you explain why the numbers of 3-permutations and 4-permutations are equal?   ▲

Computing the value of $P(n, r)$ is easy. We want to arrange r objects in a sequence. These r objects are to be selected from a pool of n items. Hence there are n ways to fill the first position. Once we settle with the first position, whatever we put there cannot be used again. We are left with $n-1$ choices for the second position. Likewise, once it is filled, there are only $n-2$ choices for the third position. Now it is clear that $P(n, r)$ is the product of r numbers of the form n, $n-1, n-2, \ldots$. What is the last number in this list? There are $r-1$ numbers before it, so it must be $n - (r-1) = n - r + 1$.

Theorem 8.3.1 *For all integers n and r satisfying $1 \leq r \leq n$,*

$$P(n, r) = n(n-1) \cdots (n - r + 1) = \frac{n!}{(n-r)!}.$$

Although the formula $P(n, r) = \frac{n!}{(n-r)!}$ is rather easy to remember, the other form

$$P(n, r) = \underbrace{n(n-1) \cdots (n - r + 1)}_{r}$$

is actually more useful in numeric computation, especially when it is done by hand. We multiply n by the next smaller integer $n-1$, and then the next smaller integer $n-2$, and so forth, until we have a product of r consecutive factors. For instance,

$$P(4, 2) = 4 \cdot 3 = 12, \qquad \text{and} \qquad P(9, 3) = 9 \cdot 8 \cdot 7 = 504.$$

How about $P(n, 1)$ and $P(n, 2)$?

The formula for $P(n, r)$ looks like a factorial; except that it stops at $n - r + 1$ instead of 1. Just remember, it contains exactly r factors.

Example 8.3.2 How would you compute the value of $P(278, 3)$ by hand, or if your calculator does not have that $_nP_r$ button?

Solution: We find $P(278, 3) = 278 \cdot 277 \cdot 276 = 21253656$.   ▲

Hands-On Exercise 8.3.1 Compute $P(21, 4)$ by hand.

△

Remark. It follows from the first version of the formula that $P(n, n) = n!$. The second version reduces to

$$n! = P(n, n) = \frac{n!}{0!}.$$

Consequently, to make the second version works, we have to define $0! = 1$.   ◇

Remark. In your homework assignments, quizzes, tests, and final exam, it is perfectly fine to use the notation $P(n, r)$ in your answers. In fact, leaving the answers in terms of $P(n, r)$ gives others a clue to how you obtained the answer.   ◇

You may leave the answers in terms of $P(n, r)$.

It is often easier and less confusing if we use the multiplication principle. Once you realize the answer involves $P(n, r)$, it is not difficult to figure out the values of n and r. A good start, *before jumping into any calculation*, is to ask yourself, how would you list the possible arrangements? Also, try constructing some examples. These can give you an idea of how many choices you have in each position.

Example 8.3.3   A police station has 12 police officers on duty. In how many ways can they be assigned to foot patrol in five different districts, assuming that we assign only one police officer per district.

Solution: Imagine you are the officer who schedules the assignments. You have to assign someone to the first district, and then another officer to the second district, and so forth.

district:	first	second	third	fourth	fifth
choices:	any officer	another officer	another different officer	...	...
# of choices:	12	11	10	9	8

There are 12 choices for the first district, 11 for the second, etc. The multiplication principle implies that the answer is $12 \cdot 11 \cdots$, which is in the form of $P(n, r)$. Since the product starts with 12, and we need a product of 5 consecutive numbers, the answer is $P(12, 5)$.   ▲

Hands-On Exercise 8.3.2   A school sends a team of six runners to a relay game. In how many ways can they be selected to participate in the 4×100 m relay?

△

Example 8.3.4   From a collection of 10 flags of different patterns, how many three-flag signals can we put on a pole?

Solution: Since the flags are arranged on a flag pole, the order is important. There are 10 choices for the top flag, 9 for the second, and 8 for the third. Therefore, $10 \cdot 9 \cdot 8 = P(10, 3)$ different signals can be formed.   ▲

Example 8.3.5   Determine the number of functions $f\colon \{1, 3, 4, 7, 9\} \to \mathbb{Z}_{22}$ if

   (a) There are no restrictions.
   (b) f is one-to-one.
   (c) f is onto.

When you get stuck, take a step back and look at a generalized problem.

Solution: To distinguish one function from another function, we have to compare their images. Hence, a function is completely determined by its images (surprise: not by its formula!). After all, we may not even know the formula behind a function, so we cannot and should not rely on the formula alone.

To determine how many functions there are from $\{1, 3, 4, 7, 9\}$ to $\mathbb{Z}_{22}$, we have to determine the number of ways to assign values to $f(1)$, $f(3)$, $f(4)$, $f(7)$ and $f(9)$.

images:	$f(1)$	$f(3)$	$f(4)$	$f(7)$	$f(9)$
choices:					
# of choices:					

(a) If there are no restrictions, we have 22 choices for each of these five images. Hence there are $22 \cdot 22 \cdot 22 \cdot 22 \cdot 22 = 22^5$ functions.

(b) If f is one-to-one, we cannot duplicate the images. So we have 22 choices for $f(1)$, 21 for $f(3)$, and so on. There are $P(22, 5)$ one-to-one functions.

(c) There are at most five distinct images, but $\mathbb{Z}_{22}$ has 22 elements, so at least 17 of them will be left unused. Hence f can never be onto. The number of onto functions is therefore zero.   ▲

Hands-On Exercise 8.3.3   How many functions are there from $\{2, 4, 6, 8, 10\}$ to $\mathbb{Z}_{15}$? How many of them are one-to-one?

△

Example 8.3.6   Let A and B be finite sets, with $|A| = s$ and $|B| = t$. Determine the number of one-to-one functions from A to B.

Solution: How can we come up with a one-to-one function from A to B? We have to specify the image of each element in A. There are t choices for the first element. Since repeated images are not allowed, we have only $t - 1$ choices for the image of the second element in A, and $t - 2$ choices for the third image, and so forth. The answer is $P(t, s)$.

What if $t < s$? We know that in such an event, there does not exist any one-to-one function from A to B because there are not enough distinct images. Does $P(t, s)$ still make sense? The product version of the formula says that $P(t, s)$ is a product of s consecutive numbers. Hence, for example,

$$P(3, 6) = 3 \cdot 2 \cdot 1 \cdot 0 \cdot (-1) \cdot (-2) = 0,$$

which means there is no one-to-one function from A to B.   ▲

$P(n, r) = 0$ if $n < r$.

Not all problems use $P(n, r)$. In many situations, we have to use $P(n, r)$ together with other numbers. The safest approach is to rely on the addition and multiplication principles.

Example 8.3.7   How many four-digit integers are there that do not contain repeated digits?

Solution: There are 10 choices for each digit, but the answer is not $P(10, 4)$, because we cannot use 0 as the first digit. To ensure that we have a four-digit integer, the first digit must be nonzero. This leaves us 9 choice for the first digit. Then we have 9 choices for the second digit, 8 and 7 for the next two. The answer is $9 \cdot 9 \cdot 8 \cdot 7$.   ▲

Example 8.3.8   Twelve children are playing "musical chairs," with 9 chairs arranged in a circle on the floor. In how many ways can they be seated?

Solution: The answer is not $P(12, 9)$ because any position can be the first position in a **circular permutation**. What matters is the relative placement of the selected objects, all we care is who is sitting next to whom. The correct answer can be found in the next theorem.   ▲

Theorem 8.3.2 *The number of circular r-permutations of an n-element set is $P(n, r)/r$.*

Proof: Compare the number of circular r-permutations to the number of linear r-permutations. Start at any position in a circular r-permutation, and go in the clockwise direction; we obtain a linear r-permutation. Since we can start at any one of the r positions, each circular r-permutation produces r linear r-permutations. This means that there are r times as many circular r-permutations as there are linear r-permutations. Therefore, the number of circular r-permutations is $P(n, r)/r$.   ∎

Alternate Proof.   Let A be the set of all linear r-permutations of the n objects, and let B be the set of all circular r-permutations. Define a function from A to B as follows. Given any

r-permutation, form its image by joining its "head" to its "tail." It becomes clear, using the same argument in the proof above, that f is an r-to-one function, which means f maps r distinct elements from A to the same image in B. Therefore A has r times as many elements as in B. This means $|A| = r \cdot |B|$. Since $|A| = P(n,r)$, we find $|B| = P(n,r)/r$.   ■

Hands-On Exercise 8.3.4   A circular cardboard has eight dots marked along its rim. In how many ways can we glue eight beads of different colors, one on each dot?

△

Hands-On Exercise 8.3.5   In how many ways can we form a necklace with eight beads of different color?

Remark: When a necklace is flipped around, it is still the same necklace. Thus, the orientation of the necklace does not matter: we can count the beads clockwise, or counterclockwise.

△

Example 8.3.9   In how many ways can we arrange 20 knights at a round table? What if two of them refuse to sit next to each other?

Solution: Without any restriction, there are $20!/20 = 19!$ ways to seat the 20 knights. To solve the second problem, use complement. If two of them always sit together, we in effect are arranging 19 objects in a circle. Among themselves, these two knights can be seated in two ways, depending on who is sitting on the left. Hence, there are $2 \cdot 19!/19 = 2 \cdot 18!$ ways to seat the 20 knights, with two of them always together. Therefore, the final answer to the second problem is $19! - 2 \cdot 18!$.   ▲

Summary and Review

- Use permutation if order matters: the keywords arrangement, sequence, and order suggest that we should use permutation.
- It is often more effective to use the multiplication principle directly.
- The number of ways to arrange n objects linearly is $n!$, and the number of ways to arrange them in a circle is $(n-1)!$.

Exercises 8.3

1. How many eight-character passwords can be formed with the 26 letters in the English alphabet, each of which can be in uppercase or lowercase, and the 10 digits? How many of them do not have repeated character?

2. How many functions are there from $\mathbb{Z}_6$ to $\mathbb{Z}_{12}$? How many of them are one-to-one?

3. The school board of a school district has 14 members. In how many ways can the chair, first vice-chair, second vice-chair, treasurer, and secretary be selected?

4. The wrestling teams of two schools have eight and 10 members respectively. In how many ways can three matches be made up between them?

5. The wrestling teams of three schools have seven, 10, and 11 members, respectively. Each school will have three matches against each of the other two school. In how many ways can these matches be arranged?

6. A teacher takes her AP calculus class of 8 students to lunch. They sit around a circular dining table.

   (a) How many seating arrangements are possible?
   (b) How many seating arrangements are there if the teacher has to sit on the chair closest to the soda fountain?
   (c) Among the students are one set of triplets. How many seating arrangements are there without all three of them sitting together?

7. Eleven students go to lunch. There are two circular tables in the dining hall, one can seat 7 people, the other can hold 4. In how many ways can they be seated?

8. Five couples attend a wedding banquet. They are seated on a long table. How many seating arrangements that alternate men and women? What if the table is circular in shape?

8.4   Combinations

In many counting problems, the order of arrangement or selection does not matter. In essence, we are selecting or forming subsets.

Example 8.4.1   Determine the number of ways to choose 4 values from 1, 2, 3, ..., 20, in which the order of selection does not matter.

Solution: Let N be the number of ways to choose the 4 numbers. Since the order in which the numbers are selected does not matter, these are *not* sequences (in which order of appearance matters). We can change a selection of 4 numbers into a sequence. The 4 numbers can be arranged in $P(4,4) = 4!$ ways. Therefore, all these 4-number selections together produce $N \cdot 4!$ sequences. The number of 4-number sequences is $P(20,4)$. Thus, $N \cdot 4! = P(20,4)$, or equivalently, $N = P(20,4)/4!$.   ▲

Definition.   The number of r-element subsets in an n-element set is denoted by

$$C(n,r) \qquad \text{or} \qquad \binom{n}{r},$$

where $\binom{n}{r}$ is read as "n choose r." It determines the number of ***combinations*** of n objects, taken r at a time (without replacement). Alternate notations such as $_nC_r$ and C_r^n can be found in other textbooks. Do *not* write it as $\left(\frac{n}{r}\right)$; this notation has a completely different meaning. ◇

Do not write $\binom{n}{r}$ as $\left(\frac{n}{r}\right)$ or $C\left(\frac{n}{r}\right)$. Instead, write it as $\binom{n}{r}$ or $C(n,r)$.

   Recall that $\binom{n}{r}$ counts the number of ways to *choose* or *select* r objects from a pool of n objects in which the order of selection does not matter. Hence, r-combinations are subsets of size r.

An r-combination is an r-element subset.

Example 8.4.2   The 2-combinations of $S = \{a, b, c, d\}$ are

$$\{a,b\}, \quad \{a,c\}, \quad \{a,d\}, \quad \{b,c\}, \quad \{b,d\}, \quad \text{and} \quad \{c,d\}.$$

Therefore $\binom{4}{2} = 6$. What are the 1-combinations and 3-combinations of S? What can you say about the values of $\binom{4}{1}$ and $\binom{4}{3}$?

Solution: The 1-combinations are the singleton sets $\{a\}$, $\{b\}$, $\{c\}$, and $\{d\}$. Hence, $\binom{4}{1} = 4$. The 3-combinations are

$$\{a, b, c\}, \quad \{a, b, d\}, \quad \{a, c, d\}, \quad \text{and} \quad \{b, c, d\}.$$

Thus, $\binom{4}{3} = 4$.   ▲

Notice that both numerator and denominator have r factors.

Theorem 8.4.1 *For all integers n and r satisfying $0 \leq r \leq n$, we have*

$$\binom{n}{r} = \frac{P(n,r)}{r!} = \frac{n(n-1)\cdots(n-r+1)}{r!} = \frac{n!}{r!\,(n-r)!}.$$

Proof: The idea is similar to the one we used in the alternate proof of Theorem 8.3.2. Let A be the set of all r-permutations, and let B be the set of all r-combinations. Define $f\colon A \to B$ to be the function that converts a permutation into a combination by "unscrambling" its order. Then f is an $r!$-to-one function because there are $r!$ ways to arrange (or shuffle) r objects. Therefore

$$|A| = r! \cdot |B|.$$

Since $|A| = P(n,r)$, and $|B| = \binom{n}{r}$, it follows that $\binom{n}{r} = P(n,r)/r!$.   ■

Example 8.4.3 There are $\binom{40}{5}$ ways to choose 5 numbers, without repetitions, from the integers $1, 2, \ldots, 40$. To compute its numeric value by hand, it is easier if we first cancel the common factors in the numerator and the denominator. We find

$$\binom{40}{5} = \frac{40 \cdot 39 \cdot 38 \cdot 37 \cdot 36}{5 \cdot 4 \cdot 3 \cdot 2 \cdot 1} = 13 \cdot 38 \cdot 37 \cdot 36,$$

which gives $\binom{40}{5} = 658008$.   ▲

Hands-On Exercise 8.4.1   Compute $\binom{12}{3}$ by hand.

           △

Hands-On Exercise 8.4.2   A three-member executive committee is to be selected from a group of seven candidates. In how many ways can the committee be formed?

           △

Hands-On Exercise 8.4.3   How many subsets of $\{1, 2, \ldots, 23\}$ have five elements?

           △

Corollary 8.4.2 *For $0 \leq r \leq n$, we have* $\dbinom{n}{r} = \dbinom{n}{n-r}$.

Proof: According to Theorem 8.4.1, we have

$$\binom{n}{n-r} = \frac{n!}{(n-r)!\,(n-(n-r))!} = \frac{n!}{(n-r)!\,r!},$$

which is precisely $\binom{n}{r}$.   ■

Example 8.4.4   To compute the numeric value of $\binom{50}{47}$, instead of computing the product of 47 factors as indicated in the definition, it is much faster if we use

$$\binom{50}{47} = \binom{50}{3} = \frac{50 \cdot 49 \cdot 48}{3 \cdot 2 \cdot 1},$$

from which we obtain $\binom{50}{47} = 19600$.   ▲

Hands-On Exercise 8.4.4   Compute, by hands, the numeric value of $\binom{529}{525}$.

△

Now we are ready to look at some mixed examples. In all of these examples, sometimes we have to use permutation, other times we have to use combination. Very often we need to use both, together with the addition and multiplication principles. You may ask, how can I figure out what to do? We suggest asking yourself these questions:

1. Use the construction approach. If you want to list all the configurations that meet the requirement, how are you going to do it systematically?

2. Are there several cases involved in the problem? If yes, we need to list them first, *before* we go through each of them one at a time. Finally, add the results to come up with the final answer.

3. Do we allow repetitions or replacements? This question can also take the form of whether the objects are distinguishable or indistinguishable.

4. Does order matter? If yes, we have to use permutation. Otherwise, use combination.

5. Sometimes, it may be easier to use the multiplication principle instead of permutation, because repetitions may be allowed (in which case, we cannot use permutation, although we can still use the multiplication principle). Try drawing a schematic diagram and decide what we need from it. If the analysis suggests a pattern that follows the one found in a permutation, you can then use the formula for permutation.

6. Do not forget: it may be easier to work with the complement.

What should we use: the addition or the multiplication principle? Permutation or combination? Here are some suggestions.

It is often not clear how to get started because there seem to be several ways to start the construction. For example, how would you distribute soda cans among a group of students? There are two possible approaches:

More suggestions.

(i) From the perspective of the students. Imagine you are one of the students, which soda would you receive?

(ii) From the perspective of the soda cans. Imagine you are holding a can of soda, to whom would you give this soda?

Depending on the actual problem, usually only one of these two approaches would work.

Example 8.4.5   Suppose we have to distribute 10 different soda cans to 20 students. It is clear that some students may not get any soda. In fact, some lucky students could receive more than one soda (the problem does not say this cannot happen). Hence, it is easier to start from the perspective of the soda cans.

We can give the first soda to any one of the 20 students, and we can also give the second soda to any one of the 20 students. In fact, we always have 20 choices for each soda. Since we have 10 sodas, there are $\underbrace{20 \cdot 20 \cdots 20}_{10} = 20^{10}$ ways to distribute the sodas.   ▲

Example 8.4.6   In how many ways can a team of three representatives be selected from a class of 885 students? In how many ways can a team of three representatives consisting of a chairperson, a vice-chairperson, and a secretary be selected?

Solution: If we are only interested in selecting three representatives, order does not matter. Hence, the answer would be $\binom{885}{3}$. If we are concerned about which offices these three representative will hold, then the answer should be $P(885, 3)$.   ▲

Hands-On Exercise 8.4.5   Mike needs some new shirts, but he has only enough money to purchase five of the eight that he likes. In how many ways can he purchase the five shirts by choosing them at random?

                                                                                                          △

Hands-On Exercise 8.4.6   Mary wants to purchase four shirts for her four brothers, and she would like each of them to receive a different shirt. She finds ten shirts that she thinks they will like. In many ways can she select them?

                                                                                                          △

Playing cards provide excellent examples for counting problems. Just in case you are not familiar with them, let us briefly review what a deck of playing cards contains.

A brief tutorial for those who do not play cards.

- There are 52 playing cards, each of them is marked with a suit and a rank.
- There are four suits: spades (♠), hearts (♡), diamonds (◇) and clubs (♣).
- Each suit has 13 ranks, labeled A, 2, 3, ..., 9, 10, J, Q, and K, where A means ace, J means jack, Q means queen, and K means king.
- Each rank has 4 suits (see above).

Example 8.4.7   Determine the number of five-card poker hands that can be dealt from a deck of 52 cards.

Solution: All we care is which five cards can be found in a hand. This is a selection problem. The answer is $\binom{52}{5}$.   ▲

Hands-On Exercise 8.4.7   In how many ways can a 13-card bridge hand be dealt from a standard deck of 52 cards?

                                                                                                          △

Example 8.4.8 In how many ways can a deck of 52 cards be dealt in a game of bridge? (In a bridge game, there are four players designated as North, East, South and West, each of them is dealt a hand of 13 cards.)

Solution: The difference between this problem and the last example is that the order of distributing the four bridge hands makes a difference. This is a problem that combines permutations and combinations. As we had suggested earlier, the best approach is to start from scratch, using the addition and/or multiplication principles, along with permutation and/or combination whenever it seems appropriate.

There are $\binom{52}{13}$ ways to give 13 cards to the first player. Now we are left with 39 cards, from which we select 13 to be given to the second player. Now, out of the remaining 26 cards, we have to give 13 to the third player. Finally, the last 13 cards will be given to the last player (there is only one way to do it). The number of ways to deal the cards in a bridge game is $\binom{52}{13}\binom{39}{13}\binom{26}{13}$.

We could have said the answer is

$$\binom{52}{13}\binom{39}{13}\binom{26}{13}\binom{13}{13}.$$

The last factor $\binom{13}{13}$ is the number of ways to give the last 13 cards to the fourth player. Numerically, $\binom{13}{13} = 1$, so the two answers are the same. Do not dismiss this extra factor as redundant. Take note of the nice pattern in this answer. The bottom numbers are 13, because we are selecting 13 cards to be given to each player. The top numbers indicate how many cards are still available for distribution at each stage of the distribution. The reasoning behind the solution is self-explanatory! ▲

Example 8.4.9 Determine the number of five-card poker hands that contain three queens. How many of them contain, in addition to the three queens, another pair of cards?

Solution: (a) The first step is to choose the three queens in $\binom{4}{3}$ ways, after which the remaining two cards can be selected in $\binom{48}{2}$ ways. Therefore, there are altogether $\binom{4}{3}\binom{48}{2}$ hands that meet the requirements.

(b) As in part (a), the three queens can be selected in $\binom{4}{3}$ ways. Next, we need to select the pair. We can select any card from the remaining 48 cards (therefore, there are 48 choices), after which we have to select one from the remaining 3 cards of the same rank. This gives $48 \cdot 3$ choices for the pair, right? The answer is *NO*!

The first card we picked could be ♡8, and the second could be ♣8. However, the first card could have been ♣8, and the second ♡8. These two selections are counted as *different* selections, but they are actually the same pair! The trouble is, we are considering "first," and "second" cards, which in effect imposes an ordering among the two cards, thereby turning it into a sequence or an *ordered* selection. We have to divide the answer by 2 to overcome the double-counting. The answer is therefore $\frac{48 \cdot 3}{2}$.

Here is a better way to count the number of pairs. An important question to ask is

> *Which one should we pick first: the suit or the rank?*

The main question is: choose the suit or the rank first?

Here, we want to pick the rank first. There are 12 choices (the pair cannot be queens) for the rank, and among the four cards of that rank, we can pick the two cards in $\binom{4}{2}$ ways. Therefore, the answer is $12\binom{4}{2}$. Numerically, the two answers are identical, because $12\binom{4}{2} = 12 \cdot \frac{4 \cdot 3}{2} = \frac{48 \cdot 3}{2}$. In summary: the final answer is $\binom{4}{3} \cdot 12\binom{4}{2}$. ▲

Hands-On Exercise 8.4.8 How many bridge hands contain exactly four spades?

△

Hands-On Exercise 8.4.9   How many bridge hands contain exactly four spades and four hearts?

△

Hands-On Exercise 8.4.10   How many bridge hands are there containing exactly four spades, three hearts, three diamonds, and three clubs?

△

Example 8.4.10   How many positive integers not exceeding 99999 contain exactly three 7s?

Solution: Regard each legitimate integer as a sequence of five digits, each of them selected from 0, 1, 2, ..., 9. For example, the integer 358 can be considered as 00358. Three out of the five positions must be occupied by 7. There are $\binom{5}{3}$ ways to select these three slots. The remaining two positions can be filled with any of the other nine digits. Hence, there are $\binom{5}{3} \cdot 9^2$ such integers.   ▲

Example 8.4.11   How many five-digit positive integers contain exactly three 7s?

Solution: Unlike the last example, the first of the five digits cannot be 0. Yet, the answer is *not* $\binom{5}{3} \cdot 9 \cdot 8$. Yes, there are $\binom{5}{3}$ choices for the placement of the three 7s, but some of these selections may have put the 7s in the last four positions. This leaves the first digit unfilled. The nine choices counted by 9 allows a zero to be placed in the first position. The result is, at best, a four-digit number. The correct approach is to consider two cases:

- Case 1. If the first digit is not 7, then there are eight ways to fill this slot. Among the remaining four positions, three of them must be 7, and the last one can be any digit other than 7. So there are $8 \cdot \binom{4}{3} \cdot 9$ integers in this category.

- Case 2. If the first digit is 7, we still have to put the other two 7s in the other four positions. There are $\binom{4}{2} \cdot 9^2$ such integers.

Together, the two cases give a total of $8 \cdot \binom{4}{3} \cdot 9 + \binom{4}{2} \cdot 9^2 = 774$ integers.   ▲

Hands-On Exercise 8.4.11   Five balls are chosen from a bag of eight blue balls, six red balls, and five green balls. How many of these five-ball selections contain exactly two blue balls?

△

Example 8.4.12   Find the number of ways to select five balls from a bag of six red balls, eight blue balls and four yellow balls such that the five-ball selections contain exactly two red balls *or* two blue balls.

Solution: The keyword "or" suggests this is a problem that involves the union of two sets, hence, we have to use PIE to solve the problem.

- How many selections contain two red balls? Following the same argument used in the last example, the answer is $\binom{6}{2}\binom{12}{3}$.

- How many selections contain two blue balls? The answer is $\binom{8}{2}\binom{10}{3}$.

- How many selections contain two red balls *and* 2 blue balls? The answer is $\binom{6}{2}\binom{8}{2}\binom{4}{1}$.

According to PIE, the final answer is

$$\binom{6}{2}\binom{12}{3} + \binom{8}{2}\binom{10}{3} - \binom{6}{2}\binom{8}{2}\binom{4}{1}.$$

In each term, the upper numbers always add up to 18, and the sum of the lower numbers is always 5. Can you explain why?   ▲

Example 8.4.13   We have 11 balls, five of which are blue, three of which are red, and the remaining three are green. How many collection of four balls can be selected such that at least two blue balls are selected? Assume that balls of the same color are indistinguishable.

Solution: The keywords "at least" mean we could have two, three, or four blue balls. There are

$$\binom{5}{2}\binom{6}{2} + \binom{5}{3}\binom{6}{1} + \binom{5}{4}\binom{6}{0}$$

ways to select four balls, with at least two of them being blue.   ▲

Hands-On Exercise 8.4.12   Jerry bought eight cans of Pepsi, seven cans of Sprite, three cans of Dr. Pepper, and six cans of Mountain Dew. He want to bring 10 cans to his pal's house when they watch the basketball game tonight. Assuming the cans are distinguishable, say, with different expiration dates, how many selections can he make if he wants to bring

(a) Exactly four cans of Pepsi?
(b) At least four cans of Pepsi?
(c) At most four cans of Pepsi?
(d) Exactly three cans of Pepsi, and at most three cans of Sprite?

△

The proof of the next result uses what we call a combinatorial or counting argument. In general, a combinatorial argument does not rely on algebraic manipulation. Rather, it uses the combinatorial significance of the situations to solve the problem.

Theorem 8.4.3 *Prove that $\sum_{r=0}^{n} \binom{n}{r} = 2^n$ for all nonnegative integers n.*

An example of
a combinatorial
argument.

Proof: Since $\binom{n}{r}$ counts the number of r-element subsets selected from an n-element set S, the summation on the left is the sum of the number of subsets of S of all possible cardinalities. In other words, this is the total number of subsets in S. We learned earlier that S has 2^n subsets, which establishes the identity immediately.   ■

Summary and Review

- Use permutation if order matters, otherwise use combination.
- The keywords arrangement, sequence, and order suggest using permutation.
- The keywords selection, subset, and group suggest using combination.
- It is best to start with a construction. Imagine you want to list all the possibilities, how would you get started?
- We may need to use both permutation and combination, and very likely we may also need to use the addition and multiplication principles.

Exercises 8.4

1. If the Buffalo Bills and the Cleveland Browns have eight and six players, respectively, available for trading, in how many ways can they swap three players for three players?

2. In the game of Mastermind, one player, the codemaker, selects a sequence of four colors (the "code") selected from red, blue, green, white, black, and yellow.

   (a) How many different codes can be formed?
   (b) How many codes use four different colors?
   (c) How many codes use only one color?
   (d) How many codes use exactly two colors?
   (e) How many codes use exactly three colors?

3. Becky likes to watch DVDs each evening. How many DVDs must she have if she is able to watch every evening for 24 consecutive evenings during her winter break?

   (a) A different subset of DVDs?
   (b) A different subset of three DVDs?

4. Bridget has n friends from her bridge club. Every Thursday evening, she invites three friends to her home for a bridge game. She always sits in the north position, and she decides which friends are to sit in the east, south, and west positions. She is able to do this for 200 weeks without repeating a seating arrangement. What is the minimum value of n?

5. Bridget has n friends from her bridge club. She is able to invite a different subset of three of them to her home every Thursday evening for 100 weeks. What is the minimum value of n?

6. How many five-digit numbers can be formed from the digits 1, 2, 3, 4, 5, 6, 7? How many of them do not have repeated digits?

7. The Mathematics Department of a small college has three full professors, seven associate professors, and four assistant professors. In how many ways can a four-member committee be formed under these restrictions:

   (a) There are no restrictions.
   (b) At least one full professor is selected.
   (c) The committee must contain a professor from each rank.

8. A department store manager receives from the company headquarters 12 football tickets to the same game (hence they can be regarded as "identical"). In how many ways can she distribute them to 20 employees if no one gets more than one ticket? What if the tickets are for 12 different games?

9. A checkerboard has 64 distinct squares arranged into eight rows and eight columns.

   (a) In how many ways can eight identical checkers be placed on the board so that no two checkers can occupy the same row or the same column?
   (b) In how many ways can two identical red checkers and two identical black checkers be placed on the board so that no two checkers of the same color can occupy the same row or the same column?

10. Determine the number of permutations of $\{A, B, C, D, E\}$ that satisfy the following conditions:

    (a) A occupies the first position.
    (b) A occupies the first position, and B the second.
    (c) A appears before B.

11. A binary string is a sequence of digits chosen from 0 and 1. How many binary strings of length 16 contain exactly seven 1s?

12. In how many ways can a nonempty subset of people be chosen from eight men and eight women so that every subset contains an equal number of men and women?

13. A poker hand is a five-card selection chosen from a standard deck of 52 cards. How many poker hands satisfy the following conditions?

    (a) There are no restrictions.
    (b) The hand contains at least one card from each suit.
    (c) The hand contains exactly one pair (the other three cards all of different ranks).
    (d) The hand contains three of a rank (the other two cards all of different ranks).
    (e) The hand is a full house (three of one rank and a pair of another).
    (f) The hand is a straight (consecutive ranks, as in 5, 6, 7, 8, 9, but not all from the same suit).
    (g) The hand is a flush (all the same suit, but not a straight).
    (h) The hand is a straight flush (both straight and flush).

14. A local pizza restaurant offers the following toppings on their cheese pizzas: extra cheese, pepperoni, mushrooms, green peppers, onions, sausage, ham, and anchovies.

    (a) How many kinds of pizzas can one order?
    (b) How many kinds of pizzas can one order with exactly three toppings?
    (c) How many kinds of vegetarian pizza (without pepperoni, sausage, or ham) can one order?

8.5   The Binomial Theorem

A binomial is a polynomial with exactly two terms. The **binomial theorem** gives a formula for expanding $(x + y)^n$ for any positive integer n.

How do we expand a product of polynomials? We pick one term from the first polynomial, multiply by a term chosen from the second polynomial, and then multiply by a term selected from the third polynomial, and so forth. In the special case of $(x + y)^n$, we are selecting either x or y from each of the n binomials $x + y$ to form a product. Some of these products will be identical, hence, we need to collect their coefficients. The expansion of $(x + y)^3$ is demonstrated below.

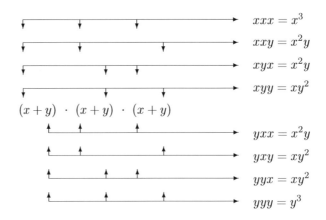

We find

$$
\begin{aligned}
(x+y)^3 &= (x+y)(x+y)(x+y) \\
&= xxx + xxy + xyx + xyy + yxx + yxy + yyx + yyy \\
&= x^3 + x^2y + x^2y + xy^2 + x^2y + xy^2 + xy^2 + y^3 \\
&= x^3 + 3x^2y + 3xy^2 + y^3.
\end{aligned}
$$

What happens when we expand $(x+y)^n$?

If we select y from k copies of the $(x+y)$s, and x from the other $n - k$ copies, their product will be $x^{n-k}y^k$. Therefore, in the expansion of $(x + y)^n$, a typical term will be of the form $x^{n-k}y^k$, where $0 \le k \le n$. The question is, what is its coefficient in the expansion, after we collect like terms? This coefficient is the number of times the product $x^{n-k}y^k$ appears when we multiply out $(x+y)^n$ in the way described above. It depends on which k copies of the $(x+y)$s we will choose y from. There are $\binom{n}{k}$ choices, hence, the product $x^{n-k}y^k$ appears $\binom{n}{k}$ times. Thus, the coefficient is $\binom{n}{k}$. For this reason, we also call $\binom{n}{k}$ the **binomial coefficients**.

Theorem 8.5.1 (Binomial Theorem) *For any positive integer n,*

$$
(x+y)^n = \sum_{k=0}^{n} \binom{n}{k} x^{n-k} y^k.
$$

Because of the symmetry in the formula, we can interchange x and y. In addition, we also have $\binom{n}{k} = \binom{n}{n-k}$. Consequently, the binomial theorem can be written in three other forms:

There are four ways to write binomial theorem; they are all equivalent.

$$
\begin{aligned}
(x+y)^n &= \sum_{k=0}^{n} \binom{n}{n-k} x^{n-k} y^k, \\
(x+y)^n &= \sum_{k=0}^{n} \binom{n}{k} x^k y^{n-k}, \\
(x+y)^n &= \sum_{k=0}^{n} \binom{n}{n-k} x^k y^{n-k}.
\end{aligned}
$$

You need not worry which one to use. They are all the same! This is how to remember these four different forms. In each term, the powers of x and y always add up to n. If the power of one of the two variables is k, where $0 \le k \le n$, then the power of the other must be $n - k$, and we need to multiply the coefficient $\binom{n}{k}$, which is the same as $\binom{n}{n-k}$, to their product.

Here is how to remember them.

When expanding $(x+y)^n$, it may be helpful if you first lay out all the terms x^n, $x^{n-1}y$, $x^{n-2}y^2$, and so forth. Then you fill in with the binomial coefficients. For instance, to expand $(x+y)^3$, we first list all the terms that we expect fo find:

$$
(x+y)^3 = \underline{\quad} x^3 + \underline{\quad} x^2y + \underline{\quad} xy^2 + \underline{\quad} y^3.
$$

Next we fill in the binomial coefficients:

$$(x+y)^3 = \binom{3}{0}x^3 + \binom{3}{1}x^2y + \binom{3}{2}xy^2 + \binom{3}{3}y^3.$$

Finally, evaluate the binomial coefficients and simplify the result.

$$(x+y)^3 = x^3 + 3x^2y + 3xy^2 + y^3.$$

In a similar way, we also find $(x-y)^3 = x^3 - 3x^2y + 3xy^2 - y^3$. Note the similarity between the two expansions.

Example 8.5.1   Compute $(x+y)^4$.

Solution: Following the steps we outlined above, we find

$$
\begin{aligned}
(x+y)^4 &= \binom{4}{0}x^4 + \binom{4}{1}x^3y + \binom{4}{2}x^2y^2 + \binom{4}{3}xy^3 + \binom{4}{4}y^4 \\
&= x^4 + 4x^3y + 6x^2y^2 + 4xy^3 + y^4.
\end{aligned}
$$

Since $\binom{n}{0} = \binom{n}{n} = 1$, the expansion always starts with x^n and ends with y^n.   ▲

Example 8.5.2   Compute $(x-y)^4$.

Solution: We find

$$
\begin{aligned}
(x-y)^4 &= [x+(-y)]^4 \\
&= \binom{4}{0}x^4 + \binom{4}{1}x^3(-y) + \binom{4}{2}x^2(-y)^2 + \binom{4}{3}x(-y)^3 + \binom{4}{4}(-y)^4 \\
&= x^4 - 4x^3y + 6x^2y^2 - 4xy^3 + y^4.
\end{aligned}
$$

Take note of the alternating signs in the expansion. This suggests that we could expand $(A-B)^n$ the exact same way we would with $(A+B)^n$, except that the signs alternate.

We can carry out the expansion by following these steps. First, list all the terms we expect to find

$$(x+y)^4 = \underline{}\ x^4\ \underline{}\ x^3y\ \underline{}\ x^2y^2\ \underline{}\ xy^3\ \underline{}\ y^4.$$

Next, fill in the signs:

$$(x+y)^4 = \underline{}\ x^4 - \underline{}\ x^3y + \underline{}\ x^2y^2 - \underline{}\ xy^3 + \underline{}\ y^4,$$

and then the binomial coefficients:

$$(x+y)^4 = \binom{4}{0}x^4 - \binom{4}{1}x^3y + \binom{4}{2}x^2y^2 - \binom{4}{3}xy^3 + \binom{4}{4}y^4.$$

Finally, compute the binomial coefficients to finish the expansion.   ▲

Example 8.5.3   Expand $(2x-3y)^5$.

Solution: The expansion yields

$$(2x)^5 - \binom{5}{1}(2x)^4(3y) + \binom{5}{2}(2x)^3(3y)^2 - \binom{5}{3}(2x)^2(3y)^3 + \binom{5}{4}(2x)(3y)^4 - (3y)^5.$$

Therefore, $(2x-3y)^5 = 32x^5 - 240x^4y + 720x^3y^2 - 1080x^2y^3 + 810xy^4 - 243y^5.$ ▲

Hands-On Exercise 8.5.1   Use the binomial theorem to expand $(3x - 5y)^4$.

△

Example 8.5.4   Find the coefficient of x^3 in the expansion of $(1 + x)^{102}$.

Solution: Since

$$(1 + x)^{102} = \sum_{k=0}^{102} \binom{102}{k} x^k,$$

the term containing x^3 is $\binom{102}{3} x^3$. Therefore, the coefficient is $\binom{102}{3}$. Depending on which form of the binomial theorem you use, you may end up with the term $\binom{102}{99} x^3$. Numerically, this gives us the same coefficient, because $\binom{102}{99} = \binom{102}{102-99} = \binom{102}{3}$.   ▲

Example 8.5.5   What is the coefficient of t^4 in the expansion of $(2 + 3t)^9$?

Solution: Since

$$(2 + 3t)^9 = \sum_{k=0}^{9} \binom{9}{k} 2^{9-k} (3t)^k,$$

we need $k = 4$. The coefficient is $\binom{9}{4} 2^5 \cdot 3^4 \cdot$.   ▲

Example 8.5.6   What is the coefficient of t^5 in the expansion of $(3 - 2t)^7$?

Solution: Since $(3 - 2t)^7 = \sum_{k=0}^{7} \binom{7}{k} 3^{7-k} (-2t)^k$, we need $k = 5$, and the coefficient is $\binom{7}{5} 3^2 \cdot (-2)^5 = -\binom{7}{5} 3^2 \cdot 2^5$.   ▲

Hands-On Exercise 8.5.2   What is the coefficient of t^5 in $(1 + 3t)^8$?

△

Hands-On Exercise 8.5.3   What is the coefficient of t^4 in the expansion of $(2 - 5t)^9$?

△

Example 8.5.7   What is the coefficient of t^6 in the expansion of $(4 + 5t^2)^8$?

Solution: The general term in the expansion is $\binom{8}{k} 4^{8-k} (5t^2)^k = \binom{8}{k} 4^{8-k} \cdot 5^k t^{2k}$. Hence, we need $k = 3$, and the coefficient is $\binom{8}{3} 4^5 \cdot 5^3$.   ▲

Hands-On Exercise 8.5.4   What is the coefficient of t^9 in the expansion of $(3 - 2t^3)^8$?

$\triangle$

The constant term in an expansion does not contain any variable. It can be interpreted as the term containing x^0.

Example 8.5.8   Find the constant term in the expansion of $\left(x + \dfrac{2}{x} \right)^8$.

Solution: The general term in the expansion is

$$\binom{8}{k} x^{8-k} \left(\frac{2}{x} \right)^k = \binom{8}{k} x^{8-k} \cdot \frac{2^k}{x^k} = \binom{8}{k} 2^k x^{8-2k}.$$

We need $8 - 2k = 0$ or $k = 4$. Therefore, the coefficient is $\binom{8}{4} 2^4$. $\blacktriangle$

Hands-On Exercise 8.5.5   Find the constant term in the expansion of the two expressions $\left(x + \dfrac{3}{x} \right)^9$ and $\left(2x - \dfrac{3}{x} \right)^{10}$.

$\triangle$

Example 8.5.9   Determine the coefficient of x^7 in the expansion of $(1 + x + x^2)(1 + x)^{10}$.

Solution: Expand $(1 + x + x^2)(1 + x)^{10}$ as follows:

$$
\begin{aligned}
(1 + x + x^2)(1 + x)^{10} &= (1 + x + x^2) \sum_{k=0}^{10} \binom{10}{k} x^k \\
&= \sum_{k=0}^{10} \binom{10}{k} x^k + \sum_{k=0}^{10} \binom{10}{k} x^{k+1} + \sum_{k=0}^{10} \binom{10}{k} x^{k+2}.
\end{aligned}
$$

So the coefficient of x^7 is $\binom{10}{7} + \binom{10}{6} + \binom{10}{5}$. $\blacktriangle$

Hands-On Exercise 8.5.6   Find the coefficient of x^8 in the expansion of $(1 - 2x + 3x^2)(1 + 2x)^{12}$.

$\triangle$

To compute the binomial coefficients quickly, one may use the **Pascal triangle**, in which the nth row ($n \geq 0$) consists of the binomial coefficients $\binom{n}{k}$, where $0 \leq k \leq n$:

$$
\begin{array}{ccccccccccccc}
 & & & & & 1 & & & & & \\
 & & & & 1 & & 1 & & & & \\
 & & & 1 & & 2 & & 1 & & & \\
 & & 1 & & 3 & & 3 & & 1 & & \\
 & 1 & & 4 & & 6 & & 4 & & 1 & \\
1 & & 5 & & 10 & & 10 & & 5 & & 1 \\
\end{array}
$$

$$
\begin{array}{ccccccccccccc}
1 & & 6 & & 15 & & 20 & & 15 & & 6 & & 1
\end{array}
$$

Constructing the Pascal triangle is easy. We generate the rows one at a time. The extreme ends are always 1. Each of the interior entries is the sum of the two entries right above it in the preceding row. For instance, the next row (for $n = 7$) should be

$$
\begin{array}{ccccccccc}
1 & 7 & 21 & 35 & 35 & 21 & 7 & 1
\end{array}
$$

Such computations produce the right binomial coefficients, because of the next result.

Theorem 8.5.2 (Pascal's Identity) *For all integers n and k satisfying $1 \leq k \leq n$,*

$$
\binom{n}{k} = \binom{n-1}{k} + \binom{n-1}{k-1}.
$$

Proof 1:   (Analytic Proof)   It follows from the definition of binomial coefficients that

$$
\begin{aligned}
\binom{n-1}{k-1} + \binom{n-1}{k} &= \frac{(n-1)!}{(k-1)!\,(n-k)!} + \frac{(n-1)!}{k!\,(n-k-1)!} \\
&= \frac{(n-1)!}{(k-1)!\,(n-k-1)!}\left(\frac{1}{n-k} + \frac{1}{k}\right) \\
&= \frac{(n-1)!}{(k-1)!\,(n-k-1)!} \cdot \frac{n}{k(n-k)} \\
&= \frac{n!}{k!\,(n-k)!}.
\end{aligned}
$$

This completes the proof.   ■

Another example of a combinatorial argument.

Proof 2:   (Combinatorial Proof)   Let A be an n-element set. Then $\binom{n}{k}$ counts the number of k-element subsets of A. These subsets can be classified according to whether they contain a fixed element, say x. If a subset contains x, then the other $k-1$ elements must be selected from the remaining $n-1$ elements of A. Otherwise, if the subset does not contain x, then all its k elements must be selected from the other $n-1$ elements of A. The numbers of these two kinds of subsets are given by $\binom{n-1}{k-1}$ and $\binom{n-1}{k}$, respectively. The theorem now follows immediately by applying the addition principle.   ■

Hands-On Exercise 8.5.7   Determine the 8th and the 9th rows in the Pascal's triangle.

△

Example 8.5.10   Use the Pascal's triangle to expand

(a) $(C - D)^5$ (b) $(2A + 5B)^3$ (c) $(3C - 4B)^4$

Solution: Draw the values of $\binom{n}{k}$ from the Pascal triangle directly. The answers are:

(a) $(C - D)^5 = C^5 - 5C^4D + 10C^3D^2 - 10C^2D^3 + 5CD^4 - D^5$.

(b) $(2a + 5B)^3 = 8A^3 + 60A^2B + 150AB^2 + 125B^3$.

(c) $(3C - 4B)^4 = 81C^4 - 432C^3B + 864C^2B^2 - 768CB^3 + 256B^4$. ▲

Many interesting results can be derived from the binomial theorem.

Example 8.5.11 Setting $x = y = 1$, we obtain a simple (analytic) proof of the familiar identity $2^n = \sum_{k=0}^{n} \binom{n}{k}$. ▲

Example 8.5.12 Letting $x = 1$ and $y = -1$ yields $0 = \sum_{k=0}^{n}(-1)^k \binom{n}{k}$. We can rewrite it as

$$\binom{n}{0} + \binom{n}{2} + \cdots = \binom{n}{1} + \binom{n}{3} + \cdots.$$

Combinatorially, this means the number of subsets of even cardinalities equals the number of subsets of odd cardinalities. ▲

Summary and Review

- The binomial theorem can be expressed in four different but equivalent forms.
- The expansion of $(x + y)^n$ starts with x^n, then we decrease the exponent in x by one, meanwhile increase the exponent of y by one, and repeat this until we have y^n.
- The next few terms are therefore $x^{n-1}y$, $x^{n-2}y^2$, etc., which end with y^n.
- In general, the sum of exponents in x and y is always n. Hence, the general term is $x^k y^{n-k}$, whose coefficient is $\binom{n}{k}$.
- The expansion of $(x + y)^n$ and $(x - y)^n$ look almost identical, except that the signs in $(x - y)^n$ alternate.

Exercises 8.5

1. Use binomial theorem to expand the following expressions:

   (a) $(x + y)^5$ (b) $(s - t)^6$ (c) $(a + 3b)^4$

2. Find the coefficient of

   (a) $x^{11}y^3$ in $(x + y)^{14}$ (b) x^4y^7 in $(2x - y)^{11}$

   (c) x^4y^3 in $(3x + 2y)^7$ (d) x^5 in $(1 - x + x^2)(1 + x)^7$

3. Find the constant term in the expansion of

   (a) $\left(x + \dfrac{1}{x}\right)^4$ (b) $\left(3x - \dfrac{2}{5x^2}\right)^9$

   (c) $\left(3x^2 - \dfrac{5}{7x^3}\right)^4$ (d) $(1 - x^2 + x^3)\left(3x^2 - \dfrac{5}{7x^3}\right)^6$

4. Show that $\sum_{k=0}^{n} \binom{n}{k} 2^k = 3^n$ for any positive integer n.

5. Let n be a positive integer. Evaluate $\sum_{k=0}^{n} \binom{n}{k} r^k$ for any real number r.

6. Find a closed form for the summation $\sum_{k=0}^{n} k\binom{n}{k}$.

   Hint: Differentiate $(1 + x)^n$ with respect to x.

7. The objective of this problem is to derive a formula for $\sum_{k=1}^{n} k^2$.

   (a) Use induction to show that

   $$\sum_{k=1}^{n} \binom{k}{1} = \frac{n(n+1)}{2}$$

   for any positive integer n.

   (b) Use induction to show that

   $$\sum_{k=1}^{n} \binom{k}{2} = \frac{n(n+1)(n-1)}{3!}$$

   for any positive integer n.

   Hint: Note that $\binom{1}{2} = 0$.

   (c) Find the integers a and b such that

   $$k^2 = a\binom{k}{2} + b\binom{k}{1}.$$

   Hint: Compare coefficients.

   (d) From part (c), we obtain

   $$\sum_{k=1}^{n} k^2 = a\sum_{k=1}^{n} \binom{k}{2} + b\sum_{k=1}^{n} \binom{k}{1}.$$

   Apply the results from parts (a) and (b) to derive a formula for $\sum_{k=1}^{n} k^2$.

8. The objective of this problem is to derive a formula for $\sum_{k=1}^{n} k^3$.

   (a) Use induction to show that

   $$\sum_{k=1}^{n} \binom{k}{3} = \frac{n(n+1)(n-1)(n-2)}{4!}$$

   for any positive integer n.

   Hint: Note that $\binom{1}{2} = 0$.

   (b) Find the integers a, b, and c such that

   $$k^3 = a\binom{k}{3} + b\binom{k}{2} + c\binom{k}{1}.$$

   Hint: Compare coefficients.

   (c) Apply the results from parts (a) and (b) to derive a formula for $\sum_{k=1}^{n} k^3$.

Appendix A

Solutions to Hands-On Exercises

Section 1.4

1. Two proofs are given below, one uses direct expansion, the other uses factorization.

   Solution 1:   Expanding the two sides *separately*, we find

   $$\frac{k(k+1)(k+2)}{3} + (k+1)(k+2) = \frac{k^3 + 3k^2 + 2k}{3} + k^2 + 3k + 2$$
   $$= \frac{k^3 + 3k^2 + 2k + 3(k^2 + 3k + 2)}{3}$$
   $$= \frac{k^3 + 6k^2 + 11k + 6}{3},$$

   and

   $$\frac{(k+1)(k+2)(k+3)}{3} = \frac{(k^2 + 3k + 2)(k+2)}{3} = \frac{k^3 + 6k^2 + 11k + 6}{3},$$

   which establish the identity.

   Solution 2:   Since

   $$\frac{k(k+1)(k+2)}{3} + (k+1)(k+2) = (k+1)(k+2)\left(\frac{k}{3}+1\right)$$
   $$= \frac{(k+1)(k+2)(k+3)}{3},$$

   the identity always holds.

Section 2.1

1. Any example of the form

   If $\boxed{\ldots \qquad \ldots}$ then $\boxed{\boxed{\ldots \qquad \ldots}}$. Therefore. if $\boxed{\ldots \quad \text{not} \quad \ldots}$ then $\boxed{\ldots \quad \text{not} \quad \ldots}$.

   will work.

2. (a) We do not know which "he" the sentence is referring to.

   (b) We do not know the values of x and y.

   (c) While the equation is true if A and B are numbers, it is not always true if A and B are matrices.

3. (a) x is an integer less than or equal to 7.

   (b) We cannot factor 144 into a product of prime numbers.

   (c) The number 64 is not a perfect square.

Section 2.2

1. x is rational and y is rational; $(x \in \mathbb{Q}) \wedge (y \in \mathbb{Q})$.

2. (a) Since "$\sqrt{30} < 5$" is false, and "$\sqrt{30} > 7$" is true, the statement "$(\sqrt{30} < 5) \wedge (\sqrt{30} > 7)$" is false.

   (b) Since "$\sqrt{30} > 5$" is true and "$\sqrt{30} < 7$" is false, the statement "$(\sqrt{30} > 5) \vee (\sqrt{30} < 7)$" is true.

3. $(5 < x) \wedge (x < 8)$.

4. The statement "$0 \geq x \geq 1$" means "$(0 \geq x) \wedge (x \geq 1)$." Since no number can be less than or equal to 0 and greater than or equal to 1 *simultaneously*, the statement "$(0 \geq x) \wedge (x \geq 1)$" is always false.

Section 2.3

1. (a) one   (b) two   (c) none

2. $x > y > 0 \Rightarrow x^2 > y^2$.

3. (a) False, because we could have $x = 3$, then "$(x - 2)(x - 3) = 0$" is true but "$x = 2$" is false. This makes the implication false.

   (b) True, because if "$x = 2$" is true, "$(x - 2)(x - 3) = 0$" would be true as well. Thus, the implication is true.

4. (a) p: The figure $PQRS$ is a square,
        q: The figure $PQRS$ is a parallelogram.

   (b) p: The number x is a prime number,
        q: The number x is an integer.

   (c) p: The function $f(x)$ is a polynomial,
        q: The function $f(x)$ is differentiable.

5. converse: if $\sqrt{p}$ is irrational, then p is prime
   inverse: if p is composite, then $\sqrt{p}$ is rational
   contrapositive: if $\sqrt{p}$ is rational, then p is composite

6. (a) $p: x > 1$; $q: x^2 > 1$.

   (b) $p: x^2 > 1$; $q: x > 1$.

Section 2.4

1. The completed statement is "n is odd $\Leftrightarrow n = 2k + 1$ for some integer k."

   Proof: Assume n is odd, then we can write $n = 2k + 1$ for some integer k. We find

   $$n^2 = (2k + 1)^2 = 4k^2 + 4k + 1 = 2(2k^2 + 2k) + 1,$$

   where $2k^2 + 2k$ is an integer. Hence, n^2 is also odd.

2. The statement "$p \Rightarrow q \wedge r$" means "$p \Rightarrow (q \wedge r)$." Below is its truth table.

p	q	r	$q \wedge r$	$p \Rightarrow (p \wedge r)$
T	T	T	T	T
T	T	F	F	F
T	F	T	F	F
T	F	F	F	F
F	T	T	T	T
F	T	F	F	T
F	F	T	F	T
F	F	F	F	T

3. We can write "$(p \wedge q) \Leftrightarrow (\overline{p} \vee \overline{q})$." To construct its truth table, we need to evaluate each component one at a time:

p	q	$p \wedge q$	$\overline{p}$	$\overline{q}$	$\overline{p} \vee \overline{q}$	$(p \wedge q) \Leftrightarrow (\overline{p} \vee \overline{q})$
T	T	T	F	F	F	F
T	F	F	F	T	T	F
F	T	F	T	F	T	F
F	F	F	T	T	T	F

Section 2.5

1. In general, if we have n statements, we need 2^n rows in the truth table.

p	q	r	$p \wedge q$	$(p \wedge q) \Rightarrow r$	$\overline{r}$	$\overline{p}$	$\overline{q}$	$\overline{p} \vee \overline{q}$	$\overline{r} \Rightarrow (\overline{p} \vee \overline{q})$	$[(p \wedge q) \Rightarrow r] \Rightarrow [\overline{r} \Rightarrow (\overline{p} \vee \overline{q})]$
T	T	T	T	T	F	F	F	F	T	T
T	T	F	T	F	T	F	F	F	F	T
T	F	T	F	T	F	F	T	T	T	T
T	F	F	F	T	T	F	T	T	T	T
F	T	T	F	T	F	T	F	T	T	T
F	T	F	F	T	T	T	F	T	T	T
F	F	T	F	T	F	T	T	T	T	T
F	F	F	F	T	T	T	T	T	T	T

2. (a)

p	q	$p \Rightarrow q$	$\overline{q}$	$\overline{p}$	$\overline{q} \Rightarrow \overline{p}$
T	T	T	F	F	T
T	F	F	T	F	F
F	T	T	F	T	T
F	F	T	T	T	T

(c)

p	q	$p \wedge q$	$\overline{p}$	$\overline{q}$	$\overline{p} \vee \overline{q}$	$\overline{\overline{p} \vee \overline{q}}$
T	T	T	F	F	F	T
T	F	F	F	T	T	F
F	T	F	T	F	T	F
F	F	F	T	T	T	F

(b)

p	p	$p \vee p$
T	T	T
F	F	F

(d)

p	q	$p \Leftrightarrow q$	$p \Rightarrow q$	$q \Rightarrow p$	$(p \Rightarrow q) \wedge (q \Rightarrow p)$
T	T	T	T	T	T
T	F	F	F	T	F
F	T	F	T	F	F
F	F	T	T	T	T

3. We need to compare the truth values of the three formulas:

$$p \veebar q, \qquad (p \vee q) \wedge \overline{p \wedge q}, \qquad \text{and} \qquad (p \wedge \overline{q}) \vee (\overline{p} \wedge q).$$

The truth table for comparing them is depicted below.

p	q	$p \veebar q$	$p \vee q$	$p \wedge q$	$\overline{p \wedge q}$	$(p \vee q) \wedge \overline{p \wedge q}$	$\overline{p}$	$\overline{q}$	$p \wedge \overline{q}$	$\overline{p} \wedge q$	$(p \wedge \overline{q}) \vee (\overline{p} \wedge q)$
T	T	F	T	T	F	F	F	F	F	F	F
T	F	T	T	F	T	T	F	T	T	F	T
F	T	T	T	F	T	T	T	F	F	T	T
F	F	F	F	F	T	F	T	T	F	F	F

4. The statement "$0 > x > 1$" means "$(0 > x) \land (x > 1)$," which is always false because no such x exists.

5. We find

$$
\begin{aligned}
(p \lor q) \land (r \lor s) &\equiv [p \land (r \lor s)] \lor [q \land (r \lor s)] \\
&\equiv (p \land r) \lor (p \land s) \lor (q \land r) \lor (q \land s).
\end{aligned}
$$

Section 2.6

1. (a) false   (b) true   (c) true

2. The first three twin primes are 3 and 5, 5 and 7, and 11 and 13.

3. (a) False, a counterexample is $x = 2$.

   (b) True.

   (c) False, because an even number is defined as an integral multiple of 2.

   (d) True, see (c).

   (e) False, $x = \sqrt{2}$ provides a counterexample.

4. False, because $0^2 = 0$.

5. True, because we can pick $y = 0$, then regardless of what x is, we always have $xy = 0 < 1$.

6. (a) There exists a prime number x such that the number $x + 1$ is prime.

   (b) There exists a prime number $x > 2$ such that the number $x + 1$ is prime.

   (c) For any integer k, the number $2k + 1$ is odd.

   (d) There exists an integer k such that $2k$ is odd.

   (e) There exists a number x such that x^2 is an integer and x is not an integer.

7. One solution is: "There is a Discrete Mathematics student who has not taken Calculus I and Calculus II." Because of De Morgan's laws, we can also state the negation as "There is a Discrete Mathematics student who has not taken Calculus I or has not taken Calculus II."

Section 3.1

1. The distance between a and $\frac{1}{3} a + \frac{2}{3} b$ is

$$
\left(\frac{1}{3} a + \frac{2}{3} b \right) - a = \frac{2}{3} b - \frac{2}{3} a = \frac{2}{3} (b - a).
$$

The distance between $\frac{1}{3} a + \frac{2}{3} b$ and b is

$$
b - \left(\frac{1}{3} a + \frac{2}{3} b \right) = \frac{1}{3} b - \frac{1}{3} a = \frac{1}{3} (b - a).
$$

Since $\frac{2}{3} (b - a) > \frac{1}{3} (b - a)$, the point $\frac{1}{3} a + \frac{2}{3} b$ is closer to b than to a.

2. $6 = 2 \cdot 3$, $40 = 2^3 \cdot 5$, $32 = 2^5 \cdot 1$, and $15 = 2^0 \cdot 15$.

3. The five consecutive integers 722, 723, 724, 725, and 726 are composite.

4. Since a and b are rational numbers, we can write $a = \frac{m}{n}$ and $b = \frac{r}{s}$ for some integers m, n, r, and s, where $n, s \neq 0$. Then the midpoint of the interval $[a, b]$ is

$$
\frac{a + b}{2} = \frac{1}{2} \left(\frac{m}{n} + \frac{r}{s} \right) = \frac{ms + nr}{2ns},
$$

where $ms + nr$ and $2ns$ are integers, and $2ns \neq 0$. Hence, $\frac{a+b}{2}$ is a rational number between a and b.

5. Using the same argument in Hands-On Exercise 3.1.4, we see that $\frac{1}{3}a + \frac{2}{3}b$ is rational, and we have learned from Hands-On Exercise 3.1.1 that it is closer to b than to a.

6. Let $g(x) = 1 + x\cos x$. Noting that $g(-\pi) = 1 - \pi < 0$ and $g(0) = 1 > 0$, we conclude that the equation $g(x) = 0$ has a real solution between $-\pi$ and 0.

Section 3.2

1. Assume n is odd, we can write $n = 2k + 1$ for some integer k. Then

$$n^3 = (2k+1)^3 = 8k^3 + 12k^2 + 6k + 1 = 2(4k^3 + 6k^2 + 2k) + 1,$$

where $4k^3 + 6k^2 + 2k$ is an integer. Thus, n^3 is odd.

2. Assume $x^3 + 6x^2 + 12x + 8 = 0$. Since

$$x^3 + 6x^2 + 12x + 8 = (x+2)^3,$$

we must have $(x+2)^3 = 0$. It follows that $x = -2$.

3. There are two cases.

   - Case 1: If n is even, then $n = 2q$ for some integer q, so that

   $$n^3 + n = (2q)^3 + 2q = 8q^3 + 2q = 2(4q^3 + q),$$

   where $4q^3 + q$ is an integer.

   - Case 2: If n is odd, then $n = 2q + 1$ for some integer q, so that

   $$n^3 + n = (2q+1)^3 + (2q+1) = 8q^3 + 12q^2 + 8q + 2 = 2(4q^3 + 6q^2 + 4q + 1),$$

   where $4q^3 + 6q^2 + 4q + 1$ is an integer.

   In both cases, we have proved that $n^3 + n$ is even.

Section 3.3

1. Assume x is a real number such that $x \neq -5$ *and* $x \neq 7$, then $x + 5 \neq 0$ and $x - 7 \neq 0$. Since $2x^2 + 5$ can never be zero, we find

$$(2x^2 + 3)(x + 5)(x - 7) \neq 0.$$

Therefore, if $(2x^2 + 3)(x + 5)(x - 7) = 0$, then either $x = -5$, or $x = 7$.

2. We shall prove the contrapositive of the given statement. Let x and y be real numbers such that $xy = 0$. Then either $x = 0$ or $y = 0$. Therefore, if $x \neq 0$ and $y \neq 0$, then $xy \neq 0$.

3. Assume $x^2 \geq 49$, we want to prove that $|x| \geq 7$. Suppose, on the contrary, $|x| < 7$. This means $-7 < x < 7$. We need to study two cases.

   - If $-7 < x < 0$, we find $0 < x^2 < 49$.
   - If $0 \leq x < 7$, we find $0 \leq x^2 < 49$.

   In both cases, we have $x^2 < 49$. This contradicts the given assumption that $x^2 \geq 49$. Therefore, we must have $|x| \geq 7$.

4. Suppose there exist some positive numbers x and y such that $\sqrt{x+y} = \sqrt{x} + \sqrt{y}$, then

$$x + y = \left(\sqrt{x} + \sqrt{y}\right)^2 = x + 2\sqrt{xy} + y,$$

implying that

$$0 = 2\sqrt{xy},$$

which is possible only when $xy = 0$. But both x and y are positive, hence, $xy \neq 0$. This contradiction shows that $\sqrt{x+y} \neq \sqrt{x} + \sqrt{y}$ for all positive numbers x and y.

5. Suppose $\sqrt{3}$ is rational, then we can write

$$\sqrt{3} = \frac{m}{n}$$

for some positive integers m and n such that m and n do not share any common divisor except 1 (hence, $\frac{m}{n}$ is in its simplest term). Squaring both sides and cross-multiplying gives

$$3n^2 = m^2.$$

Thus 3 divides m^2, consequently 3 must also divide m. Then we can write $m = 3s$ for some integer s. The equation above becomes

$$3n^2 = m^2 = (3s)^2 = 9s^2.$$

Hence,

$$n^2 = 3s^2,$$

which implies that 3 divides n^2, thus 3 also divides n. We have proved that both m and n are divisible by 3. This contradicts the assumption that m and n do not share any common divisor. Therefore, $\sqrt{3}$ must be irrational.

6. ($\Rightarrow$) If n is odd, we can write $n = 2k + 1$ for some integer k. Then

$$n^2 = (2k+1)^2 = 4k^2 + 4k + 1 = 2(2k^2 + 2k) + 1,$$

where $2k^2 + 2k$ is an integer. Hence, n^2 is odd.

($\Leftarrow$) We shall prove its contrapositive: if n is even, then n^2 is even. If n is even, we can write $n = 2k$ for some integer k. Then

$$n^2 = (2k)^2 = 4k^2 = 2 \cdot 2k^2,$$

where $2k^2$ is an integer, which means n^2 is even.

Section 3.4

1. We proceed by induction on n. When $n = 1$, the left-hand side reduces to $1 \cdot 2 = 2$, and the right-hand side becomes $\frac{1 \cdot 2 \cdot 3}{3} = 2$. Hence, the identity holds when $n = 1$. Assume the identity holds when $n = k$ for some integer $k \geq 1$; that is, assume

$$1 \cdot 2 + 2 \cdot 3 + 3 \cdot 4 + \cdots + k(k+1) = \frac{k(k+1)(k+2)}{3}$$

for some integer $k \geq 1$. We want to show that it also holds when $n = k+1$; that is, we want to show that

$$1 \cdot 2 + 2 \cdot 3 + 3 \cdot 4 + \cdots + (k+1)(k+2) = \frac{(k+1)(k+2)(k+3)}{3}.$$

It follows from the inductive hypothesis that

$$
\begin{aligned}
1\cdot 2 + 2\cdot 3 + \cdots + (k+1)(k+2) &= 1\cdot 2 + 2\cdot 3 + \cdots + k(k+1) + (k+1)(k+2) \\
&= \frac{k(k+1)(k+2)}{3} + (k+1)(k+2) \\
&= (k+1)(k+2)\left(\frac{k}{3}+1\right) \\
&= (k+1)(k+2)\left(\frac{k+3}{3}\right).
\end{aligned}
$$

This completes the induction.

2. We proceed by induction on n. When $n=1$, the left-hand side reduces to $1\cdot 2\cdot 3 = 6$, and the right-hand side reduces to $\frac{1\cdot 2\cdot 3\cdot 4}{4}=6$. Hence, the identity holds when $n=1$. Assume it holds when $n=k$ for some integer $k\geq 1$; that is, assume

$$
\sum_{i=1}^{k} i(i+1)(i+2) = \frac{k(k+1)(k+2)(k+3)}{4}
$$

for some integer $k\geq 1$. We want to show that it also holds when $n=k+1$; that is, we want to show that

$$
\sum_{i=1}^{k+1} i(i+1)(i+2) = \frac{(k+1)(k+2)(k+3)(k+4)}{4}.
$$

It follows from the inductive hypothesis that

$$
\begin{aligned}
\sum_{i=1}^{k+1} i(i+1)(i+2) &= \left(\sum_{i=1}^{k} i(i+1)(i+2)\right) + (k+1)(k+2)(k+3) \\
&= \frac{k(k+1)(k+2)(k+3)}{4} + (k+1)(k+2)(k+3) \\
&= (k+1)(k+2)(k+3)\left(\frac{k}{4}+1\right) \\
&= (k+1)(k+2)(k+3)\left(\frac{k+4}{4}\right).
\end{aligned}
$$

This completes the induction.

3. We proceed by induction on n. When $n=1$, the left-hand side reduces to $1+4=5$, and the right-hand side becomes $\frac{1}{3}(4^2-1)=5$. Hence, the identity holds when $n=1$. Assume it holds when $n=k$ for some integer $k\geq 1$; that is, assume that

$$
1+4+4^2+\cdots+4^k = \frac{1}{3}\left(4^{k+1}-1\right)
$$

for some integer $k\geq 1$. We want to show that it also holds when $n=k+1$; that is, we want to show that

$$
1+4+4^2+\cdots+4^{k+1} = \frac{1}{3}\left(4^{k+2}-1\right).
$$

It follows from the inductive hypothesis that

$$
\begin{aligned}
1+4+4^2+\cdots+4^{k+1} &= 1+4+4^2+\cdots+4^k+4^{k+1} \\
&= \tfrac{1}{3}\left(4^{k+1}-1\right)+4^{k+1} \\
&= \tfrac{1}{3}\left(4^{k+1}-1+3\cdot 4^{k+1}\right) \\
&= \tfrac{1}{3}\left(4\cdot 4^{k+1}-1\right) \\
&= \tfrac{1}{3}\left(4^{k+2}-1\right).
\end{aligned}
$$

This completes the induction.

Section 3.5

1. We use induction to prove the claim. Note that $n^2 + 3n + 2 = 6$ when $n = 1$, so the claim is true. Assume it is true when $n = k$ for some integer $k \geq 1$, so we can write

$$k^2 + 3k + 2 = 2q$$

for some integer q. We want to show that the claim is still true when $n = k + 1$, that is,

$$(k + 1)^2 + 3(k + 1) + 2 = 2Q$$

for some integer Q. We find

$$
\begin{aligned}
(k + 1)^2 + 3(k + 1) + 2 &= k^2 + 5k + 6 \\
&= (k^2 + 3k + 2) + 2k + 4 \\
&= 2q + 2k + 4 \\
&= 2(q + k + 2),
\end{aligned}
$$

where $q + k + 2$ is an integer. Thus, the claim is still true when $n = k + 1$, thereby completing the induction.

2. Proceed by induction on n. Since $1 < 2^1$, the inequality is valid when $n = 1$. Assume it is valid when $n = k$ for some integer $k \geq 1$; that is, assume

$$k < 2^k$$

for some integer $k \geq 1$. We want to show that

$$k + 1 < 2^{k+1}.$$

Notice that for $k \geq 1$, we have $1 < 2^k$. Hence, it follows from the inductive hypothesis that

$$k + 1 < 2^k + 1 < 2^k + 2^k = 2 \cdot 2^k = 2^{k+1}.$$

This completes the induction and the proof of the given inequality.

3. Proceed by induction on n. When $n = 0$, the LHS of the identity reduces to 1, and the RHS of the identity becomes $3\left(1 - \frac{2}{3}\right) = 3 \cdot \frac{1}{3} = 1$. Thus, the identity holds when $n = 0$. Assume it holds when $n = k$ for some integer $k \geq 0$. That is, assume

$$1 + \frac{2}{3} + \frac{4}{9} + \cdots + \left(\frac{2}{3}\right)^k = 3\left[1 - \left(\frac{2}{3}\right)^{k+1}\right]$$

for some integer $k \geq 0$. We want to show that it also holds when $n = k + 1$. That is, we want to show that

$$1 + \frac{2}{3} + \frac{4}{9} + \cdots + \left(\frac{2}{3}\right)^{k+1} = 3\left[1 - \left(\frac{2}{3}\right)^{k+2}\right].$$

According to the inductive hypothesis,

$$
\begin{aligned}
1 + \frac{2}{3} + \frac{4}{9} + \cdots + \left(\frac{2}{3}\right)^{k+1} &= 1 + \frac{2}{3} + \frac{4}{9} + \cdots + \left(\frac{2}{3}\right)^k + \left(\frac{2}{3}\right)^{k+1} \\
&= 3\left[1 - \left(\frac{2}{3}\right)^{k+1}\right] + \left(\frac{2}{3}\right)^{k+1} \\
&= 3\left[1 - \left(\frac{2}{3}\right)^{k+1} + \frac{1}{3}\left(\frac{2}{3}\right)^{k+1}\right]
\end{aligned}
$$

$$= 3 \left[1 - \frac{2}{3} \cdot \left(\frac{2}{3} \right)^{k+1} \right]$$

$$= 3 \left[1 - \left(\frac{2}{3} \right)^{k+2} \right].$$

This completes the induction and the proof of the given identity.

Section 3.6

1. Proceed by induction on n. When $n = 1, 2$, the proposed formula for c_n says $c_1 = 5 \cdot 3 - 4 \cdot 2 = 7$, and $c_2 = 5 \cdot 9 - 4 \cdot 4 = 29$. They agree with the given initial values, so the formula holds for $n = 1, 2$. Assume the formula is valid for $n = 1, 2, \ldots, k$ for some integer $k \geq 2$. In particular, assume

$$c_k = 5 \cdot 3^k - 4 \cdot 2^k, \qquad \text{and} \qquad c_{k-1} = 5 \cdot 3^{k-1} - 4 \cdot 2^{k-1}.$$

We want to show that the formula still works when $n = k + 1$. In other words, we want to show that

$$c_{k+1} = 5 \cdot 3^{k+1} - 4 \cdot 2^{k+1}.$$

Using the recurrence relation and the inductive hypothesis, we find

$$
\begin{aligned}
c_{k+1} &= 5c_k - 6c_{k-1} \\
&= 5(5 \cdot 3^k - 4 \cdot 2^k) - 6(5 \cdot 3^{k-1} - 4 \cdot 2^{k-1}) \\
&= 25 \cdot 3^k - 20 \cdot 2^k - 30 \cdot 3^{k-1} + 24 \cdot 2^{k-1} \\
&= 25 \cdot 3^k - 20 \cdot 2^k - 10 \cdot 3 \cdot 3^{k-1} + 12 \cdot 2 \cdot 2^{k-1} \\
&= 25 \cdot 3^k - 20 \cdot 2^k - 10 \cdot 3^k + 12 \cdot 2^k \\
&= 15 \cdot 3^k - 8 \cdot 2^k \\
&= 5 \cdot 3 \cdot 3^k - 4 \cdot 2 \cdot 2^k \\
&= 5 \cdot 3^{k+1} - 4 \cdot 2^{k+1},
\end{aligned}
$$

which is what we want to establish. This completes the induction, and hence, the claim that $b_n = 2^n + 3^n$.

2. Proceed by induction on n. The claim is true for $n = 2, 3$, because

$$
\begin{aligned}
2 &= 2 \cdot 1 + 3 \cdot 0, \\
3 &= 2 \cdot 0 + 3 \cdot 1.
\end{aligned}
$$

Assume the claim holds when $n = 2, 3, \ldots, k$ for some integer $k \geq 3$. In particular, since $k - 1 \geq 2$, we may assume that

$$k - 1 = 2x + 3y$$

for some nonnegative integers x and y. We want to show that the claim is still true when $n = k + 1$. We find

$$
\begin{aligned}
k + 1 &= (k - 1) + 2 \\
&= (2x + 3y) + 2 \\
&= 2(x + 1) + 3y,
\end{aligned}
$$

where $x + 1$ and y are nonnegative integers. Therefore, the claim is still true when $n = k + 1$. This completes the induction.

Section 4.1

1. $\{-4, -3, -2, -1, 0, 1, 2, 3, 4\}$, and $\{1, 2, 3, 4\}$.

2. $\{1, 4, 9, 16\}$.

3. $\{\ldots, -5, -3, -1, 1, 3, 5, \ldots\}$.

4. $\{\ldots, -9, -6, -3, 0, 3, 6, 9, \ldots\}$.

5. Only $\{x \in \mathbb{R} \mid 1 < x < 7\}$ can be represented by the interval notation $(1, 7)$, because we have to include all the real numbers between 1 and 7.

6. Because $[2, 7] = \{x \in \mathbb{R} \mid 2 \le x \le 7\}$ includes decimal numbers and integers, but $\{2, 3, 4, 5, 6, 7\}$ contains only integers.

7. False, because the interval $(-2, 3)$ contains decimal numbers as well as integers, but the set $\{-1, 0, 1, 2\}$ contains only integers.

8. $\mathbb{Z}^-$.

9. The notation $[7, 7]$ means $\{x \in \mathbb{R} \mid 7 \le x \le 7\}$. Since equality is allowed, this set contains only one number, namely, the number 7. In other words, $[7, 7] = \{7\}$. But the sets $(7, 7)$, $(7, 7]$ and $[7, 7)$ are empty.

10. Both sets have two elements. The elements of $\{0, \{1\}\}$ are 0 and $\{1\}$, one of them is an integer, the other is a set. The elements of $\{\{0\}, \{1\}\}$ are the two sets $\{0\}$ and $\{1\}$.

11. (a) 0   (b) the set is infinite   (c) 1

12. It is incorrect to say $|\emptyset| = \emptyset$ because $|\emptyset|$ is a number (its value is 0), but $\emptyset$ is a set, they are incompatible.

Section 4.2

1. (a) true   (b) true

2. False, because $3 \in [3, 4)$ but $3 \notin (3, 4)$.

3. Since $(3, 4)$ consists of numbers strictly between 3 and 4, every number we can find in $(3, 4)$ also appears as a member of $[3, 4]$. However, the interval $[3, 4]$ also contains the two numbers 3 and 4, which are not members of the interval $(3, 4)$. Therefore, it is true that $(3, 4) \subset [3, 4]$. Likewise, we also have $(3, 4) \subset (3, 4]$.

4. (a) According to Theorem 4.2.2, the empty set is the subset of any set, including $\{\emptyset\}$. Thus, the statement is true.

   (b) For $S \subseteq T$, every element of S must be an element of T as well. Here, the set $\{1\}$ has only one element: the number 1, which is also an element of $\{1, \{1, 2\}\}$. Therefore, the statement is true.

   (c) This time, 1 does not appear in $\{\{1\}, \{1, 2\}\}$ as an *element*. Notice that $\{\{1\}, \{1, 2\}\}$ has two elements, both of which are *sets*, namely, $\{1\}$ and $\{1, 2\}$. Therefore, the statement is false. It would have been true if it were $\{1\} \in \{\{1\}, \{1, 2\}\}$.

5. The completed table is listed below.

size	subset
0	$\emptyset$
1	$\{1\}, \{2\}, \{3\}, \{4\}$
2	$\{1, 2\}, \{1, 3\}, \{1, 4\}, \{2, 3\}, \{2, 4\}, \{3, 4\}$
3	$\{1, 2, 3\}, \{1, 2, 4\}, \{1, 3, 4\}, \{2, 3, 4\}$
4	$\{1, 2, 3, 4\}$

The final answer is

$$\wp(\{1,2,3,4\}) = \{\emptyset, \{1\}, \{2\}, \{3\}, \{4\}, \{1,2\}, \{1,3\}, \{1,4\}, \{2,3\}, \{2,4\}, \{3,4\},$$
$$\{1,2,3\}, \{1,2,4\}, \{1,3,4\}, \{2,3,4\}, \{1,2,3,4\}\}.$$

6. The set $\emptyset$ has no element, but the set $\{\emptyset\}$ has one element (namely, the empty set). In terms of cardinality, $|\emptyset| = 0$, and $|\{\emptyset\}| = 1$. Yes, it is true that $\wp(\emptyset) = \{\emptyset\}$.

7. There are $2^3 = 8$ elements in $\wp(\{\alpha, \beta, \gamma\})$. They are

$$\emptyset, \quad \{\alpha\}, \quad \{\beta\}, \quad \{\gamma\}, \quad \{\alpha, \beta\}, \quad \{\alpha, \gamma\}, \quad \{\beta, \gamma\}, \quad \text{and} \quad \{\alpha, \beta, \gamma\}.$$

8. Since $|\emptyset| = 0$, the power set $\wp(\emptyset)$ has only $2^0 = 1$ element, which is $\emptyset$ itself. Therefore, $\wp(\emptyset) = \{\emptyset\}$.

9. Yes, because $|A|$ is a number, and $2^{|A|}$ does equal to $|\wp(A)|$. The notation 2^A is illegal because A is a set, hence, it does not make much sense to raise 2 to a power that is not a number.

Section 4.3

1. $A \cap B = \{\text{John}\}$, $A \cup B = \{\text{John}, \text{Mary}, \text{Dave}, \text{Larry}, \text{Lucy}\}$, $A - B = \{\text{Mary}, \text{Dave}\}$, $B - A = \{\text{Larry}, \text{Lucy}\}$, $\overline{A} = \{\text{Lucy}, \text{Peter}, \text{Larry}, \}$, $\overline{B} = \{\text{John}, \text{Mary}, \text{Dave}\}$.

2. $\emptyset$.

3. (a) Because $\{-1, -2, -3, \ldots\}$ and $\{1, 2, 3, \ldots\}$ are sets, but 0 is not, we cannot form their set union. To fix it, we should write $\mathbb{Z} = \{-1, -2, -3, \ldots\} \cup \{0\} \cup \{1, 2, 3, \ldots\}$.

   (b) This is worse than (a): all three components are not sets! Of course, it does not make much sense to take the union of things that are not even sets. To fix it, we need to insert curly braces (set brackets) as in (a).

   (c) Same problem as in (b), plus a wrong notation for set union. To fix it, insert curly braces and change the symbol $+$ to $\cup$.

   (d) Same as (a).

4. $[-1, 3)$ and $(0, 3)$.

5. *Solution 1:* Let $x \in A \cap (B \cup C)$. Then $x \in A$, and $x \in B \cup C$. We know that $x \in B \cup C$ implies that $x \in B$ or $x \in C$. So we have

   (i) $x \in A$ and $x \in B$, or
   (ii) $x \in A$ and $x \in C$;

   equivalently,

   (i) $x \in A \cap B$, or
   (ii) $x \in A \cap C$.

   Thus, $x \in (A \cap B) \cup (A \cap C)$. We have proved that $A \cap (B \cup C) \subseteq (A \cap B) \cup (A \cap C)$.

   Now let $x \in (A \cap B) \cup (A \cap C)$. Then $x \in A \cap B$ or $x \in A \cap C$. From the definition of intersection, we find

   (i) $x \in A$ and $x \in B$, or
   (ii) $x \in A$ and $x \in C$.

   Both conditions require $x \in A$, so we can rewrite them as

   (i) $x \in A$, and
   (ii) $x \in B$ or $x \in C$;

equivalently,

   (i) $x \in A$, or
   (ii) $x \in B \cup C$.

Thus, $x \in A \cap (B \cup C)$. This proves that $(A \cap B) \cup (A \cap C) \subseteq A \cap (B \cup C)$. Together with $A \cap (B \cup C) \subseteq (A \cap B) \cup (A \cap C)$, we conclude that $A \cap (B \cup C) = (A \cap B) \cup (A \cap C)$.

Solution 2:   We note that

$$
\begin{aligned}
x \in A \cap (B \cup C) &\Leftrightarrow x \in A \wedge x \in (B \cup C) &&\text{(defn. of intersection)} \\
&\Leftrightarrow x \in A \wedge (x \in B \vee x \in C) &&\text{(defn. of union)} \\
&\Leftrightarrow (x \in A \wedge x \in B) \vee (x \in A \wedge x \in C) &&\text{(distributive law)} \\
&\Leftrightarrow (x \in A \cap B) \vee (x \in A \cap C) &&\text{(defn. of intersection)} \\
&\Leftrightarrow x \in (A \cap B) \cup (A \cap C) &&\text{(defn. of union)}
\end{aligned}
$$

it follows that $A \cap (B \cup C) = (A \cap B) \cup (A \cap C)$.

6. Assume $A \subseteq B$ and $A \subseteq C$. We want to show that $A \subseteq B \cap C$. To achieve this goal, let $x \in A$. Since $A \subseteq B$, we also have $x \in B$. Likewise $A \subseteq C$ implies that $x \in C$. Now $x \in B$ and $x \in C$ together imply that, according to the definition of set intersection, $x \in B \cap C$. We have proved that $x \in A$ implies that $x \in B \cap C$; it follows that $A \subseteq B \cap C$.

Section 4.4

1. $A \times B = \{(a,r),(a,s),(a,t),(b,r),(b,s),(b,t),(c,r),(c,s),(c,t),(d,r),(d,s),(d,t)\}$,

   $B \times A = \{(r,a),(r,b),(r,c),(r,d),(s,a),(s,b),(s,c),(s,d),(t,a),(t,b),(t,c),(t,d)\}$,

   $B \times B = \{(r,r),(r,s),(r,t),(s,r),(s,s),(s,t),(t,r),(t,s),(t,t)\}$.

2. $\big\{(a,\emptyset),(a,\{d\}),(b,\emptyset),(b,\{d\}),(c,\emptyset),(c,\{d\})\big\}$.

3. $\{(x,y) \mid 1 \le x \le 3, 2 \le y \le 4\}$.

4. $\{(1,a,r),(1,a,s),(1,a,t),(1,b,r),(1,b,s),(1,b,t),$
   $(2,a,r),(2,a,s),(2,a,t),(2,b,r),(2,b,s),(2,b,t)\}$.

5. $\big\{\big((1,a),r\big),\big((1,a),s\big),\big((1,a),t\big),\big((1,b),r\big),\big((1,b),s\big),\big((1,b),t\big),$
   $\big((2,a),r\big),\big((2,a),s\big),\big((2,a),t\big),\big((2,b),r\big),\big((2,b),s\big),\big((2,b),t\big)\big\}$.

Section 4.5

1. $\bigcup_{i=1}^{n} B_i = [0, 2n)$, and $\bigcap_{i=1}^{n} B_i = [0, 2)$.

2. $\bigcup_{i=1}^{\infty} B_i = [0, \infty)$, and $\bigcap_{i=1}^{\infty} B_i = [0, 2)$.

3. $\bigcup_{i=1}^{\infty} C_i = [0, 1)$, and $\bigcap_{i=1}^{\infty} C_i = \{0\}$.

4. $\bigcup_{i=1}^{\infty} E_i = (-\infty, 2)$, and $\bigcap_{i=1}^{\infty} E_i = [-1, 1]$.

5. $\bigcup_{i=1}^{\infty} F_i = \mathbb{N}$, and $\bigcap_{i=1}^{\infty} F_i = \emptyset$.

6. We find

$$\bigcup_{i \in J} A_i = A_1 \cup A_4 \cup A_5 = \{1, 4, 23\} \cup \{5, 17, 22\} \cup \{3, 6, 23\} = \{1, 3, 4, 5, 6, 17, 22, 23\},$$

and

$$\bigcap_{i \in J} A_i = A_1 \cap A_4 \cap A_5 = \{1, 4, 23\} \cap \{5, 17, 22\} \cap \{3, 6, 23\} = \emptyset.$$

7. For $I = \{\text{Mary}, \text{Joe}, \text{Lucy}\}$, we have

$$\bigcup_{i \in I} = A_{\text{Mary}} \cup A_{\text{Joe}} \cup A_{\text{Lucy}} = \{7, 11, 23\} \cup \{3, 6, 9\} \cup \{3, 6, 23\} = \{3, 6, 7, 9, 11, 23\}.$$

These will be the numbers on their Lotto tickets if Mary, Joe, and Lucy pool their money together.

8. I leave them to you as exercises.

9. The union $\bigcup_{i \in I} A_i$ represents the set of people who is friend to at least one student in I. The intersection $\bigcap_{i \in I} A_i$ represents the set of people who knows everyone in I.

Section 5.1

1. The subset $(0, 1)$ does not have a smallest element. Thus $[0, 1]$ is not well-ordered.

Section 5.2

1. (a) 18, 2   (b) -19, 5   (c) -25, 11

2.

b	a	$b \operatorname{div} a$	$b \bmod a$
234	15	22	4
234	-15	-22	4
-234	15	-23	11
-234	-15	23	11

3. $11q + 4$, 2.

4. Thursday.

Section 5.3

1. $35 = 5 \cdot 7,$ $35 = 8 \cdot 4 + 3,$ $35 = 25 \cdot 1 + 10,$ $14 = 7 \cdot 2,$ $-14 = 2 \cdot (-7),$
   $14 = 14 \cdot 1.$

2. When an odd integer is divided by 2, the remainder is 1. Hence, we have

   - If n is even, then $n = 2q$ for some integer q.
   - If n is odd, then $n = 2q + 1$ for some integer q.

3. If n is not divisible by 3, then $n = 3q + 1$ or $n = 3q + 2$ for some integer q.

4. 1, 2, 3, 4, 6, 11, 12, 22, 33, 44, and 66.

5. 27, 29, 31, 37, and 41.

6. Assume $a \mid b$ and $a \mid c$. There exist integers x and y such that $b = ax$ and $c = ay$. Then

$$bc = ax \cdot ay = a^2 \cdot xy,$$

where xy is an integer. Thus, $a^2 \mid bc$.

Section 5.4

1. The only common divisors of 3 and 5 are ± 1. Hence, $\gcd(3, 5) = 1$.

2. The largest positive divisor of -8 is 8, which also divides 0. Thus, $\gcd(0, -8) = 8$.

3. By applying the theorem repeatedly, we have

$$
\begin{array}{llll}
732 & = & 153 \cdot 4 + 120, & \gcd(732, 153) & = & \gcd(153, 120) \\
153 & = & 120 \cdot 1 + 33, & \gcd(153, 120) & = & \gcd(120, 33) \\
120 & = & 33 \cdot 3 + 21, & \gcd(120, 33) & = & \gcd(33, 21) \\
33 & = & 21 \cdot 1 + 12, & \gcd(33, 21) & = & \gcd(21, 12) \\
21 & = & 12 \cdot 1 + 9, & \gcd(21, 12) & = & \gcd(12, 9) \\
12 & = & 9 \cdot 1 + 3, & \gcd(12, 9) & = & \gcd(9, 3) \\
9 & = & 3 \cdot 3 + 0, & \gcd(9, 3) & = & \gcd(3, 0) = 3.
\end{array}
$$

Therefore, $\gcd(732, 153) = 3$.

4. By applying division repeatedly, we find

$$
\begin{array}{llll}
6958 & = & 2478 \cdot 2 + 2002 & \gcd(6958, 2478) & = & \gcd(2478, 2002), \\
2478 & = & 2002 \cdot 1 + 476 & \gcd(2478, 2002) & = & \gcd(2002, 476), \\
2002 & = & 476 \cdot 4 + 98 & \gcd(2002, 476) & = & \gcd(476, 98), \\
476 & = & 98 \cdot 4 + 84 & \gcd(476, 98) & = & \gcd(98, 84), \\
98 & = & 84 \cdot 1 + 14 & \gcd(98, 84) & = & \gcd(84, 14), \\
84 & = & 14 \cdot 6 + 0 & \gcd(84, 14) & = & \gcd(14, 0) = 14.
\end{array}
$$

Therefore, $\gcd(6958, 2478) = 14$.

5. We find $\gcd(732, 153) = 3$, as follows:

4	732	153	1
1	612	120	
3	120	33	1
1	99	21	
1	21	12	1
1	12	9	
3	9	3	
		9	
		0	

6. We find $\gcd(6958, 2478) = 14$, as follows:

2	6958	2478	1
	4956	2002	
4	2002	476	4
	1904	392	
1	98	84	6
	84	84	
	14	0	

7. From the linear combinations

$$
\begin{array}{rcrcl}
7(5m + 7n) & - & 5(7m + 5n) & = & 24n, \\
-5(5m + 7n) & + & 7(7m + 5n) & = & 24m,
\end{array}
$$

we know that $\gcd(5m + 7n, 7m + 5n)$ divides both $24n$ and $24m$. Since $\gcd(m, n) = 1$, we conclude that $\gcd(5m + 7n, 7m + 5n)$ divides 24. Thus, $\gcd(5m + 7n, 7m + 5n)$ equals to 1, 2, 3, 4, 6, 8, 12, or 24.

8. The following computation

s_k	t_k	q_k			
0	1				
1	0	4	732	153	1
-4	1	1	612	120	
5	-1	3	120	33	1
-19	4	1	99	21	
24	-5	1	21	12	1
-43	9	1	12	9	
67	-14	3	9	3	
			9		
			0		

shows that $3 = \gcd(153, 732) = 67 \cdot 153 - 14 \cdot 732$.

9. The following computation

s_k	t_k	q_k			
0	1				
1	0	2	6958	2478	1
-2	1	1	4956	2002	
3	-1	4	2002	476	4
-14	5	4	1904	392	
59	-21	1	98	84	6
-73	26	6	84	84	
			14	0	

shows that $14 = \gcd(2478, 6958) = -73 \cdot 2478 + 26 \cdot 6958$.

Section 5.5

1. $-43 \cdot 133 + 40 \cdot 143 = 1$.

2. $-512 \cdot 757 + 319 \cdot 1215 = 1$.

3. Suppose $\sqrt{7}$ is rational, then we can write

$$\sqrt{7} = \frac{m}{n}$$

for some positive integers m and n that do not share any common divisor except 1. Squaring both sides and cross-multiplying gives

$$7n^2 = m^2.$$

Thus 7 divides m^2. Since 7 is prime, Euclid's lemma asserts that 7 must also divide m. Then we can write $m = 7s$ for some integer s. The equation above becomes

$$7n^2 = m^2 = (7q)^2 = 49q^2.$$

Hence,

$$n^2 = 7q^2,$$

which implies that 7 divides n^2. Again, since 7 is prime, Euclid's lemma implies that 7 also divides n. We have proved that both m and n are divisible by 7. This contradicts the assumption that m and n do not share any common divisor. Therefore, $\sqrt{7}$ must be irrational.

Section 5.6

1. Since $153 = 3 \cdot 3 \cdot 17$, and $72 = 2 \cdot 2 \cdot 3 \cdot 61$, we determine that $\gcd(153, 72) = 3$.

2. By writing the factorizations as

$$
\begin{aligned}
2^3 \cdot 5 \cdot 7 \cdot 11^2 &= 2^3 \cdot 3^0 \cdot 5^1 \cdot 7^1 \cdot 11^2, \\
2^2 \cdot 3^2 \cdot 5^2 \cdot 7^2 &= 2^2 \cdot 3^2 \cdot 5^2 \cdot 7^2 \cdot 11^0,
\end{aligned}
$$

   it becomes clear that $\gcd(2^3 \cdot 5 \cdot 7 \cdot 11^2, 2^2 \cdot 3^2 \cdot 5^2 \cdot 7^2) = 2^2 \cdot 3^0 \cdot 5^1 \cdot 7^1 \cdot 11^0 = 4 \cdot 5 \cdot = 140$.

3. We find $\operatorname{lcm}(2^3 \cdot 5 \cdot 7 \cdot 11^2, 2^2 \cdot 3^2 \cdot 5^2 \cdot 7^2) = 2^3 \cdot 3^2 \cdot 5^2 \cdot 7^2 \cdot 11^2 = 10672200$.

4. We find $\operatorname{lcm}(246, 426) = \dfrac{246 \cdot 426}{\gcd(246, 426)} = \dfrac{246 \cdot 426}{6} = 17466$.

5. Since $\operatorname{lcm}(35, 42) = 210$, the two comets will return to Earth together in 2222.

6. From the linear combinations

$$
\begin{aligned}
6(4m - 6n) &- 4(6m + 4n) = -52n, \\
4(4m - 6n) &+ 6(6m + 4n) = 52m,
\end{aligned}
$$

   we know that $\gcd(4m - 6n, 6m + 4n)$ divides both $-52n$ and $52m$. Since $\gcd(m, n) = 1$, we conclude that $\gcd(4m - 6n, 6m + 4n)$ divides 52. Consequently, $\gcd(4m - 6n, 6m + 4n)$ equals to 1, 2, 4, 13, 26, or 52. It follows that $\operatorname{lcm}(4m - 6n, 6m + 4n)$ equals to mn, $mn/2$, $mn/4$, $mn/13$, $mn/26$, or $mn/52$.

7. Assume $x \in 4\mathbb{Z} \cap 6\mathbb{Z}$, then $x \in 4\mathbb{Z}$ and $x \in 6\mathbb{Z}$. This means x is a multple of both 4 and 6. Consequently, x is a multiple of $\operatorname{lcm}(4, 6) = 12$, which means $x \in 12\mathbb{Z}$. Thus, $4\mathbb{Z} \cap 6\mathbb{Z} \subseteq 12\mathbb{Z}$.

   Next, assume $x \in 12\mathbb{Z}$, then x is a multiple of 12. Consequently, x is a multiple of 3, as well as a multiple of 4. This means $x \in 4\mathbb{Z}$, and $x \in 6\mathbb{Z}$. As a result, $x \in 4\mathbb{Z} \cap 6\mathbb{Z}$. Thus, $12\mathbb{Z} \subseteq 4\mathbb{Z} \cap 6\mathbb{Z}$. Together with $4\mathbb{Z} \cap 6\mathbb{Z} \subseteq 12\mathbb{Z}$, we conclude that $4\mathbb{Z} \cap 6\mathbb{Z} = 12\mathbb{Z}$.

Section 5.7

1. Wednesday.

2. 13.

3. 3.

4. 8.

5. There are five cases to consider:

$n \pmod 5$	$n^5 - n \pmod 5$
0	$0^5 - 0 = 0$
1	$1^5 - 1 = 0$
2	$2^5 - 2 = 30 \equiv 0$
3	$3^5 - 3 = 340 \equiv 0$
4	$4^5 - 4 = 1020 \equiv 0$

   Therefore, for any integer n, we always have $n^5 - n \equiv 0 \pmod 5$, which means $5 \mid (n^5 - n)$.

6. $7^{45} = 7^{32} \cdot 7^8 \cdot 7^4 \cdot 7 \equiv 5 \cdot 9 \cdot 3 \cdot 7 \equiv 10 \pmod{11}$.

7. $9^{58} = 9^{32} \cdot 9^{16} \cdot 9^8 \cdot 9^2 \equiv 18 \cdot 8 \cdot 13 \cdot 12 \equiv 16 \pmod{23}$.

8. 17.

9. 38.

Section 6.1

1. The domain is $\mathbb{R}$, and the codomain is $\mathbb{Z}$.

2. The range is $\mathbb{R}^+ \cup \{0\}$. Hence, the square root function is not onto.

3. No, because $\mathbb{R}^+$ is a set, and 0 is a number. We can only take union of two sets.

Section 6.2

1. Only f is a well-defined function. The rule for g does not assign any value to a. In other words, $g(a)$ is undefined. For h, two values are associated to b. That is, there are two possible values for the image $h(b)$, which is not allowed.

2. No, r is not a well-defined function because the value of $r(x)$ should be the same regardless of which day of the week it is.

3. No, s is not a well-defined function because the images $s(x)$ are undefined for $2 \leq x \leq 3$.

4. We also have
$$n(\{a,b\}) = n(\{a,d\}) = n(\{b,c\}) = n(\{c,d\}) = 2.$$

   The value of $n(S)$ must be between 0 and 4, inclusive.

5.

n	0	1	2	3	4	5	6	7	8	9
$g(n)$	0	3	1	4	2	0	3	1	4	2

6.

$$
\begin{array}{c}
 \\
0 \\ 1 \\ 2 \\ 3 \\ 4 \\ 5 \\ 6 \\ 7 \\ 8 \\ 9
\end{array}
\begin{pmatrix}
1 & 0 & 0 & 0 & 0 \\
0 & 0 & 0 & 1 & 0 \\
0 & 1 & 0 & 0 & 0 \\
0 & 0 & 0 & 0 & 1 \\
0 & 0 & 1 & 0 & 0 \\
1 & 0 & 0 & 0 & 0 \\
0 & 0 & 0 & 1 & 0 \\
0 & 1 & 0 & 0 & 0 \\
0 & 0 & 0 & 0 & 1 \\
0 & 0 & 1 & 0 & 0
\end{pmatrix}
$$

with column headings $0\ 1\ 2\ 3\ 4$.

Section 6.3

1. Assume $g(x_1) = g(x_2)$, then
$$5 - 7x_1 = 5 - 7x_2,$$

   which clearly implies $x_1 = x_2$. Hence, g is one-to-one.

2. Assume $h(x_1) = h(x_2)$, then
$$\sqrt{x_1 - 2} = \sqrt{x_2 - 2}.$$

   Squaring both sides yields $x_1 - 2 = x_2 - 2$, which clearly implies $x_1 = x_2$. Hence, h is one-to-one.

3. Assume $k(x_1) = k(x_2)$, then
$$\ln x_1 = \ln x_2.$$

   Raising both sides to the power of e, we find
$$e^{\ln x_1} = e^{\ln x_2},$$

   which simplifies to $x_1 = x_2$. Thus, k is a one-to-one function.

Alternatively, we can look at the derivative $k'(x) = 1/x$. Since $k'(x) > 0$ for all $x > 0$, the function k is increasing. Thus, k is one-to-one.

4. First, we use the two-point form to find the equation of the line:

$$\frac{y-2}{x-3} = \frac{5-2}{1-3} = -\frac{3}{2}.$$

This simplifies to $y = -\frac{3}{2}x + \frac{13}{2}$. However, this is not the correct answer. We want a function, so the answer should be

$$f\colon [1,3] \to [2,5], \qquad f(x) = -\frac{3}{2}x + \frac{13}{2}.$$

5. There are many possible answers, we only give two here, their graphs are the straight lines that join the opposite corners of the rectangle framed by the domain and codomain. The straight line joining the two corners $(3,2)$ and $(8,5)$ yields the example

$$f\colon [3,8] \to [2,5], \qquad f(x) = \frac{3}{5}x + \frac{1}{5},$$

and the line joining the two corners $(3,5)$ and $(8,2)$ gives the example

$$g\colon [3,8] \to [2,5], \qquad g(x) = -\frac{3}{5}x + \frac{34}{5}.$$

6. Assume $h(x_1) = h(x_2)$, then

$$4x_1 - 11 \equiv 4x_2 - 11 \pmod{15}.$$

Adding 11 to both sides yields

$$4x_1 \equiv 4x_2 \pmod{15}.$$

Multiplying 4 to both sides leads to

$$16x_1 \equiv 16x_2 \pmod{15},$$

which simplifies to $x_1 \equiv x_2 \pmod{15}$. Therefore, h is one-to-one.

7. We find, for example, $k(3) \equiv k(6) \equiv 4 \pmod{15}$. Hence, k is not one-to-one.

8. Assume $h(n_1) = h(n_2)$. Since the image is either odd or even, we have to consider two cases.

   - If both $h(n_1)$ and $h(n_2)$ are odd, then

     $$2n_1 + 1 = 2n_2 + 1,$$

     hence, $n_1 = n_2$.
   - If both $h(n_1)$ and $h(n_2)$ are even, then

     $$-2n_1 = -2n_2,$$

     hence, $n_1 = n_2$.

In both cases, we find $n_1 = n_2$. Therefore, h is one-to-one.

Section 6.4

1. We can use, for example, a straight line graph that connects the points $(1, 2)$ and $(3, 5)$. This leads to the function $f : [1, 3] \to [2, 5]$ defined by $f(x) = \frac{3}{2}x + \frac{1}{2}$.

2. We can use, for example, a straight line graph that connects the points $(1, 2)$ and $(3, 4)$, see Figure 6.4.

3. $[0, \infty)$.

4. The midpoint of the interval $(2, 9)$ is $\frac{11}{2}$, and its width is 7. The transformation of x to $x - \frac{11}{2}$ shifts the interval to $\left(-\frac{7}{2}, \frac{7}{2}\right)$. Hence, we can set $h(x) = \tan\left[\frac{\pi}{7}\left(x - \frac{11}{2}\right)\right]$.

5. Let $y = 3x + 11$, then
$$x = \frac{y - 11}{3},$$
which is, of course, an element of the domain. Hence, g is onto.

6. It is obvious that the graphs $y = 3x + 1$ and $y = 4x$ are increasing. For $x \leq 2$, the y-values cover the range $(-\infty, 7)$. For $x > 2$, the y-values cover the range $(8, \infty)$. Hence, the y-values in the interval $[7, 8]$ are never used as images. For example, there is no x-value which would give $f(x) = \frac{15}{2}$. Therefore, f is not onto.

7. Let $y \equiv 5x + 8 \pmod{23}$. Then
$$5x \equiv y - 8 \pmod{23}.$$
Since $5^{-1} \equiv 14 \pmod{23}$, we find
$$x \equiv 5^{-1}(y - 8) \equiv 14(y - 8) \pmod{23}.$$
Therefore, h is onto.

8. No! Since $v(n) \geq 2$, there does not exist $n \in \mathbb{N}$ such that $v(n) = 1$.

9. No! Someone in the tree would have no daughter. She could be you, or your sisters, or one of their infant daughters, or someone higher up in the tree. For this individual y, we cannot find any x such that $h_1(x) = y$, because this would make x a daughter of x.

Section 6.5

1. $(11, \infty)$; $\mathbb{R}$.

2. Since
$$x^2 - x - 7 = \left(x - \frac{1}{2}\right)^2 - \frac{29}{4} \geq -\frac{29}{4},$$
we determine that $\operatorname{im} g = \left(-\frac{29}{4}, \infty\right)$.

3. Remember that $h(\{0, 3, 4\})$ is a set, so we need to use a set notation. The answer is $\{4, 9\}$.

4. $\{0, 1, 2, 3, 4, 5\}$.

5. Let $y \in f(C_1 \cap C_2)$, we want to show that $y \in f(C_1) \cap f(C_2)$. Having $y \in f(C_1 \cap C_2)$ means there exists $x \in C_1 \cap C_2$ such that $f(x) = y$. Now that $x \in C_1 \cap C_2$ requires $x \in C_1$ and $x \in C_2$.

   - For $x \in C_1$, we find $y = f(x) \in f(C_1)$.
   - For $x \in C_2$, we find $y = f(x) \in f(C_2)$.

We conclude that $y = f(x)$ belongs to *both* $f(C_1)$ and $f(C_2)$. Thus, $f(x) \in f(C_1) \cap f(C_2)$, proving that $f(C_1 \cap C_2) \subseteq f(C_1) \cap f(C_2)$.

6. We want to find x such that
$$x^2 - x - 7 = 3.$$

This is equivalent to solving the equation
$$x^2 - x - 10 = 0.$$

Its solutions are $x = \frac{1 \pm \sqrt{41}}{2} \notin \mathbb{Q}$. Therefore, $k^{-1}(\{3\}) = \emptyset$.

7. $h^{-1}(\{4\}) = \{0, 3, 6, 9, 12\}; \qquad h^{-1}(\{2\}) = \emptyset$.

8. First, we want to prove that $f^{-1}(D_1 \cap D_2) \subseteq f^{-1}(D_1) \cap f^{-1}(D_2)$. Let $x \in f^{-1}(D_1 \cap D_2)$, then $f(x) \in D_1 \cap D_2$. This means either $f(x) \in D_1$ and $f(x) \in D_2$.

   - For $f(x) \in D_1$, we find $x \in f^{-1}(D_1)$.
   - For $f(x) \in D_2$, we find $x \in f^{-1}(D_2)$.

Since x belongs to both $f^{-1}(D_1)$ and $f^{-1}(D_2)$, we determine that $x \in f^{-1}(D_1) \cap f^{-1}(D_2)$. Therefore, $f^{-1}(D_1 \cap D_2) \subseteq f^{-1}(D_1) \cap f^{-1}(D_2)$.

Next, we want to prove that $f^{-1}(D_1) \cap f^{-1}(D_2) \subseteq f^{-1}(D_1 \cap D_2)$. Let $x \in f^{-1}(D_1) \cap f^{-1}(D_2)$. Then x belongs to both $f^{-1}(D_1)$ and $x \in f^{-1}(D_2)$.

   - For $x \in f^{-1}(D_1)$, we find $f(x) \in D_1$.
   - For $x \in f^{-1}(D_2)$, we find $f(x) \in D_2$.

Hence, $f(x)$ belongs to both D_1 and D_2, which means $f(x) \in D_1 \cap D_2$. Thus, $x \in f^{-1}(D_1 \cap D_2)$. We have proved that $f^{-1}(D_1) \cap f^{-1}(D_2) \subseteq f^{-1}(D_1 \cap D_2)$. Together with $f^{-1}(D_1 \cap D_2) \subseteq f^{-1}(D_1) \cap f^{-1}(D_2)$, we conclude that $f^{-1}(D_1 \cap D_2) = f^{-1}(D_1) \cap f^{-1}(D_2)$.

Section 6.6

1. $f^{-1} \colon [0, \infty) \to [-3, \infty), \qquad f^{-1}(x) = x^2 - 3$.

2. $g^{-1} \colon (0, \infty) \to \mathbb{R}, \qquad g^{-1}(x) = \ln x$.

3. Following the same idea used in Example 6.6.3, we find
$$g^{-1} \colon \mathbb{R} \to \mathbb{R}, \qquad g^{-1}(x) = \begin{cases} \frac{1}{3}(x - 5) & \text{if } x \leq 23, \\ \frac{1}{5}(x + 7) & \text{if } x > 23. \end{cases}$$

4. Let $y \equiv 49x - 3 \pmod{57}$. Interchanging x and y yields
$$x \equiv 49y - 3 \pmod{57}.$$

Hence,
$$y \equiv 49^{-1}(x + 3) \equiv 7(x + 3) \pmod{57}.$$

Therefore, $h^{-1} \colon \mathbb{Z}_{57} \to \mathbb{Z}_{57}$ is defined by $h^{-1}(x) = 7(x + 3) \bmod 57$.

5. Following the same idea used in Example 6.6.6, we find
$$f^{-1} \colon \mathbb{N} \to \mathbb{Z}, \qquad f^{-1}(n) = \begin{cases} -\frac{n}{2} & \text{if } n \text{ is even}, \\ \frac{n-1}{2} & \text{if } n \text{ is odd}. \end{cases}$$

6. $(0, 0, 0, 0, 0, 0, 0, 0); \qquad \{a_1, a_3, a_4, a_5\}$.

Section 6.7

1. We find $p \circ q : \mathbb{R} \to \mathbb{R}$ and $q \circ p : \mathbb{R} \to \mathbb{R}$ defined by $(p \circ q)(x) = 2x^2 + 7$, and $(q \circ p)(x) = 4x^2 + 20x + 26$.

2. Direct computation yields

$$f(g(x)) \equiv 7g(x) + 2 \equiv 7(5x - 3) + 2 \equiv 11x + 5 \pmod{12}.$$

   Hence, $f \circ g : \mathbb{Z}_{12} \to \mathbb{Z}_{12}$ is defined by $(f \circ g)(x) \equiv 11x + 5 \pmod{12}$.

3. Since $(f \circ g)(x) = f(g(x)) = 3g(x) + 2$, the function $f \circ g : \mathbb{R} \to \mathbb{R}$ is defined by

$$(f \circ g)(x) \;=\; \begin{cases} 3x^2 + 2 & \text{if } x \leq 5 \\ 3(2x - 1) + 2 & \text{if } x > 5 \end{cases}$$
$$=\; \begin{cases} 3x^2 + 2 & \text{if } x \leq 5 \\ 6x - 1 & \text{if } x > 5 \end{cases}$$

4. The composite function $f \circ g : \mathbb{Z} \to \mathbb{Z}$ is defined by

$$(f \circ g)(n) = \begin{cases} n - 6 & \text{if } n \text{ is even,} \\ n + 2 & \text{if } n \text{ is odd.} \end{cases}$$

   This is how we obtained the answer. If n is even, then $f(n) = n + 1$ is odd, so we have to use the second branch in g to evaluate $g(f(n))$. We find, for even n, $g(f(n)) = g(n + 1) = (n + 1) - 7 = n - 6$. In a similar manner, when n is odd, $f(n) = n - 1$ is even, therefore $g(f(n)) = g(n - 1) = (n - 1) + 3 = n + 2$.

5. The composite function $h \circ g$ is easy to obtain:

$$h \circ g : \mathbb{Z} \to \mathbb{R}, \qquad (h \circ g)(x) = \left(\sqrt{|x|} - 5 \right)^2.$$

   To compute $g \circ h$, we start with h, whose codomain is $\mathbb{R}$. This means the result from h could be a real number. But the domain of g is $\mathbb{Z}$, therefore $g \circ h$ is not a well-defined composite function.

6. We find

$$(f \circ g)(x) = f(g(x)) = e^{g(x)} = e^{\ln x} = x,$$
$$(g \circ f)(x) = g(f(x)) = \ln f(x) = \ln e^x = x.$$

   Therefore, f and g are inverse functions of each other.

Section 7.1

1. False, false, true, true, true.

2. Yes, we can write either $(2, 0.5) \in G$, or $2\, G\, 0.5$.

   No, $(4, 0.5) \notin G$, which can also be written as $4\, \cancel{G}\, 0.5$.

   No, $(10, 3) \notin G$, and we can also write $10\, \cancel{G}\, 3$.

3. No, $(0, 3) \notin G$, or $0\, \cancel{G}\, 3$. No, $(1, -1) \notin G$, or $1\, \cancel{G}\, -1$. Yes, $\left(\frac{1}{\sqrt{2}}, \sqrt{2} \right) \in G$, or $\frac{1}{\sqrt{2}}\, G\, \sqrt{2}$.

4. $S = \{(2, 2), (2, 4), (2, 6), (2, 8), (2, 10), (2, 12), (3, 3), (3, 6), (3, 9), (3, 12),$
   $(4, 4), (4, 8), (4, 12)\}$.

5. $\operatorname{dom} S = \{2, 3, 4\} = S - \{7\}$, $\operatorname{im} S = \{2, 3, 4, 6, 8, 9, 10, 12\} = S - \{1, 5, 7, 11\}$.

6.
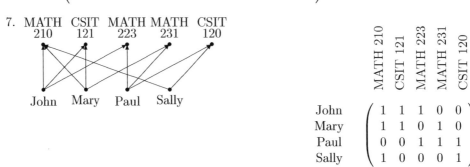

$$\begin{array}{c} 2 \\ 3 \\ 4 \\ 7 \end{array} \begin{pmatrix} 0 & 1 & 0 & 1 & 0 & 1 & 0 & 1 & 0 & 1 & 0 & 1 \\ 0 & 0 & 1 & 0 & 0 & 1 & 0 & 0 & 1 & 0 & 0 & 1 \\ 0 & 0 & 0 & 1 & 0 & 0 & 0 & 1 & 0 & 0 & 0 & 1 \\ 0 & 0 & 0 & 0 & 0 & 0 & 0 & 0 & 0 & 0 & 0 & 0 \end{pmatrix}$$

7.
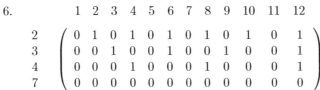

$$\begin{array}{c} \text{John} \\ \text{Mary} \\ \text{Paul} \\ \text{Sally} \end{array} \begin{pmatrix} 1 & 1 & 1 & 0 & 0 \\ 1 & 1 & 0 & 1 & 0 \\ 0 & 0 & 1 & 1 & 1 \\ 1 & 0 & 0 & 0 & 1 \end{pmatrix}$$

with columns MATH 210, CSIT 121, MATH 223, MATH 231, CSIT 120.

Section 7.2

1. We find the following.

   - The relation R is reflexive since $a \leq a$ for all a; hence, it cannot be irreflexive.
   - It is not symmetric, because $2 \leq 3$ but $3 \not\leq 2$.
   - Since $a \leq b$ and $b \leq a$ does imply that $a = b$, the relation R is antisymmetric.
   - Finally, it is transitive because $a \leq b$ and $b \leq c$ imply that $a \leq c$.

   The relation R is reflexive, antisymmetric, and transitive.

2. This is how the analysis may proceed:

   - Since $a \cdot a = a^2$ is always positive for any $a \in \mathbb{R}^*$ (question: is it still true if $A = \mathbb{R}$?), the relation S is reflexive, hence, it is not irreflexive.
   - Since $ab = ba$, it follows that whenever $ab > 0$, we also have $ba > 0$. Therefore, S is symmetric.
   - However, S is not antisymmetric. For example, $2 \cdot 3 > 0$ and $3 \cdot 2 > 0$, but $2 \neq 3$.
   - Since $ab > 0$ only when a and b have the same sign, if we also have $bc > 0$, then c must have the same sign as b, hence, the same sign as a, which in turn implies that $ac > 0$. Thus, S is transitive.

   The given relation is reflexive, symmetric, and transitive.

3. The is how the analysis goes:

   - The relation T is reflexive because $a \mid a$ for any positive integer a. Consequently, T is not irreflexive.
   - Since $2 \mid 6$ but $6 \nmid 2$, we find T non-symmetric.
   - However, if $a \mid b$ and $b \mid a$, we must have $a = b$, thus T is antisymmetric.
   - Finally, $a \mid b$ and $b \mid c$ do imply that $a \mid c$, hence, T is transitive.

   The relation is reflexive, antisymmetric, and transitive.

4. The argument is similar to Hands-On Exercise 7.2.3, the relation is reflexive and transitive.

5. The argument is similar to Hands-On Exercise 7.2.3, the relation R is reflexive, antisymmetric, and transitive.

6. We obtain these conclusions:

- Anyone and himself (or herself) must have the same last name, hence, W is reflexive, which immediately implies that W cannot be irreflexive.
- If two people a and b have the same last name, then so are b and a. Thus, W is symmetric.
- It is not antisymmetric. For example, John Doe and Jane Doe are two different persons having the same last name.
- It is obvious that W is transitive.

This relation is reflexive, symmetric, and transitive.

Section 7.3

1. The proof is similar to Example 7.3.2.

2. The proof is similar to Example 7.3.2.

3. $[0], [1], [2], [3], [4], [5]$.

4. $[0], [1], [2], \ldots, [n-1]$.

5. Example 7.2.5: $[1] = \mathbb{Q}$, and $[x] = x\mathbb{Q}$, where x is any irrational number.

   Example 7.2.7: $[0]$ and $[1]$.

   Hands-On Exercise 7.2.2: $[1] = \mathbb{R}^+$, and $[-1] = \mathbb{R}^-$.

   Hands-On Exercise 7.2.6: each equivalence class consists of individuals with the same last name.

6. Since $x - x = 0$ is an integer, we find $x \sim x$, hence, $\sim$ is reflexive. If $x \sim y$, then $x - y = m$ for some integer m. It follows that $y - x = -(x - y) = -m$, where $-m$ is an integer. Hence, $y \sim x$ as well, which means $\sim$ is symmetric. If $x \sim y$ and $y \sim z$, then $x - y = m$ and $y - z = n$ for some integers m and n. Then

$$x - z = (x - y) + (y - z) = m + n$$

is an integer. Hence, $x \sim z$, which means $\sim$ is transitive. Therefore, $\sim$ is an equivalence relation.

7. The proof is identical to that of Hands-On Exercise 7.3.6. However, $-2.14 \notin [5.14]$, because $5.14 - (-2.14) = 7.28 \notin \mathbb{Z}$.

8. Two points are related if they both lie on the same line $y = 5x + b$ for some specific b. To obtain a more precise formulation, let (x_1, y_1) and (x_2, y_2) be the two points. Then $y_1 = 5x_1 + b$ and $y_2 = 5x_2 + b$. Since b is fixed, we find $b = y_1 - 5x_1 = y_2 - 5x_2$. Therefore

$$(x_1, y_1) \sim (x_2, y_2) \Leftrightarrow y_1 - 5x_1 = y_2 - 5x_2$$

is the relation induced by the partition.

9. From the incidence matrix

	1	2	3	4	5	6
1	1	0	0	1	0	0
2	0	1	0	0	1	1
3	0	0	1	0	0	0
4	1	0	0	1	0	0
5	0	1	0	0	1	1
6	0	1	0	0	1	1

$\rightsquigarrow$

	1	4	2	5	6	3
1	1	1	0	0	0	0
4	1	1	0	0	0	0
2	0	0	1	1	1	0
5	0	0	1	1	1	0
6	0	0	1	1	1	0
2	0	0	0	0	0	1

it is clear that the relation S is an equivalence relation, and its equivalence classes are $[1] = \{1, 4\}$, $[2] = \{2, 5, 6\}$, and $[3] = \{3\}$.

10. $\{(a,a),(a,d),(b,b),(b,c),(b,g),(c,b),(c,c),(c,g),(d,a),(d,d),$

   $(e,e),(e,f),(f,e),(f,f),(g,b),(g,c),(g,g)\}$

Section 7.4

1. The "divides" relation is reflexive and transitive over $\mathbb{Z}^*$, but it is not antisymmetric. For example, $(-2) \mid 2$, and $2 \mid (-2)$; yet $-2 \neq 2$.

2. The relation $\sqsubseteq$ is reflexive and transitive, but not antisymmetric. For example, $\{a,b\} \sqsubseteq \{b\}$, and $\{b\} \sqsubseteq \{a,b\}$; yet $\{a,b\} \neq \{b\}$.

3. The Hasse diagram is displayed below, on the left.

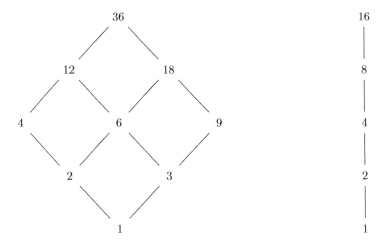

4. The Hasse diagram is displayed above, on the right.

5. The Hasse diagram for the poset $(\wp(\{a,b,c\}), \subseteq)$ is shown below.

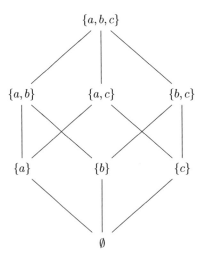

Section 8.2

1. 7, 11.

2. Let A and B denote the *sets* of people who attended the two games, then we are looking for the value of $|A \cup B|$. Since $|A| = 72397$, $|B| = 69211$ and $|A \cap B| = 45713$, we find

$$|A \cup B| = |A| + |B| - |A \cap B| = 72397 + 69211 - 45713 = 95895.$$

Conclusion: 95895 different people attended the two games.

3. This time, we have $|A| = 72397$, $|B| = 69211$ and $|A \cup B| = 93478$, hence,

$$|A \cap B| = |A| + |B| - |A \cup B| = 72397 + 69211 - 93478 = 48130.$$

Conclusion: 48130 people attended both games.

4. The answer is $(47 + 43 + 32) - (33 + 27 + 25) - 22 = 59$.

5. 100000.

6. 999.

7. $9 \cdot 9 \cdot 8 \cdot 7 \cdot 6 \cdot 5 = 136080$.

8. There are $9 \cdot 10 \cdot 10 = 900$ natural numbers with 3 digits. Among them there are 10 of the form $44x$, and 9 of the form $x44$, for some digit x. However, 444 is counted in both groups, so there are actually $10 + 9 - 1 = 18$ integers with repeated 4s. Hence, the number of 3-digit natural numbers that do not have repeated 4s is $900 - 18 = 882$.

9. (a) There are 26 choices each for the first two letters, and 10 choices for each of the remaining four digits. Hence, there are $26^2 \cdot 10^4$ choices for the PINs.

(b) There are seven cases: from 0 to 6 digits following the first two letters, thus the total count is $26^2(1 + 10 + 10^2 + \cdots + 10^6) = 26^2(10^7 - 1)/9$.

(c) Similar to (b), the total number of PINS equals to $26^2(10^2 + 10^3 + \cdots + 10^6) = 26^2 \cdot 10^2(1 + 10 + \cdots + 10^4) = 260^2(10^5 - 1)/9$.

Section 8.3

1. $21 \cdot 20 \cdot 19 \cdot 18 = 143640$.

2. $6 \cdot 5 \cdot 4 \cdot 3 = P(6,4) = 360$.

3. 15^5; $15 \cdot 14 \cdot 13 \cdot 12 \cdot 11 = P(15,5) = 360360$.

4. $7! = 5040$.

5. $7!/2 = 2520$.

Section 8.4

1. $\binom{12}{3} = \frac{12 \cdot 11 \cdot 10}{3 \cdot 2 \cdot 1} = 2 \cdot 11 \cdot 10 = 220$.

2. The order in which the committee members are selected does not matter. This problem essentially counts the number of 3-element subsets. The answer is $\binom{7}{3}$.

3. There are $\binom{23}{5}$ subsets with 5 elements.

4. $\binom{529}{525} = \binom{529}{4} = \frac{529 \cdot 528 \cdot 527 \cdot 526}{4 \cdot 3 \cdot 2 \cdot 1} = 3226076876$.

5. $\binom{8}{5}$.

6. $P(10,4)$.

7. $\binom{52}{13}$.

8. A bridge hand is a 13-element subset, so it is a combination problem. The four spades can be chosen in $\binom{13}{4}$ ways. The remaining nine cards must be selected from the remaining 39 cards (the non-spades), hence, they can be chosen in $\binom{39}{9}$ ways. Together, we determine that the number of bridge hands with exactly four spades is $\binom{13}{4}\binom{39}{9}$. Note that the upper numbers add up to 52, the total number of cards available, and the lower numbers add up to 13, the total number of cards selected.

9. The spades can be selected in $\binom{13}{4}$ ways, and the hearts in $\binom{13}{4}$ ways. The remaining five cards must be selected from the remaining 26 cards other than spades and hearts, they can be selected in $\binom{26}{5}$ ways. Hence, there are $\binom{13}{4}\binom{13}{4}\binom{26}{5}$. Again, take note that the upper numbers add up to 52, and the lower numbers add up to 13.

10. Following the same approach in the last two hands-on exercises, we find the total number to be $\binom{13}{4}\binom{13}{3}\binom{13}{3}\binom{13}{3}$, which can be written as $\binom{13}{4}\binom{13}{3}^3$.

11. There are $\binom{8}{2}$ ways to choose the two blue balls. The other three balls must be either red or green, so we have to choose 3 balls from $6 + 5 = 11$ balls. There are $\binom{11}{3}$ choices. Together, there are $\binom{8}{2}\binom{11}{3}$ selections with exactly two blue balls.

12. This is a combination problem, because we are selecting soda cans without worrying about the order of selection.

    (a) The 4 cans of Pepsi can be selected in $\binom{8}{4}$ ways. The other 6 cans can be selected from the remaining 16 cans, and there are $\binom{16}{6}$ ways to do so. The total number of selections is therefore $\binom{8}{4}\binom{16}{6}$. Note that the upper numbers add up to 24, the total number of soda cans, and the lower numbers add up to 10, the number of cans selected.

    (b) "At least 4 cans of Pepsi" means we can choose from 4 to 8 cans. Following the argument used above, the number of selections is

    $$\binom{8}{4}\binom{16}{6} + \binom{8}{5}\binom{16}{5} + \binom{8}{6}\binom{16}{4} + \binom{8}{7}\binom{16}{3} + \binom{8}{8}\binom{16}{2},$$

    which can be written as $\sum_{k=4}^{8}\binom{8}{k}\binom{16}{10-k}$.

    (c) This time, the number of Pepsi is between 0 to 4 cans. The number of selections is

    $$\binom{8}{0}\binom{16}{10} + \binom{8}{1}\binom{16}{9} + \binom{8}{2}\binom{16}{8} + \binom{8}{3}\binom{16}{7} + \binom{8}{4}\binom{16}{6},$$

    or simply $\sum_{k=0}^{4}\binom{8}{k}\binom{16}{10-k}$.

    (d) This is a more elaborate version of the previous problems. The 3 Pepsi cans can be selected in $\binom{8}{3}$. Now we have to pick the other 7 cans. The number of Sprite could vary from 0 to 3 cans. Once we have picked the Sprite cans, the other cans must be selected from the remaining 9 cans of Dr. Pepper and Mountain Dew. Thus, the total count is

    $$\binom{8}{3}\left[\binom{7}{0}\binom{9}{7} + \binom{7}{1}\binom{9}{6} + \binom{7}{2}\binom{9}{5} + \binom{7}{3}\binom{9}{4}\right].$$

    Using the sigma notation, we can write $\binom{8}{3}\sum_{k=0}^{3}\binom{7}{k}\binom{9}{7-k}$.

Section 8.5

1. $81x^4 - 540x^3y + 1350x^2y^2 - 1500xy^3 + 625y^4$.

2. Since $(1 + 3t)^8 = \sum_{k=0}^{8}\binom{8}{k}(3t)^k$, we need $k = 5$. The coefficient is $\binom{8}{5}3^5$.

3. Since $(2 - 5t)^9 = \sum_{k=0}^{9} \binom{9}{k} 2^{9-k}(-5t)^k$, we need $k = 4$, which implies that the coefficient of t^4 is $\binom{9}{4} 2^5 \cdot (-5)^4$.

4. Since $(3 - 2t^3)^8 = \sum_{k=0}^{8} \binom{8}{k} 3^{8-k}(-2t^3)^k = \sum_{k=0}^{8} \binom{8}{k} 3^{8-k}(-2)^k t^{3k}$, we need $3k = 9$, or $k = 3$. The coefficient is $\binom{8}{3} 3^5 (-2)^3$.

5. Since
$$\left(x + \frac{3}{x} \right)^9 = \sum_{k=0}^{9} \binom{9}{k} x^{9-k} \left(\frac{3}{x} \right)^k = \sum_{k=0}^{9} \binom{9}{k} 3^k x^{9-2k},$$
we need $9 - 2k = 0$, which has no integral solutions. Hence, the constant term in $(x + 3/x)^9$ is zero.

For the second problem, since
$$\left(2x - \frac{3}{x} \right)^{10} = \sum_{k=0}^{10} \binom{10}{k} (2x)^{10-k} \left(-\frac{3}{x} \right)^k = \sum_{k=0}^{10} \binom{10}{k} 2^{10-k}(-3)^k x^{10-2k},$$
we need $10 - 2k = 0$ or $k = 5$. The constant term is $\binom{10}{5} 2^5 (-3)^5$.

6. $\binom{12}{8} \cdot 2^8 - 2\binom{12}{7} \cdot 2^7 + 3\binom{12}{6} \cdot 266$.

7. The 7th, 8th, and 9th rows of Pascal's triangle are displayed below.

		1		7		21		35		35		21		7		1		
	1		8		28		56		70		56		28		8		1	
1		9		36		84		126		126		84		36		9		1

Appendix B

Answers to Selected Exercises

Section 2.1

1. Only (a), (c), and (e) are statements.

3. (a) false   (b) false   (c) false   (d) true

5. (a) $\pi \notin \mathbb{Z}$ (b) $1^3 + 2^3 + 3^3 \neq 3^2 \cdot 4^2/4$ (c) u is not a vowel
   (d) This statement is either true or false.

7. (a) true   (b) true   (c) true   (d) false   (e) false   (f) true

9. By definition, a rational number can be written as a ratio of two integers. After multiplying the numerator by 7, we still have a ratio of two integers. Conversely, given any rational number x, we can multiply the denominator by 7, we obtain another rational number y such that $7y = x$. Hence, the two sets $7\mathbb{Q}$ and $\mathbb{Q}$ contain the same collection of rational numbers. In contrast, $0\mathbb{Q}$ contains only one number, namely, 0. Therefore, $0\mathbb{Q} \neq \mathbb{Q}$.

Section 2.2

1. (a) $p \wedge q$ (b) $\bar{q} \wedge r$ (c) $\bar{p} \vee \bar{q}$ (d) $(p \vee q) \wedge \overline{p \wedge q}$

3. (a) $p \wedge q$; always false regardless of the value of r.
   (b) $p \vee q$; always true regardless of the value of r.
   (c) $(p \wedge q) \vee r$; true if r is true, and false if r is false.
   (d) $\bar{q} \wedge r$; true if r is true, and false if r is false.

5. (a) false   (b) true

7. (a) $(4 \leq x) \wedge (x \leq 7)$ (b) $(4 < x) \wedge (x \leq 7)$ (c) $(4 \leq x) \wedge (x < 7)$

Section 2.3

1. (a) $p \Rightarrow q$ (b) $r \Rightarrow p$ (c) $\bar{p} \Rightarrow q$ (d) $\bar{p} \Rightarrow r$ (e) $(\bar{p} \wedge q) \Rightarrow r$

3. (a) $p \Rightarrow q$, which is false.
   (b) $p \Rightarrow r$, which is true if r is true, and is false if r is false.
   (c) $(p \vee q) \Rightarrow r$, which is true if r is true, and is false if r is false.

5. (a) $x^3 - 3x^2 + x - 3 = 0 \Rightarrow x = 3$
   (b) $x^3 - 3x^2 + x - 3 = 0 \Rightarrow x = 3$
   (c) $x = 3 \Rightarrow x^3 - 3x^2 + x - 3 = 0$

7.

p	q	r	$p \wedge q$	$(p \wedge q) \vee r$
T	T	T	T	T
T	T	F	T	T
T	F	T	F	T
T	F	F	F	F
F	T	T	F	T
F	T	F	F	F
F	F	T	F	T
F	F	F	F	F

p	q	r	$p \vee q$	$p \wedge r$	$(p \vee q) \Rightarrow (p \wedge r)$
T	T	T	T	T	T
T	T	F	T	F	F
T	F	T	T	T	T
T	F	F	T	F	F
F	T	T	T	F	F
F	T	F	T	F	F
F	F	T	F	F	T
F	F	F	F	F	T

9. (a) Using a truth table, we find that the implication $(p \wedge q) \Rightarrow (q \vee r)$ is always true. Hence, no truth value of p would make $(p \wedge q) \Rightarrow (q \vee r)$ false.

(b) From a truth table, we find that, $(q \wedge r) \Rightarrow (p \wedge q)$ is false only when p is false. We can draw the same conclusion without using any truth table. An implication is false only when its hypothesis (in this case, $q \wedge r$) is true *and* its conclusion (in this case, $p \wedge q$) is false. For $q \wedge r$ to be true, we need both q and r to be true. Now q is true and $p \wedge q$ is false require p to be false.

Section 2.4

1. (a) $p \Leftrightarrow q$ (b) $r \Leftrightarrow \overline{p}$ (c) $r \Leftrightarrow (q \wedge \overline{p})$ (d) $r \Leftrightarrow (p \wedge q)$

3. (a) $p \Leftrightarrow q$, which is false.

(b) $p \Leftrightarrow r$, which is true if r is true, and is false if r is false.

(c) $(p \vee q) \Leftrightarrow r$, which is true if r is true, and is false if r is false.

5. (a) true   (b) false   (c) false   (d) false

7. We say n is odd if and only if $n = 2q + 1$ for some integer q.

Section 2.5

1.

p	q	$p \vee q$	$\overline{p \vee q}$	$\overline{p}$	$\overline{q}$	$\overline{p} \wedge \overline{q}$
T	T	T	F	F	F	F
T	F	T	F	F	T	F
T	T	T	F	T	F	F
T	F	F	T	T	T	T

3. Only (b) is a tautology, as indicated in the truth tables below.

(a)

p	q	$\overline{p}$	$\overline{p} \vee q$	$(\overline{p} \vee q) \Rightarrow p$
T	T	F	T	T
T	F	F	F	T
F	T	T	T	F
F	F	T	T	F

(b)

p	q	$p \Rightarrow q$	$\overline{q}$	$p \Rightarrow \overline{q}$	$(p \Rightarrow q) \vee (p \Rightarrow \overline{q})$
T	T	T	F	F	T
T	F	F	T	T	T
F	T	T	F	T	T
F	F	F	T	T	T

(c)

p	q	r	$p \Rightarrow q$	$(p \Rightarrow q) \Rightarrow r$
T	T	T	T	T
T	T	F	T	F
T	F	T	F	T
T	F	F	F	T
F	T	T	T	T
F	T	F	T	F
F	F	T	T	T
F	F	F	T	F

5. The proofs are displayed below without explanations. Be sure to fill them in.

(b) $(p \wedge q) \Rightarrow r \equiv \overline{p \wedge q} \vee r \qquad ($ $)$

$\equiv (\overline{p} \vee \overline{q}) \vee r \qquad ($ $)$

$\equiv \overline{p} \vee (\overline{q} \vee r) \qquad ($ $)$

$\equiv p \Rightarrow (\overline{q} \vee r) \qquad ($ $)$

(c) $(p \Rightarrow \overline{q}) \wedge (p \Rightarrow \overline{r}) \equiv (\overline{p} \vee \overline{q}) \wedge (\overline{p} \vee \overline{r}) \qquad ($ $)$

$\equiv \overline{p} \vee (\overline{q} \wedge \overline{r}) \qquad ($ $)$

$\equiv \overline{p} \vee \overline{q \vee r} \qquad ($ $)$

$\equiv \overline{p \wedge (q \vee r)} \qquad ($ $)$

7. (a) Converse: If triangle ABC is a right triangle, then ABC is isosceles and contains an angle of 45 degrees.

Inverse: If triangle ABC is not isosceles or does not contain an angle of 45 degrees, then ABC is not a right triangle.

Contrapositive: If triangle ABC is not a right triangle, then ABC is not isosceles or does not contain an angle of 45 degrees.

(b) Converse: If quadrilateral $ABCD$ is both a rectangle and a rhombus, then $ABCD$ is a square.

Inverse: If quadrilateral $ABCD$ is not a square, then it is not a rectangle or not a rhombus.

Contrapositive: If quadrilateral $ABCD$ is not a rectangle or not a rhombus, then $ABCD$ is not a square.

9. (a) true   (b) true   (c) false

11. Only (b).

13. (a) $p \wedge q$ (b) $p \wedge \overline{q}$ (c) $p \wedge q$

Section 2.6

1. (a) There exists an integer n such that n is prime and n is even.

(b) For all integers n, if $n > 2$, then n is prime or n is even.

(c) There exists an integer n such that n is prime, and either n is even or $n > 2$.

(d) For all integers n, if n is prime and n is even, then $n \leq 2$.

3. (a) true   (b) true   (c) false   (d) false   (e) true

5. (a) $\exists x < 0 \, \exists y, z \in \mathbb{R} \, (y < z \wedge xy \leq xz)$

(b) $\exists x \in \mathbb{Z} \, [\overline{p(x)} \wedge \overline{q(x)}]$

(c) $\exists x, y \in \mathbb{R} \, [p(x,y) \wedge \overline{q(x,y)}]$

7. (a) $\forall x, y \in \mathbb{R}\,(x + y = y + x)$
    $\exists x, y \in \mathbb{R}\,(x + y \neq y + x)$
    There exist real numbers x and y such that $x + y \neq y + x$.

   (b) $\forall x \in \mathbb{R}^+ \exists y \in \mathbb{R}\,(y^2 = x)$
    $\exists x \in \mathbb{R}^+ \forall y \in \mathbb{R}\,(y^2 \neq x)$
    There exists a positive real number x such that for all real numbers y, $y^2 \neq x$.

   (c) $\exists y \in \mathbb{R}\,\forall x \in \mathbb{Z}\,(2x^2 + 1 > x^2 y)$
    $\forall y \in \mathbb{R}\,\exists x \in \mathbb{Z}\,(2x^2 + 1 \leq x^2 y)$
    For every real number y, there exists an integer x such that $2x^2 + 1 \leq x^2 y$.

9. The statement "a square must be a parallelogram" means, symbolically,

$$\forall PQRS\,(PQRS \text{ is a square} \Rightarrow PQRS \text{ is a parallelogram}),$$

   but the statement "a square must not be a parallelogram" means

$$\forall PQRS\,(PQRS \text{ is a square} \Rightarrow PQRS \text{ is not a parallelogram}).$$

   The second statement is not the negation of the first. The correct negation, in symbol, is

$$\exists PQRS\,(PQRS \text{ is a square} \wedge PQRS \text{ is a parallelogram}).$$

   In words, it means "there exists a square that is not a parallelogram."

Section 3.1

1. Placing six dominoes horizontally in each row covers the entire chessboard.

3. Let $f(x) = x^3 - 12x + 2$. From the following chart

x	-4	-3	-2	-1	0	1	2	3	4
$f(x)$	-14	12	18	13	2	-9	-14	-7	18

   we conclude there $x^3 - 12x + 2 = 0$ has a solution between -4 and -3, another one between 0 and 1, and a third one between 3 and 4. So it has at least three real solutions.

   Remark. The Fundamental Theorem of Algebra asserts that a real polynomial of degree n has at most n real roots. Hence, the given equation has exactly three real solutions.

7. $n = 3$.

Section 3.2

1. No, $2^3 + 1 = 9$ is composite.

7. According to (i), the number $\sqrt{2}$ is irrational. It follows from (ii) that $\sqrt[4]{2} = \sqrt{\sqrt{2}}$ is also irrational. Applying (ii) one more time, we conclude that $\sqrt[8]{2} = \sqrt{\sqrt[4]{2}}$ is irrational.

8. (a) The statement is false, because $(-3)^2 > (-2)^2$, but $-3 \not> -2$.

   (b) The statement is false, because when $n = 41$,

$$n^2 + n + 41 = 41^2 + 41 + 41 = 41(41 + 1 + 1) = 41 \cdot 43$$

   is composite.

Section 3.3

1. (a) We will prove the contrapositive of the given statement. That is, we will prove that if n is odd, then n^2 is odd. If n is odd, we can write $n = 2q + 1$ for some integer q. Then

$$n^2 = (2q + 1)^2 = 4q^2 + 4q + 1 = 2(2q^2 + 2q) + 1,$$

where $2q^2 + 2q$ is an integer. This shows that n^2 is odd.

(b) Suppose the given statement is false. That is, suppose n^2 is even, but n is odd. Since n is odd, $n = 2q + 1$ for some integer q. Then

$$n^2 = (2q + 1)^2 = 4q^2 + 4q + 1 = 2(2q^2 + 2q) + 1,$$

where $2q^2 + 2q$ is an integer. This shows that n^2 is odd, which contradicts the assumption that n^2 is even. Therefore, the given statement must be true.

9. Suppose there exist some numbers $a \neq b$ such that $a^2 + b^2 = 2ab$. Then

$$0 = a^2 - 2ab + b^2 = (a - b)^2$$

would have implied that $a = b$. This contradicts the assumption that $a \neq b$. Therefore, $a^2 + b^2 \neq 2ab$.

15. Suppose $(p \Rightarrow q) \vee (p \Rightarrow \overline{q})$ is false for some logical statements p and q. For a disjunction to be false, we need

- $p \Rightarrow q$ to be false, and
- $p \Rightarrow \overline{q}$ to be false.

They in turn require

- p to be true and q to be false, and
- p to be true and $\overline{q}$ to be false.

Having $\overline{q}$ false would imply q is true, which contradicts what we found. Therefore, the given logical formula is always true, hence, a tautology.

Section 3.4

1. We proceed by induction on n. When $n = 1$, the left-hand side of the identity reduces to $1^3 = 1$, and the right-hand side becomes $\frac{1^2 \cdot 2^2}{4} = 1$. Hence, the identity holds when $n = 1$. Assume the identity holds when $n = k$ for some integer $k \geq 1$; that is, assume

$$1^3 + 2^3 + 3^3 + \cdots + k^3 = \frac{k^2(k + 1)^2}{4}$$

for some integer $k \geq 1$. We want to show that it also holds when $n = k + 1$; that is, we want to show that

$$1^3 + 2^3 + 3^3 + \cdots + (k + 1)^3 = \frac{(k + 1)^2(k + 2)^2}{4}.$$

Using the inductive hypothesis, we find

$$
\begin{aligned}
1^3 + 2^3 + 3^3 + \cdots + (k + 1)^3 &= 1^3 + 2^3 + 3^3 + \cdots + k^3 + (k + 1)^3 \\
&= \frac{k^2(k + 1)^2}{4} + (k + 1)^3 \\
&= \frac{(k + 1)^2[k^2 + 4(k + 1)]}{4} \\
&= \frac{(k + 1)^2(k^2 + 4k + 4)}{4} \\
&= \frac{(k + 1)^2(k + 2)^2}{4}.
\end{aligned}
$$

Therefore, the identity also holds when $n = k + 1$. This completes the induction.

Section 3.5

1. We proceed by induction on n. When $n = 1$, the product $n(n+1)(n+2)$ becomes $1 \cdot 2 \cdot 3 = 6$, which is obviously a multiple of 3. Hence, the claim holds when $n = 1$. Assume the claim holds when $n = k$ for some integer $k \geq 1$; that is, assume that $k(k+1)(k+2)$ is a multiple of 3 for some integer $k \geq 1$. Then we can write

$$k(k+1)(k+2) = 3q$$

for some integer q. We want to show that the claim is still valid when $n = k + 1$. That is, we want to show that $(k+1)(k+2)(k+3)$ is also a multiple of 3. So we want to find an integer Q such that

$$(k+1)(k+2)(k+3) = 3Q.$$

We note that, using the inductive hypothesis,

$$
\begin{aligned}
(k+1)(k+2)(k+3) &= k(k+1)(k+2) + 3(k+1)(k+2) \\
&= 3q + 3(k+1)(k+2) \\
&= 3\left[q + (k+1)(k+2)\right],
\end{aligned}
$$

where $q + (k+1)(k+2)$ is an integer. Hence, $(k+1)(k+2)(k+3)$ is a multiple of 3. This completes the induction.

11. (b) $S_n = 1 - \frac{1}{(n+1)!}$ for all integers $n \geq 1$.

12. (b) $T_n = \frac{n+1}{2n+3}$ for all integers $n \geq 0$.

Section 3.6

1. We proceed by induction on n. When $n = 1$, the left-hand side of the identity reduces to $F_1^2 = 1^2 = 1$, and the right-hand side becomes $F_1 F_2 = 1 \cdot 1 = 1$. Hence, the identity holds when $n = 1$. Assume the identity holds when $n = k$ for some integer $k \geq 1$; that is, assume

$$F_1^2 + F_2^2 + F_3^2 + \cdots + F_k^2 = F_k F_{k+1}$$

for some integer $k \geq 1$. We want to show that it also holds when $n = k + 1$; that is, we want to show that

$$F_1^2 + F_2^2 + F_3^2 + \cdots + F_{k+1}^2 = F_{k+1} F_{k+2}.$$

Using the inductive hypothesis, we find

$$
\begin{aligned}
F_1^2 + F_2^2 + F_3^2 + \cdots + F_{k+1}^2 &= F_1^2 + F_2^2 + F_3^2 + \cdots + F_k^2 + F_{k+1}^2 \\
&= F_k F_{k+1} + F_{k+1}^2 \\
&= F_{k+1}(F_k + F_{k+1}) \\
&= F_{k+1} F_{k+2}.
\end{aligned}
$$

Therefore, the identity also holds when $n = k + 1$. This completes the induction.

Section 4.1

1. (a) $\{-5, -4, -3, -2, -1, 0, 1, 2, 3\}$ (b) $\{1, 2, 3\}$ (c) $\{0, -2, 3\}$ (d) $\{-3, 3\}$

3. (a) $\{n \in \mathbb{Z} \mid n < 0\}$

   (b) $\{n \in \mathbb{Z} \mid n \text{ is a perfect cube}\}$

   (c) $\{n \in \mathbb{Z} \mid n \text{ is a perfect square}\}$

5. (a) $\mathbb{Z}^-$ (d) $5\mathbb{Z}$ (f) $4 + 6\mathbb{Z}$

   Remark. We cannot write (b) as $\mathbb{Z}^3$ and (c) as $\mathbb{Z}^2$, because $\mathbb{Z}^3$ and $\mathbb{Z}^2$ mean something else. If we drop 0 from (e), then $\{4, 8, 12, \ldots\} = 4\mathbb{N}$. However, the inclusion of 0 makes it harder to describe (d) in the form of $4S$.

7. (a) $(-4, 7)$ (b) $(-4, 7]$ (c) $(0, 7]$

9. (a) 10   (b) 11   (c) 7

11. (a) true   (b) true   (c) true   (d) false

13. (a) It is incorrect to write $(3, 7] = 3 < x \le 7$ because $(3, 7]$ is a set, but $3 < x \le 7$ is a logical statement.

    (b) No, because both $\{x \in \mathbb{R} \mid x^2 < 0\}$ and $\emptyset$ are sets, so we should use an equal sign to compare them. The notation $\equiv$ only applies to logical statements. The correct way to say it is "$\{x \in \mathbb{R} \mid x^2 < 0\} = \emptyset$."

Section 4.2

1. (a) true   (b) true   (c) true   (d) true   (e) true   (f) false

3. We have $\mathbb{Z} \subseteq \mathbb{N}$ because every integer n is also a rational number, as we can write it as the rational number $\frac{n}{1}$.

5. Yes, this is the transitive property.

7. (e) $\{\emptyset, \{a\}, \{\{b\}\}, \{a, \{b\}\}\}$

11. (a) False, because the set $\{a\}$ cannot be found in $\{a, b, c\}$ as an element.

    (b) False, because a, the sole element in $\{a\}$, cannot be found in $\{\{a\}, b, c\}$ as an element.

    (c) False. For $\{a\} \in \wp(\{\{a\}, b, c\})$, the set $\{a\}$ must be a subset of $\{\{a\}, b, c\}$. This means a must belong to $\{\{a\}, b, c\}$, which is not true.

Section 4.3

1. (a) $\{-4, -3, -2, -1, 0, 1, 2, 3, 4\}$

   (b) $\{-3, -2, -1, 0, 1, 2, 3, 4\}$

   (c) $\{-3, -2, -1, 0, 1, 2, 3, \ldots\}$

3. (a) false   (b) false

5. (a) $E \cap D$ (b) $\overline{E} \cup B$

7. For example, take $A = \{x\}$, and $B = \{\{x\}, x\}$.

9. Assume $A \subseteq C$ and $B \subseteq C$, we want to show that $A \cup B \subseteq C$. In this regard, let $x \in A \cup B$, we want to show that $x \in C$ as well. Since $x \in A \cup B$, the definition of set union asserts that either $x \in A$ or $x \in B$.

   - Case 1: If $x \in A$, then $A \subseteq C$ implies that $x \in C$.
   - Case 2: If $x \in B$, then $B \subseteq C$ implies that $x \in C$.

   In both cases, we find $x \in C$. This proves that $A \cup B \subseteq C$.

13. (a) The notation $\cap$ is used to connect two sets, but "$x \in A$" and "$x \in B$" are both logical statements. We should also use $\Leftrightarrow$ instead of $\equiv$. The statement should have been written as "$x \in A \wedge x \in B \Leftrightarrow x \in A \cap B$."

(b) If we read it aloud, it sounds perfect:

If x belongs to A and B, then x belongs to $A \cap B$.

The trouble is, every notation has its own meaning and specific usage. In this case, $\wedge$ is not exactly a replacement for the English word "and." Instead, it is the notation for joining two logical statements to form a conjunction. Before $\wedge$, we have "$x \in A$," which is a logical statement. But, after $\wedge$, we have "B," which is a set, and not a logical statement. It should be written as "$x \in A \wedge x \in B \Rightarrow x \in A \cap B$."

Section 4.4

1. (a) $\{(-2,0),(-2,4),(2,0),(2,4)\}$

   (b) $\{(-2,-3),(-2,0),(-2,3),(-2,-3),(-2,0),(-2,3)\}$

3. $2 \cdot 2 \cdot 2 \cdot 3 = 24$.

5. (a) $\{(-2,\emptyset),(-2,\{-2\}),(-2,\{2\}),(-2,\{-2,2\}),(2,\emptyset),(2,\{-2\}),(2,\{2\}),(2,\{-2,2\})\}$

Section 4.5

1. $\bigcap_{n=1}^{\infty} A_n = [0,2)$, $\bigcup_{n=1}^{\infty} A_n = (-1,\infty)$.

3. $\bigcap_{n=0}^{\infty} C_n = \emptyset$, $\bigcup_{n=0}^{\infty} C_n = \mathbb{N} \cup \{0\}$.

5. $\bigcap_{n \in \mathbb{N}} E_n = E_0 = \{0\}$, $\bigcup_{n \in \mathbb{N}} E_n = \mathbb{Z}$.

7. $\bigcup_{i \in I} A_i = [1,\infty)$, $\bigcap_{i \in I} A_i = \{1\}$.

9. $\bigcap_{x \in (1,2)} (1-2x, x^2) = [-1,1]$, $\bigcup_{x \in (1,2)} (1-2x, x^2) = (-3.4)$.

11. $\bigcap_{r \in (0,\infty)} A_r = \{(0,0)\}$, $\bigcup_{r \in (0,\infty)} A_r = \mathbb{R}^* \times \mathbb{R}^+ \cup \{(0,0)\}$.

Section 5.1

1. (a) 3   (b) 3   (c) 3   (d) 1

3. We claim that the subset $(3,5)$ does not have a smallest element. To see why, suppose it has a smallest element x. The midpoint between 3 and x is the number $\frac{3+x}{2}$, and

$$3 < \frac{3+x}{2} < x < 5.$$

This means $\frac{3+x}{2}$ is also inside the interval $(3,5)$, and is smaller than x. This contradicts the minimality of x. Thus, the interval $(3,5)$ does not have a smallest element. Consequently, the interval $(3,5]$ is not well-ordered.

5. We know that $\mathbb{N}$ is well-ordered. Since $2\mathbb{N}$ is a subset of $\mathbb{N}$, and $2\mathbb{N}$ is clearly nonempty, we conclude from Problem 4 that $2\mathbb{N}$ is also well-ordered.

Section 5.2

1. (a) 23, 1   (b) −11, 1   (c) −6, 13

3. This is an immediate consequence of Corollary 5.2.2.

5. (a) Let n be any integer. Then $n \bmod 3 = 0, 1, 2$.

   - Case 1: if $n \bmod 3 = 0$, then $n = 3q$ for some integer q, and
   $$n^3 - n = (3q)^3 - 3q = 27q^3 - 3q = 3(9q^2 - q),$$
   where $9q^2 - q$ is an integer.
   - Case 2: if $n \bmod 3 = 1$, then $n = 3q + 1$ for some integer q, and
   $$n^3 - n = (3q + 1)^3 - (3q + 1) = 27q^3 + 27q^2 + 6q = 3(9q^3 + 9q^2 + 2q),$$
   where $9q^3 + 9q^2 + 2q$ is an integer.
   - Case 2: if $n \bmod 3 = 2$, then $n = 3q + 2$ for some integer q, and
   $$n^3 - n = (3q + 2)^3 - (3q + 2) = 27q^3 + 54q^2 + 33q + 6 = 3(9q^3 + 18q^2 + 11q + 2),$$
   where $9q^3 + 18q^2 + 11q + 2$ is an integer.

   In all three cases, we have shown that $n^3 - n$ is a multiple of 3.

   (b) We note that
   $$n^3 - n = n(n^2 - 1) = n(n - 1)(n + 1) = (n - 1)n(n + 1)$$

   is a product of three consecutive integers. As we have seen in Problem 4, any three consecutive integers must contain a multiple of 3. It follows that their product is also a multiple of 3.

7. (a) $s + t$ (b) 4

Section 5.3

1. Assume $a \mid b$ and $c \mid (-a)$. There exist integers x and y such that $b = ax$ and $-a = cy$. Then
   $$b = ax = (-a)(-x) = cy \cdot (-x) = (-c) \cdot xy,$$
   where xy is an integer. Thus, $(-c) \mid b$.

7. There are three cases, depending on the remainder when an integer is divided by 3.

   - $(3q)^2 = 9q^2 = 3 \cdot 3q^2$.
   - $(3q + 1)^2 = 9q^2 + 6q + 1 = 3(3q^2 + 2q) + 1$.
   - $(3q + 2)^2 = 9q^2 + 12q + 4 = 9q^2 + 12q + 3 + 1 = 3(3q^2 + 4q + 1) + 1$.

   In each case, we have shown that the square of an integer is of the form $3k$ or $3k + 1$.

Section 5.4

1. (a) $1 \cdot 27 + 0 \cdot 81 = 27$ (b) $-3 \cdot 24 + 1 \cdot 84 = 12$ (c) $-35 \cdot 1380 + 16 \cdot 3020 = 20$

7. 1, 2, 17, and 34.

Section 5.5

1. Since
$$-3 \cdot (2n + 1) + 2 \cdot (3n + 2) = 1,$$
we deduce that $\gcd(2n + 1, 3n + 2) = 1$.

5. Let a, b, and c be positive integers such that $a \mid c$, $b \mid c$, and $\gcd(a, b) = 1$. Then there exist integers x and y such that $c = ax$ and $c = by$; and there exist integers s and t such that $sa + tb = 1$. It follows that
$$c = c \cdot 1 = c(sa + tb) = csa + ctb.$$
Using $c = ax$ and $c = by$, we find
$$c = csa + ctb = by \cdot sa + ax \cdot tb = ab(ys + xt),$$
where $ys + xt$ is an integer. Thus, $ab \mid c$.

Section 5.6

1. (a) $3^2 \cdot 5^2 \cdot 7$ \qquad (b) $2 \cdot 3^2 \cdot 7^2 \cdot 11$

2. (a) 81 \qquad (b) 168

3. Every 50 days.

5. Assume $x \in 10\mathbb{Z} \cap 15\mathbb{Z}$, then $x \in 10\mathbb{Z}$ and $x \in 15\mathbb{Z}$. This means x is a multiple of both 10 and 15. Consequently, x is a multiple of $\mathrm{lcm}(10, 15) = 30$, which means $x \in 30\mathbb{Z}$. Thus, $10\mathbb{Z} \cap 15\mathbb{Z} \subseteq 30\mathbb{Z}$.

   Next, assume $x \in 30\mathbb{Z}$, then x is a multiple of 30. Consequently, x is a multiple of 10, as well as a multiple of 15. This means $x \in 10\mathbb{Z}$, and $x \in 15\mathbb{Z}$. As a result, $x \in 10\mathbb{Z} \cap 15\mathbb{Z}$. Thus, $30\mathbb{Z} \subseteq 10\mathbb{Z} \cap 15\mathbb{Z}$. Together with $10\mathbb{Z} \cap 15\mathbb{Z} \subseteq 30\mathbb{Z}$, we conclude that $10\mathbb{Z} \cap 15\mathbb{Z} = 30\mathbb{Z}$.

7. (a) When p is divided by 4, its remainder is 0, 1, 2, or 3. But p is odd, hence, p is of the form $4k + 1$ or $4k + 3$ for some integer k. Since $p \geq 3$, we also need k to be a nonnegative integer.

   (b) When p is divided by 6, its remainder is 0, 1, 2, 3, 4, or 5. But p is odd, hence, p is of the form $6k + 1$, $6k + 3$, or $6k + 5$. We rule out the form $6k + 3$ because this would make p a multiple of 3. Hence, p is of the form $6k + 1$ or $6k + 5$ for some nonnegative integer k.

Section 5.7

1. The addition and multiplication tables for $\mathbb{Z}_8$ are listed below.

+	0	1	2	3	4	5	6	7
0	0	1	2	3	4	5	6	7
1	1	2	3	4	5	6	7	0
2	2	3	4	5	6	7	0	1
3	3	4	5	6	7	0	1	2
4	4	5	6	7	0	1	2	3
5	5	6	7	0	1	2	3	4
6	6	7	0	1	2	3	4	5
7	7	0	1	2	3	4	5	6

·	0	1	2	3	4	5	6	7
0	0	0	0	0	0	0	0	0
1	0	1	2	3	4	5	6	7
2	0	2	4	6	0	2	4	6
3	0	3	6	1	4	7	2	5
4	0	4	0	4	0	4	0	4
5	0	5	2	7	4	1	6	3
6	0	6	4	2	0	6	4	2
7	0	7	2	5	4	3	2	1

Only 1, 3, 5, and 7 have multiplicative inverses. In fact, $1^{-1} = 1$, $3^{-1} = 3$, $5^{-1} = 5$, and $7^{-1} = 7$.

3. The sum is 9, and the product is 7.

5. From the following computation

m (mod 7)	$m^2 + 1$ (mod 7)
0	$0^2 + 1 = 1$
± 1	$1^2 + 1 = 2$
± 2	$2^2 + 1 = 5$
± 3	$3^2 + 1 = 10 \equiv 3$

we determine that $m^2 + 1 \not\equiv 0$ (mod 7). Hence, $m^2 + 1$ is not a multiple of 7 for all integers m.

7. Both methods give $4^{45} = 1$ in $\mathbb{Z}_{11}$.

9. (a) 9

Section 6.1

1.

x	5.7	π	e	-7.2	-0.8	9
$\lfloor x \rfloor$	5	3	2	-8	-1	9
$\lceil x \rceil$	6	4	3	-7	0	9
$[x]$	6	3	3	-7	-1	9

3. $[0, \infty)$.

Section 6.2

1. $\left[\frac{7}{3}, \infty\right)$.

3. Only g is a well-defined function. The image $f(4)$ is undefined, and there are two values for $h(3)$. Hence, both f and h are not well-defined functions.

5. (a) Yes, because no division by zero will ever occur.

7.

x	1	2	3	4
$p(x)$	3	1	2	2

x	1	2	3	4
$q(x)$	2	3	1	3

9. (a) 7   (b) 7   (c) 3

Section 6.3

1. (a) No. For example, $f(0) = f(2) = 1$.

   (b) Yes, since $g'(x) = 3x^2 - 4x = x(3x - 4) > 0$ for $x > 2$.

3. Because the domain and the codomain are half-open intervals, we need to be careful with the inclusion and exclusion of the endpoints. We can use the graph displayed below on the left.

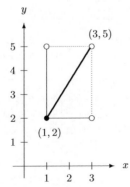 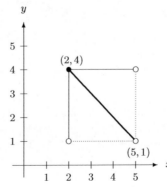

We find $f(x) = \frac{3}{2}x + \frac{1}{2}$.

5. (a) One-to-one   (b) Not one-to-one

7. (a) Not one-to-one   (b) One-to-one

9. There are twelve one-to-one functions from $\{1, 2\}$ to $\{a, b, c, d\}$. The images of 1 and 2 under them are listed below.

	f_1	f_2	f_3	f_4	f_5	f_6	f_7	f_8	f_9	f_{10}	f_{11}	f_{12}
1	a	a	a	b	b	b	c	c	c	d	d	d
2	b	c	d	a	c	d	a	b	d	a	b	c

11. (a) One-to-one   (b) Not one-to-one   (c) Not one-to-one

Section 6.4

1. (a) Yes! It is not easy to express x in terms of y from the equation $y = x^3 - 2x^2 + 1$. However, from its graph, we can tell that the y-values cover all the possible real values in the codomain.

   (b) No, because $g(x) \geq 1$.

5. (b) Not onto   (c) Onto

7. (b) Not onto   (c) Onto

9. No, because we have at most two distinct images, but the codomain has four elements.

11. (a) Onto   (b) Not onto   (c) Not onto

Section 6.5

1. (a) $f_1(A) = \{a, b\}$, $f_1^{-1}(B) = \{2, 3, 4, 5\}$

   (b) $f_2(A) = \{a, c\}$, $f_2^{-1}(B) = \{2, 4\}$

   (c) $f_3(A) = \{b, d\}$, $f_3^{-1}(B) = \emptyset$

   (d) $f_4(A) = \{e\}$, $f_4^{-1}(B) = \{5\}$

3. The images of s are tabulated below.

x	0	1	2	3	4	5	6	7	8	9	10	11
$s(x)$	7	11	3	7	11	3	7	11	3	7	11	3

   (a) $\{3, 11\}$ (b) $\{0, 3, 6, 9\}$ (c) $\{3, 7, 11\}$

5. (a) $[20, 26)$; $\{20, 23, 26\}$ (b) $[-3, -\frac{4}{3})$; $\{-2\}$

7. (a) $\{\frac{3}{5}, \frac{9}{5}, \frac{27}{5}, 3, 9, 27, 15, 45, 135\}$ (b) $\{(-3, 2)\}$ (c) $\mathbb{N} \times \{0\}$

9. For a function to be well-defined, each row sum must be 1. For the function to be one-to-one, each column sum must be at most 1. For the function to be onto, each column sum must be at least 1 (hence, no column sum is zero).

13. Let $y \in f(C_1) - f(C_2)$, we want to show that $y \in f(C_1 - C_2)$ as well. Since $y \in f(C_1) - f(C_2)$, we know there exists $x \in A$ such that $f(x) = y$. Having $y \in f(C_1) - f(C - 2)$ means $y \in f(C_1)$ but $y \notin f(C_2)$. Hence, $x \in C_1$ but $x \notin C_2$. In other words, $x \in C_1 - C_2$. This leads to $y = f(x) \in f(C_1 - C_2)$. This completes the proof that $f(C_1) - f(C_2) \subseteq f(C_1 - C_2)$.

17. $\{0, 1, 4, 9\}$; $\{0, \pm 1, \pm 2, \pm 3\}$.

Section 6.6

1. Only (e) is bijective.

3. Their inverse functions $f^{-1}, g^{-1}: (4,7) \to (1,3)$ are defined by

$$f^{-1}(x) = \frac{2}{3}\left(x - \frac{5}{2}\right), \qquad \text{and} \qquad g^{-1}(x) = -\frac{2}{3}\left(x - \frac{17}{2}\right).$$

5. $g^{-1}: [4,7] \to [1,3]$, where $g^{-1}(x) = \begin{cases} x - 3 & \text{if } 4 \leq x < 5, \\ \frac{1}{2}(11 - x) & \text{if } 5 \leq x \leq 7. \end{cases}$

7. $s^{-1}: (-\infty, -3) \to \mathbb{R}$, where $s^{-1}(x) = \frac{1}{2} \ln\left(\frac{4-x}{7}\right)$.

9. (a) $u^{-1}: \mathbb{Q} \to \mathbb{Q}, \qquad u^{-1}(x) = (x+2)/3$

11. The images under $\alpha^{-1}: \{a,b,c,d,e,f,g,h\} \to \{1,2,3,4,5,6,7,8\}$ are given below.

x	a	b	c	d	e	f	g	h
$\alpha^{-1}(x)$	2	5	8	3	6	7	1	4

Section 6.7

1. Both $f \circ g$ and $g \circ f$ are from $\mathbb{R}$ to $\mathbb{R}$, where $(f \circ g)(x) = 15x^2 + 19$, and $(g \circ f)(x) = 75x^2 - 30x + 7$.

3. We do not need to find the formula of the composite function, as we can evaluate the result directly: $f(g(f(0))) = f(g(1)) = f(2) = -5$.

5. (a) $g \circ f: \mathbb{Z} \to \mathbb{Q}, \quad (g \circ f)(n) = 1/(n^2 + 1)$

   (b) $g \circ f: \mathbb{R} \to (0,1), \quad (g \circ f)(x) = x^2/(x^2 + 1)$

7. (a) $g \circ f: \{1,2,3,4,5\} \to \{1,2,3,4,5\}$,

   $(g \circ f)(1) = 2, (g \circ f)(2) = 5, (g \circ f)(3) = 1, (g \circ f)(4) = 3, (g \circ f)(5) = 4$

9. $g \circ f: \mathbb{Z} \to \mathbb{Z}, \qquad (g \circ f)(n) = \begin{cases} 3(2n - 1) & \text{if } n \geq 0, \\ 2n + 1 & \text{if } n < 0. \end{cases}$

11. (a) $f \circ g: \mathbb{Z} \to \mathbb{Z}, \qquad (f \circ g)(n) = 3 - n$

   $(f \circ g)^{-1}: \mathbb{Z} \to \mathbb{Z}, \qquad (f \circ g)^{-1}(n) = 3 - n$

   $f^{-1}: \mathbb{Z} \to \mathbb{Z}, \qquad f^{-1}(n) = 2 - n$

   $g^{-1}: \mathbb{Z} \to \mathbb{Z}, \qquad g^{-1}(n) = n - 1$

   $g^{-1} \circ f^{-1}: \mathbb{Z} \to \mathbb{Z}, \qquad (g^{-1} \circ f^{-1})(n) = 3 - n$

Section 7.1

1. (a)

(b)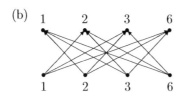

$$\begin{array}{c} \\ 1 \\ 2 \\ 3 \\ 6 \end{array} \begin{array}{cccc} 1 & 2 & 3 & 6 \\ \begin{pmatrix} 0 & 1 & 1 & 1 \\ 1 & 0 & 1 & 1 \\ 1 & 1 & 0 & 1 \\ 1 & 1 & 1 & 0 \end{pmatrix} \end{array}$$

(c)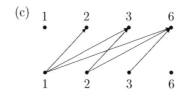

$$\begin{array}{c} \\ 1 \\ 2 \\ 3 \\ 6 \end{array} \begin{array}{cccc} 1 & 2 & 3 & 6 \\ \begin{pmatrix} 0 & 1 & 1 & 1 \\ 0 & 0 & 1 & 1 \\ 0 & 0 & 0 & 1 \\ 0 & 0 & 0 & 0 \end{pmatrix} \end{array}$$

2. (a) domain = image = $\{1, 2, 3, 6\}$.

   (b) domain = image = $\{1, 2, 3, 6\}$.

   (c) domain = $\{1, 2, 3\}$, image = $\{2, 3, 6\}$.

7.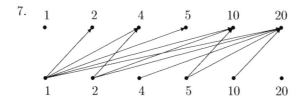

$$\begin{array}{c} \\ 1 \\ 2 \\ 4 \\ 5 \\ 10 \\ 20 \end{array} \begin{array}{cccccc} 1 & 2 & 4 & 5 & 10 & 20 \\ \begin{pmatrix} 0 & 1 & 1 & 1 & 1 & 1 \\ 0 & 0 & 1 & 0 & 1 & 1 \\ 0 & 0 & 0 & 0 & 0 & 1 \\ 0 & 0 & 0 & 0 & 1 & 1 \\ 0 & 0 & 0 & 0 & 0 & 1 \\ 0 & 0 & 0 & 0 & 0 & 0 \end{pmatrix} \end{array}$$

9.

$$\begin{array}{c} \\ \emptyset \\ \{1\} \\ \{2\} \\ \{1,2\} \end{array} \begin{array}{cccc} \emptyset & \{1\} & \{2\} & \{1,2\} \\ \begin{pmatrix} 0 & 0 & 0 & 0 \\ 0 & 1 & 0 & 1 \\ 0 & 0 & 1 & 1 \\ 0 & 1 & 1 & 1 \end{pmatrix} \end{array}$$

Section 7.2

1. (a) Reflexive, symmetric, antisymmetric, and transitive.

   (b) Irreflexive, and symmetric.

   (c) Irreflexive, and transitive.

2. (a) Antisymmetric.

   (b) Reflexive, symmetric, and transitive.

   (c) Irreflexive, symmetric, and transitive.

3. Reflexive, symmetric, and transitive.

4. Antisymmetric, and transitive.

5. Irreflexive, and antisymmetric.

6. Symmetric.

7. (a) A is not reflexive because $(X, X) \notin A$ if $X \neq \emptyset$.

(b) A is not irreflexive because $(\emptyset, \emptyset) \in A$.

(c) No. For example, consider $S = \{a, b, c\}$, $X = \{a\}$, $Y = \{b\}$, and $Z = \{a, c\}$. Then $(X, Y) \in A$, $(Y, Z) \in A$, but $(X, Z) \notin A$.

(d)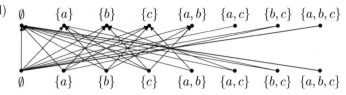

$$
\begin{array}{c}
\\
\emptyset \\
\{a\} \\
\{b\} \\
\{c\} \\
\{a,b\} \\
\{a,c\} \\
\{b,c\} \\
\{a,b,c\}
\end{array}
\begin{array}{cccccccc}
\emptyset & \{a\} & \{b\} & \{c\} & \{a,b\} & \{a,c\} & \{b,c\} & \{a,b,c\} \\
\left(\begin{array}{cccccccc}
1 & 1 & 1 & 1 & 1 & 1 & 1 & 1 \\
1 & 0 & 1 & 1 & 0 & 0 & 1 & 0 \\
1 & 1 & 0 & 1 & 0 & 1 & 0 & 0 \\
1 & 1 & 1 & 0 & 1 & 0 & 0 & 0 \\
1 & 0 & 0 & 1 & 0 & 0 & 0 & 0 \\
1 & 0 & 1 & 0 & 0 & 0 & 0 & 0 \\
1 & 1 & 0 & 0 & 0 & 0 & 0 & 0 \\
1 & 0 & 0 & 0 & 0 & 0 & 0 & 0
\end{array} \right)
\end{array}
$$

8. (a) Symmetric.

(b) Reflexive, and symmetric.

9. (a) Reflexive, antisymmetric, and transitive.

(b) Reflexive, symmetric, and transitive.

(c) Symmetric.

10. (a) Reflexive, antisymmetric, and transitive.

(b) Symmetric.

(c) Symmetric, and transitive.

11. (a) Reflexive, and transitive.

(b) Symmetric,

(c) Reflexive, symmetric, and transitive.

12. (a) Symmetric, and transitive.

(b) Reflexive, symmetric, and transitive.

(c) Reflexive, and transitive.

Section 7.3

1. (a) The equivalence classes are of the form $\{3 - k, 3 + k\}$ for some integer k. For instance, $[3] = \{3\}$, $[2] = \{2, 4\}$, $[1] = \{1, 5\}$, and $[-5] = \{-5, 11\}$.

(b) There are three equivalence classes: $[0] = 3\mathbb{Z}$, $[1] = 1 + 3\mathbb{Z}$, and $[2] = 2 + 3\mathbb{Z}$.

3. (a) True

(b) False

(c) $[\{1, 5\}] = \big\{ \{1\}, \{1, 2\}, \{1, 4\}, \{1, 5\}, \{1, 2, 4\}, \{1, 2, 5\}, \{1, 4, 5\}, \{1, 2, 4, 5\} \big\}$

(d) $[X] = \{(X \cap T) \cup Y \mid Y \in \wp(\overline{T})\}$. In other words, $S \sim X$ if S contains the same element in $X \cap T$, plus possibly some elements not in T.

5. (a) Yes, with $[(a,b)] = \{(x,y) \mid y = x + k \text{ for some constant } k\}$. In other words, the equivalence classes are the straight lines of the form $y = x + k$ for some constant k.

(b) No. For example, $(2,5) \sim (3,5)$ and $(3,5) \sim (3,7)$, but $(2,5) \not\sim (3,7)$. Hence, the relation $\sim$ is not transitive.

7. We find $[0] = \frac{1}{2}\mathbb{Z} = \{\frac{n}{2} \mid n \in \mathbb{Z}\}$, and $[\frac{1}{4}] = \frac{1}{4} + \frac{1}{2}\mathbb{Z} = \{\frac{2n+1}{4} \mid n \in \mathbb{Z}\}$.

Section 7.4

1. The Hasse diagram is shown below.

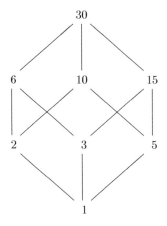

3. Let $a \in B$, since $B \subseteq A$, we also find $a \in A$. Since $(A, \preceq)$ is a poset, the relation $\preceq$ on A is reflexive, hence, $a \preceq a$. This shows that $\preceq$ is still reflexive when restricted to B. Antisymmetry and transitivity are proved with a similar argument.

5. (b) The Hasse diagram is shown below.

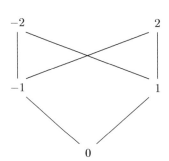

7. $B = \{\emptyset, \{a\}, \{a,b\}, \{a,b,c\}, \{a,b,c,d\}\}$.

Section 8.2

1. 6.

3. 70.

5. $7 \cdot 5 + 7 \cdot 4 + 5 \cdot 4$

7. $4^5, \qquad 4^5 - 3 \cdot 4^2$

9. (a) 52^4 (b) 39^4 (c) $4 \cdot 13^4$ (d) $4 \cdot 48 \cdot 52^3$ (e) $52^4 - 48^4$

11. (a) $9 \cdot 10^3$ (b) $8 \cdot 9^3$ (c) $9 \cdot 10^3 - 8 \cdot 9^3$ (d) $9 \cdot 10$

13. (a) 8^6 (b) $8 \cdot 7 \cdot 6 \cdot 5 \cdot 4 \cdot 3$ (c) 0 (d) $8^6 - 4^6$ (e) $4 \cdot 8^4$ (f) 7^5

Section 8.3

1. 62^8, $P(62, 8)$.

3. $P(14, 5)$.

5. $p(7, 3) \cdot P(10, 3) + P(7, 3) \cdot P(11, 3) + P(10, 3) \cdot P(11, 3)$.

7. $P(11, 7) \cdot 3!/7$.

Section 8.4

1. $\binom{6}{3}\binom{8}{3}$.

3. (a) at least 5   (b) at least 7

5. 10.

7. (a) $\binom{14}{4}$ (b) $\binom{14}{4} - \binom{11}{4}$ (c) $\binom{3}{2}\binom{7}{1}\binom{4}{1} + \binom{3}{1}\binom{7}{2}\binom{4}{1} + \binom{3}{1}\binom{7}{1}\binom{4}{2}$

9. (a) $8!$ (b) $\binom{8}{2} P(8, 2) \left[\binom{6}{2} P(8, 2) + 2 \cdot 7 \cdot 6 \cdot 7 + 7 \cdot 6\right]$

11. $\binom{16}{7}$.

13. (a) $\binom{52}{5}$ (b) $4\binom{13}{2} 13^3$ (c) $13\binom{4}{2}\binom{12}{3} 4^3$ (d) $13\binom{4}{3}\binom{12}{2} 4^2$

   (e) $13\binom{4}{3} 12\binom{4}{2}$ (f) $10 \cdot (4^5 - 1)$ (g) $4\left[\binom{13}{5} - 10\right]$ (h) $4 \cdot 10$

Section 8.5

1. (a) $x^5 + 5x^4 y + 10x^3 y^2 + 10x^2 y^3 + 5xy^4 + y^5$

   (b) $s^6 - 6s^5 t + 15s^4 t^2 - 20s^3 t^3 + 15s^2 t^4 - 6st^5 + t^6$

   (c) $a^4 + 12a^3 b + 54a^2 b^2 + 108ab^3 + 81b^4$

3. (a) $\binom{4}{2} = 6$ (b) $-\binom{9}{3} 3^6 \left(\frac{2}{5}\right)^3 = -\frac{489888}{125}$ (c) 0 (d) $-\binom{6}{3} 3^3 \left(\frac{5}{7}\right)^3 = -\frac{67500}{343}$

5. $\sum_{k=0}^{n} \binom{n}{k} r^k = (1 + r)^n$

7. (c) $k^2 = 2\binom{k}{2} + \binom{k}{1}$ (d) $\sum_{k=1}^{n} k^2 = \frac{1}{6} n(n + 1)(2n + 1)$

Index

Made in the USA
Middletown, DE
08 January 2020